A PICTURE SPEAKS A THOUSAND WORDS

The most common issue between buyers and suppliers is the lack of communication and unclear specifications for products that leads to mistakes.

By Stanley Brahams

A DEFINITIVE APPROACH TO SPECIFICATION WRITING

The Fashiondex, Inc.
New York NY
212 647 0051
E-Mail: info@fashiondex.com
Web Site: www.fashiondex.com
Printed in the Australia, United Kingdom and United States of America.
ISBN: 978-0-9851058-1-5

Also published by Fashiondex:

The Apparel Industry Sourcebook
The Apparel Production Sourcebook/America
The Apparel Design and Production Handbook (A Technical Reference)
The Small Design Company's Guide to Wholesale Fabrics
The Directory of Brand-Name Apparel Manufacturers
The Design Detail Book/Editions 1 and 2
The Color Book/Editions 1, 2 and 3
The Designer's Book of Bridal Gowns
Poses
Birnbaum's Global Guide to Winning the Great Garment War
Birnbaum's Global Guide to Material Sourcing
Crisis in the 21st Century Garment Industry
The Birnbaum Report/Strategic Sourcing for Garment Importers
Sourcing A,B,C'S
The Vendor Compliance Handbook with Forms and Data Templates
How to Start a Fashion Company

ACKNOWLEDGEMENTS

The team at Fashiondex for guiding me through the unknown territory of writing a first book.
My wife Andrea and family for their encouragement over the last three years.

Stanley Brahams

TABLE OF CONTENTS

DEDICATION

To my first grandchild Oliver.

If something is worth doing, then it is worth the time and effort to see it through to the end.

Stanley Brahams

INTRODUCTION

A Picture Speaks a Thousand Words

As manufacturing is now a global business, most companies place some or all production offshore, often in countries whose language is different from their own.

This book demonstrates the use of computer–aided design to create clearly detailed technical information for factories through the stages of design, development and manufacture, using graphic illustration wherever possible.

The specification is a critical document to be shared by all involved in the buying, selling, design and manufacture of the product. A style can be amended many times before the start of production, and specifications created by CAD can be quickly amended in minutes and circulated to everyone involved.

The book takes the reader through a variety of specifications step by step and explains the reasoning behind creating each page; a complete detailed specification may have up to 20 pages depending on the style and construction detail. This book is a practical, hands-on approach to the subject written with many years experience in the industry. The message is that good graphics is an international language, which helps to avoid misunderstandings; details that are in text can be lost in translation.

A recent quote from a source in China states that the most common issue between buyers and suppliers is the lack of communication and unclear specifications for products that leads to mistakes and that Quality Control is your most effective tool to getting the correct product when your specifications/ expectations are clear.

This book is a definitive approach to specification writing for the clothing and related industries, demonstrating the advantages of using CAD.

This book will help those working in the industry and students starting textile courses to view specifications as an integral part of product development, quality assurance and manufacturing.

My purpose for writing the book

The idea for writing the book first came to me when the CEO of the company I worked for was showing customers around our department. Picking up a specification that I was working on, he commented. "A picture speaks a thousand words". This prompted me to view the value of my work in a different light, because when compared to specifications I had seen from other companies I became convinced that my approach to writing specifications had much more to offer due to the positive feedback I was getting from customers and factories, and I was curious to see what books were available on the subject of writing specifications for the textile industry. To sum up, I found plenty of information on measuring and illustrating garments but that was the limit of what was available. I realized that I could offer much more substance to the subject.

I think that generally the subject of specifications has been overlooked. The reason may well be that very few people in the clothing industry have had the opportunity to work full-time as a Specification Technologist/Writer, since over a period of approximately 10 years I can only remember seeing four positions for specification writers advertised in the textile industry and I have held two of them. But there are thousands of Designers, Pattern Cutters and Technologists who write specifications as part of their many other responsibilities.

My wish is to share the methods I have discovered and challenges that I have come across over the years in my role as a Technologist.

Being responsible for a range from initial design to delivery to the customer is a very rewarding job especially when the products are flying out of your customer's stores and catalogues and they turn to you to place large repeat orders wanted in their warehouse yesterday!

Below is a typical example of a job brief for a Technologist. Producing specifications is one of many responsibilities, but the specification is fundamental in linking all the parts of the job together.

- Maintain consistency of Quality standards on specific product.
- Work as part of a team.
- Assist in the update of quality standard documents.
- Monitor and achieve critical path dates from sample development to sign off for final production.
- Manage PRM files ensuring detail is correct at all times.
- **Develop new specs from design brief.**
- Ensure all product testing is complete and production wash codes are confirmed in line with the critical path.
- Ensure all shipment samples are in and approved ahead of shipment.
- Assist the technical manager on any production return issues.
- Travel to the warehouse on a regular basis to review and check product.
- Maintain the companies' established blocks and grade rules.
- Ensure changes in blocks are signed off with technical manager prior to rolling out to suppliers.
- Organize and prepare for fit meetings.
- Ensure comments sent to suppliers are clear and concise.
- Develop a good working relationship with the Design team and offshore suppliers.
- Keep the Technical Manager up to date of sealing status and flag any anticipated production delays.
- Travel as required to countries of production to check production and complete factory evaluations.

What is the purpose of writing a specification? The obvious answer is to provide information, but there are other advantages that might not be so obvious but are just as important to a business. Today companies are not only looking for the cheapest prices, but are also looking for reliable suppliers who have a good infrastructure as well as sound quality assurance procedures. Companies need to reduce the risks involved in buying from factories in other countries or that are several days travel from their head office, and it is common now to assess suppliers' procedures from design to the finished product being delivered to the warehouse.

That's why a specification is such an important document; it is a blue print of the product and should ideally show all style features, components inside and out, packaging and the methods of construction which demonstrates a professional approach enhancing your companies standing with its customers.

Changes and updates can be added and circulated to all concerned in minutes, all made possible by CAD and e-mail.

Why is such detail necessary? **As a general rule as little as possible should be left to interpretation by the factories because to do so is inviting problems.** It is far better to communicate information by picture/illustration wherever possible. Visual Imagery has always played an important part in our lives. Illustration is a common language and often the best way to convey ideas and information. It is not always practical or possible to send a sample for factories to copy. Speed and quick responses are essential today, especially in the fashion business, but accuracy is equally important.

Having worked successfully for several companies as a full-time Specification Writer and Technical Illustrator, I know what the key elements are to writing a good specification and how it benefits a company. Focusing entirely on specification writing gave me the opportunity to develop a structured approach to the job, which aims to comprehensively cover every aspect of the product and CAD is now becoming more widely accepted as a tool for specification writing.

If only we all spoke the same language life would be so much easier–how many times have we heard that said? IKEA assembly instructions are an excellent example of using illustration instead of text. Any country in the world where their products are sold can follow the instructions; they don't need translating into different languages as they rely entirely on the illustrations.

All companies write a specification for their products, but the amount of detail varies greatly depending on the type of business and the demands of their customers. Whatever market we are supplying every detail should be important. Of course the selling price is a limiting factor, but does it cost more to achieve good fit rather than a bad one, ensure pockets are the right size, correctly positioned and constructed, buttons and button holes are positioned correctly, and top stitching is the right width and color?

Designers and product developers work hard to achieve a well designed, aesthetically pleasing garment. So it is important to follow through and specify exactly what you want from the factories. Attention to detail can make the difference between success and failure and establishing customer loyalty.

The aim of this book is to show the advantages of using CAD and how to achieve the best results. Once a company uses CAD they become aware of the many possibilities open to them of illustrating detail that was not possible before with text and hand drawings. Simply put, companies understand the advantages of showing step by step and in detail what their requirements are as this can avoid costly mistakes.

Download all the style drawings for free at:
http://www.fashiondex.com/store/proddetail.php?prod=912
At checkout use dicount code SDPWTW82 and the download will be free.

CHAPTER 1

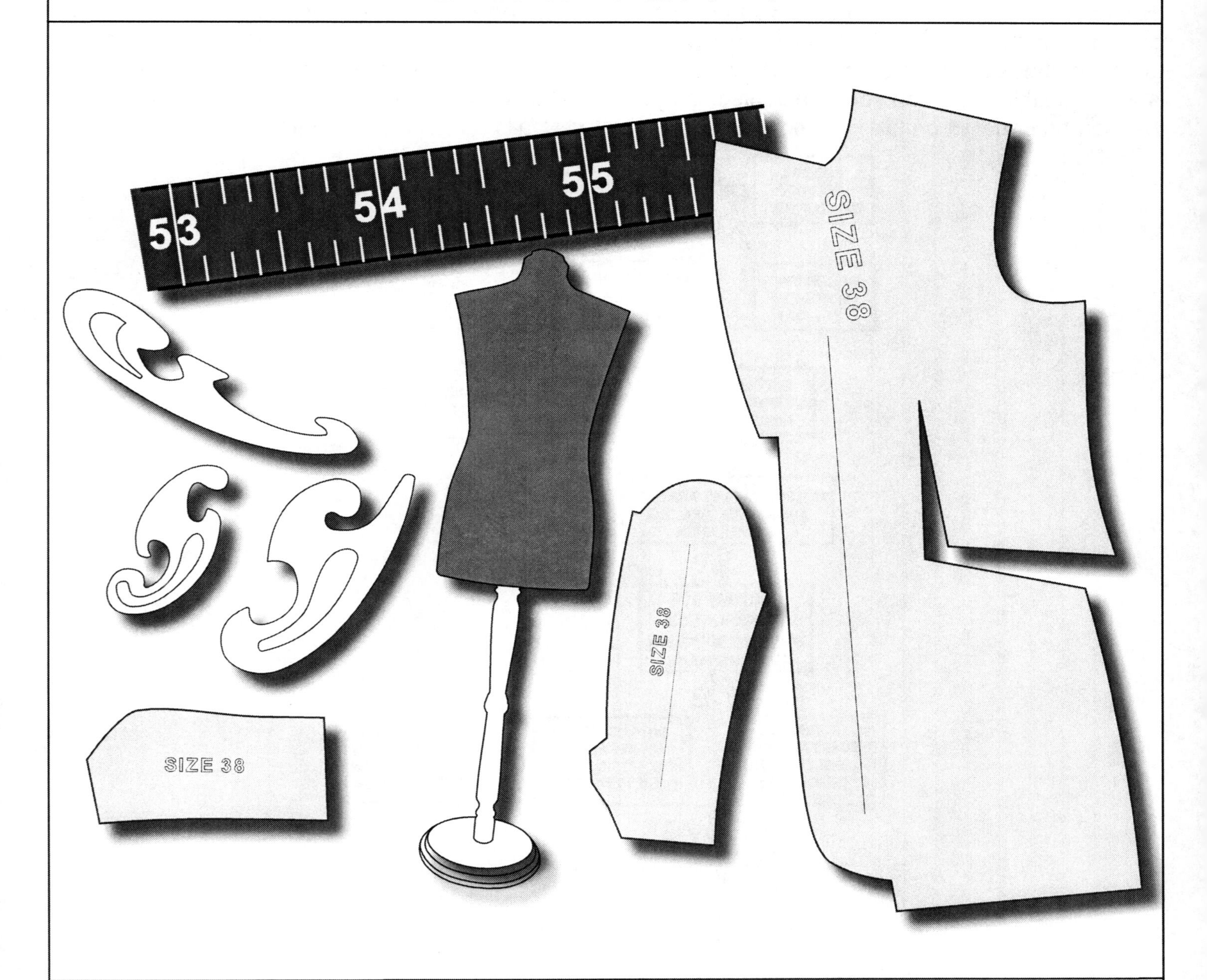

PRODUCT DEVELOPMENT

Product development is now a continuous process in most companies, to keep ahead of the competition, improve quality and improve profit margins. Let's take a typical scenario of a company putting a range together. The range could consist of reworking previous styles and the introduction of new styles. The company could be a retailer with its own design and technical department who work directly with factories or an importer who will source new items from its own factories.

Designing a range can be done in several ways, such as looking around shops, buying in samples, researching the internet and discussion with customers. As the ideas develop we put them down on paper and quickly the initial designs takes shape. This may be in the form of a sketch that needs to be translated into flat drawings to create the specification. First samples or mock-ups could be made at the head office to check fit or style details and at this stage more detail can be added to the specification. With the style finalized and fabric and trim agreed upon, specification can be sent to the factory for a costing and first samples.

The flow chart

This shows how the specification becomes an integral part of the development process from the initial designs to delivery to the customer. The specification is an essential tool for quality control when compared to the sealed sample which, is used to check workmanship. The specification is much easier to use to check the garment measurements, pocket sizes, button positions, style detail and labeling. It is also possible that even after the sealed sample has been approved that minor changes can be made that can be updated on the specification and circulated to all concerned in minutes.

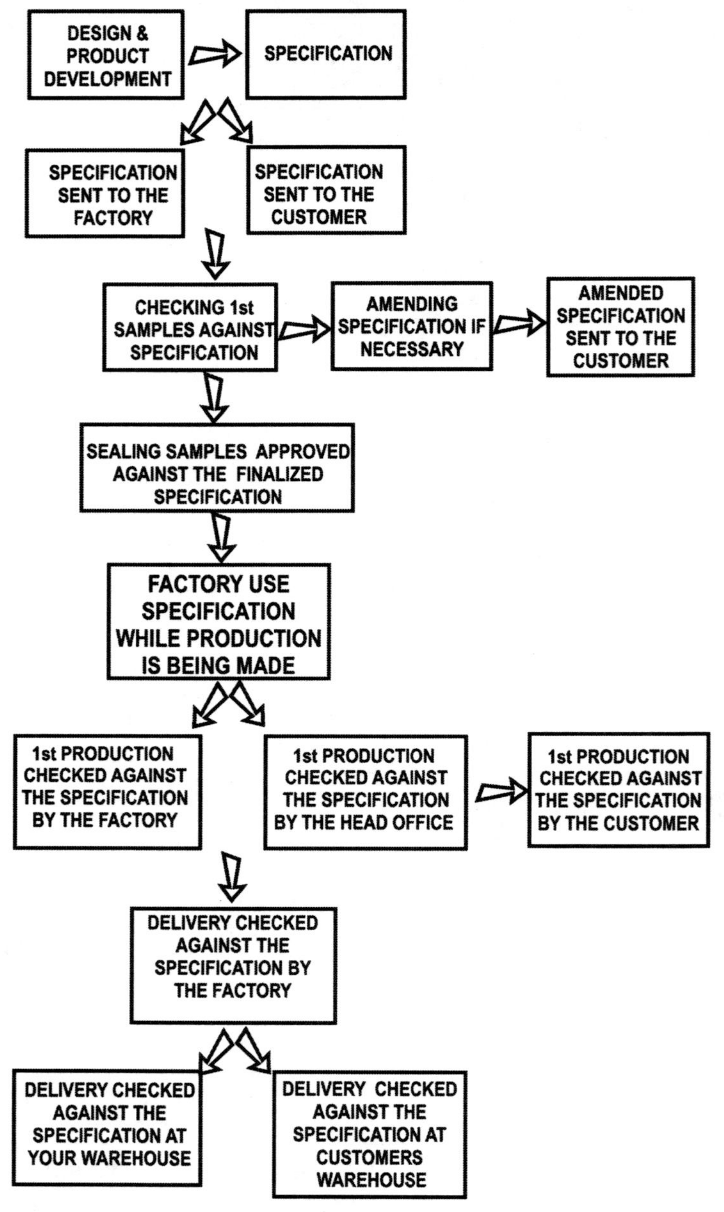

Planning ahead is very important and we would like to think that every style will be a winner, but we can never be sure why one style sells well and another does not. The merchandiser plays a key role in trying to forecast how many sales each style will achieve, but it is not an exact science and they don't want to be left with surplus stock. Merchandisers look carefully at how a new style sells at the beginning of the season and quickly identify which styles are selling well and where new orders will have to quickly be placed to meet demand through the season.

At this point companies go into overdrive. Firstly contacting the original supplier to see how quickly they can make repeats, and then companies will also contact alternative suppliers in case the first supplier cannot meet the increased demand in time. Most companies work with a number of factories making the same type of product and often have to switch production. The clock is ticking away and every hour counts. Sending a correct sample if one is available by courier takes at least two to three days, but sending a detailed specification by e-mail takes minutes. The specification can be sent to any number of factories greatly increasing your chances of finding one or more factories able to quickly supply counter samples at the right price.

If a garment is a winner we want the repeats to be reproduced where possible with every detail of the original production, because if there is any compromise over quality or style details this subsequently may affect future sales. It is possible and sometimes absolutely necessary to supply every piece of information about the materials, style and construction of a product especially on items that could cause injury if the specification is not detailed enough. Generally with textiles and clothing we have some flexibility, in as much as that if we don't give enough information, the finished product might not be what we expected, but this will not cause physical harm–it only damage our profits. If we select factories that have a good track record and we give them sufficient information they should be able to fill in the gaps that we may not have covered.

The term Product specification would suggest that it contains all the information required for the product, but often it is presented in two documents: the style and technical specification and the Bill of Materials. The latter itemizes the quantity and quality of every piece of fabric, trim, button, zip, shoulder pads, types of sewing thread, label, bag, carton required for the product, which the specification writer needs to constantly cross reference the specification against the Bill of Materials. The factory also needs to know the following:

Quantity and size ratio

Delivery date

Shipping

Insurance

Some companies provide all the materials and arrange insurance and shipping themselves as well as supply the patterns, while others rely on the factories to source all the materials, patterns and build the shipping cost into their price.

I start a new specification by working on the illustrations first and add text later. The first drawings will represent the style and overall appearance of the product and from these more detail will evolve by having the capability to focus on specific areas and enlarge the illustration without having to re-draw the detail (See the boot as an example). The original drawing is copied and pasted, parts that are not needed are deleted to make extra room on the page to show more detail or a factory might request clarification on certain measurements. You will see examples of this in the following chapters.

It is essential that a detailed specification is finalized and agreed upon by both the customer and the factory before production starts.

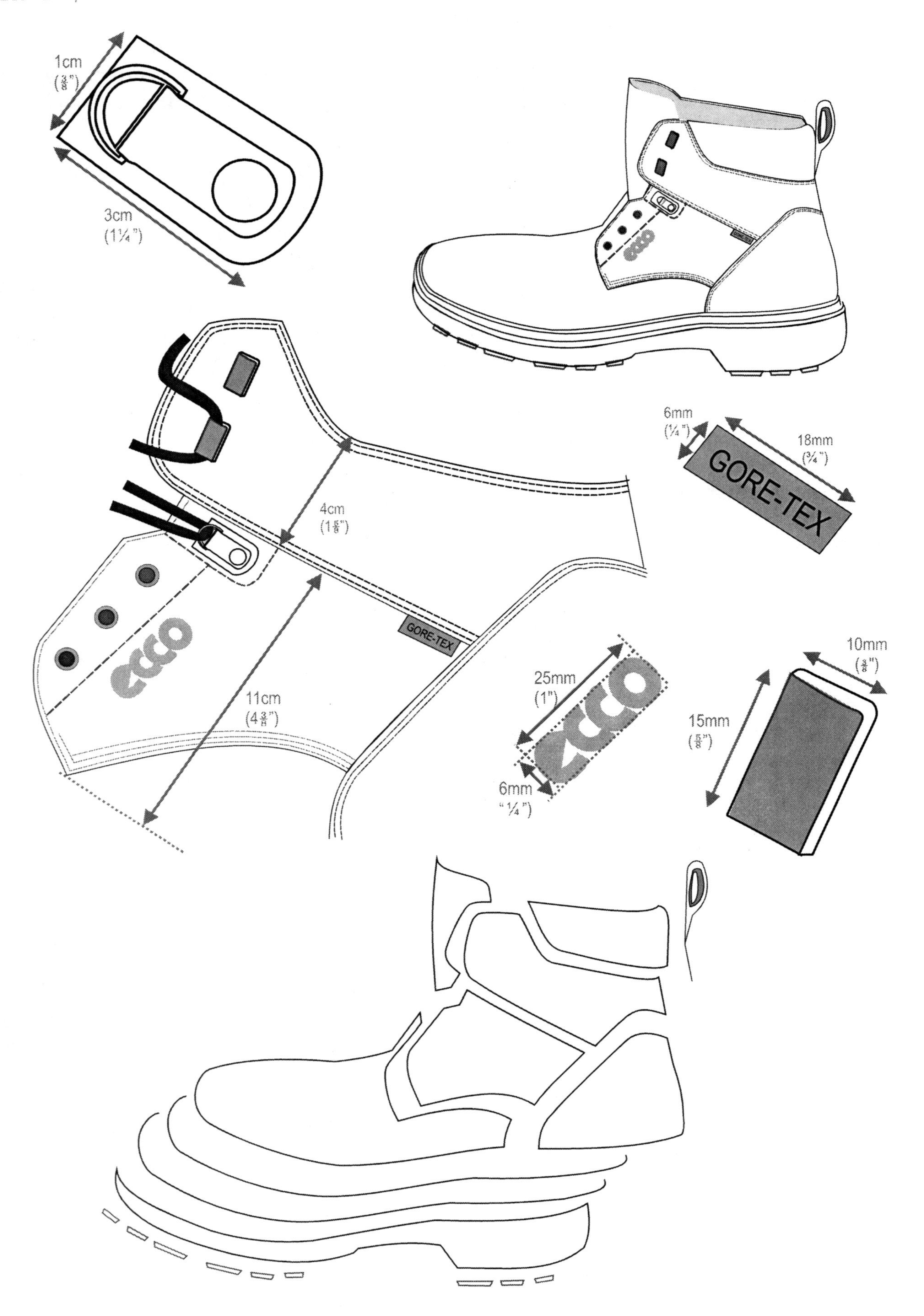

1cm
(⅜")
3cm
(1¼")
6mm
(¼")
18mm
(¾")
GORE-TEX
4cm
(1⅝")
GORE-TEX
ecco
11cm
(4⅜")
10mm
(⅜")
25mm
(1")
15mm
(⅝")
ecco
6mm
"¼")

Throughout the book I vary my approach to writing specifications because to manage our time efficiently we need to consider how much detail is necessary to put into the specification. This is not contradicting what I said earlier about nothing being be left to the factories' interpretation, but time is a precious commodity and we need to put the extra time into a specification when required.

There are basically two main ways of doing business offshore-----

1. Using a group of factories that we may alternate our production between while sourcing new factories looking for better prices and quality.
2. Working with established factories, possibly owned by your company, whose methods of manufacturing we know and they know your standards.

With method one, a detailed specification is always advisable; with method two, we can rely more on the factory to know the correct method of construction. It is possible that a company uses both methods of manufacturing and the type of specification we do should be carefully considered.

The other factor to consider is the complexity of the product. As an example the construction of a pair of jeans is fairly standard and once we have approved a factory's standard, we can concentrate on detailing the other style features. The same applies to many unstructured, unlined garments, where the construction would normally be 5–thread over–locked as standard.

Prepare the specification as if you are the end user, think what information you would want and how you would like it presented. I've varied the amount of text between specifications–some factories may prefer both, but it becomes obvious how good graphics replace the need for all but the minimum of text.

Text should be highlighted with bullet points to show where one instruction starts and finishes, also use different colors. For example, measurements can be put in bold type so they stand out from the rest of the detail.

Order of making

Always try and keep to one format, so that the factories become familiar with your specifications and know where to find any particular piece of information. As an example with the Reefer Overcoat or any tailored coat I follow this format.

Interlinings
Fronts and pockets first, then the back
Sleeve, cuff and the shoulder straps
Collars
Lining
Buttoning
Packaging

Text and illustration should always be together wherever possible to give a complete picture for that particular part of the garment so you do not have to go from page to page to find all the information.

A detail can be missed if there is too much information on a page, specific detail can be highlighted on a separate page. Detailed specifications save time in the long run and will achieve better results and fewer mistakes.

A poorly written specification will throw up as many queries as points it answers, which will cause delays and mistakes.

CHAPTER 2

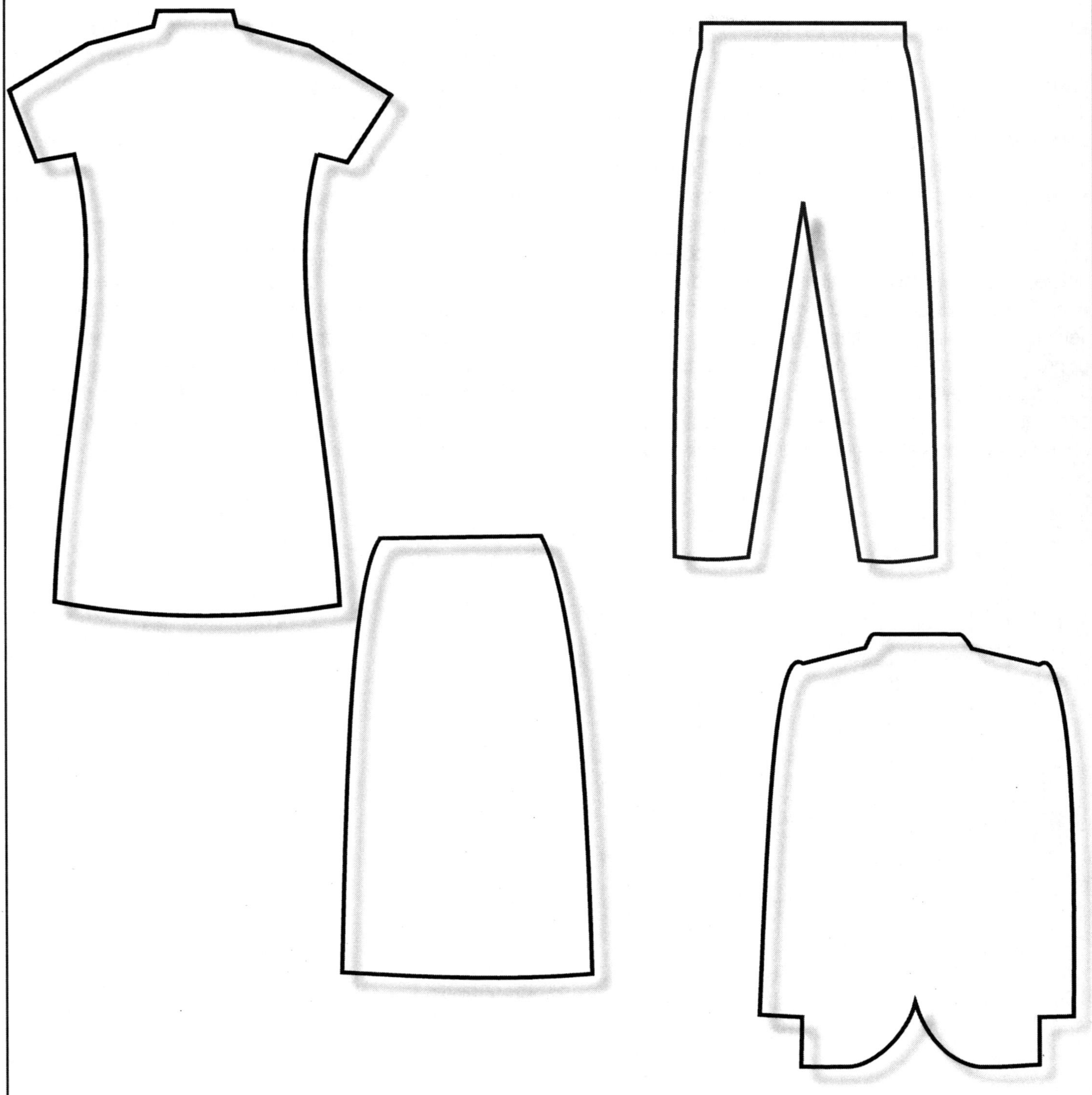

TEMPLATES

All the following define the word template and all are relevant in the process of writing specifications. Prototype, Model, Precedent, Established practice, Arrangement, Shape, Structure, Benchmark.

Maintaining consistency is very important when writing specifications, so we need to develop trusted, proven shapes, structures and methods for our illustrations which can be confidently used over and over again making the most of the advantages of CAD. This chapter deals in detail with creating a variety of templates. When I first started drawing, I had great difficulty in drawing objects to scale. This was mainly due to starting to draw an object usually from the top and then finding it was too big and would not fit on the page. I would start again making the drawing smaller, but would then find that when starting the next part of the drawing this was not in proportion to what I had already drawn. Do not rush to complete the drawing, but develop the outline first, height and width are crucial to getting the correct proportions. Once you think you have the right outline start to add a small amount of detail such as the outline of seams, pockets, lapels and keep checking that you are still happy with the appearance. At this stage you might start to see shapes or angles that you did not notice before and might need to adjust the drawing again. As a technical illustrator every drawing is a potential template to be used or amended for future work. Personal computers were unheard of when I first started work as a Technologist for a national mail–order company. During my first week at the company I was given a tour of all the departments, including the computer dept. It was like going into a place of worship with the staff being the equivalent of high priests. There were cabinet after cabinet of whirring discs in a spotless room with the temperature carefully controlled. This was the future but not yet for us mere mortals. After the visit I never saw a computer again for many years. Unless you were a talented drawer each Technologist assembled a collection of cardboard templates for the different garment shapes. To myself and the other Technologists this was cutting edge technology. My first lesson was if the outline was correct then you stood a good chance of producing a reasonable drawing. The templates on the previous page are approximately the size we worked with so they could fit neatly into boxes on the specification form. Style detail then had to carefully added. The chapters in the book show how computer–aided design have revolutionised style/technical drawings to create very professional specifications, enabling designers and technologists to “think outside the box” and present information in different ways.

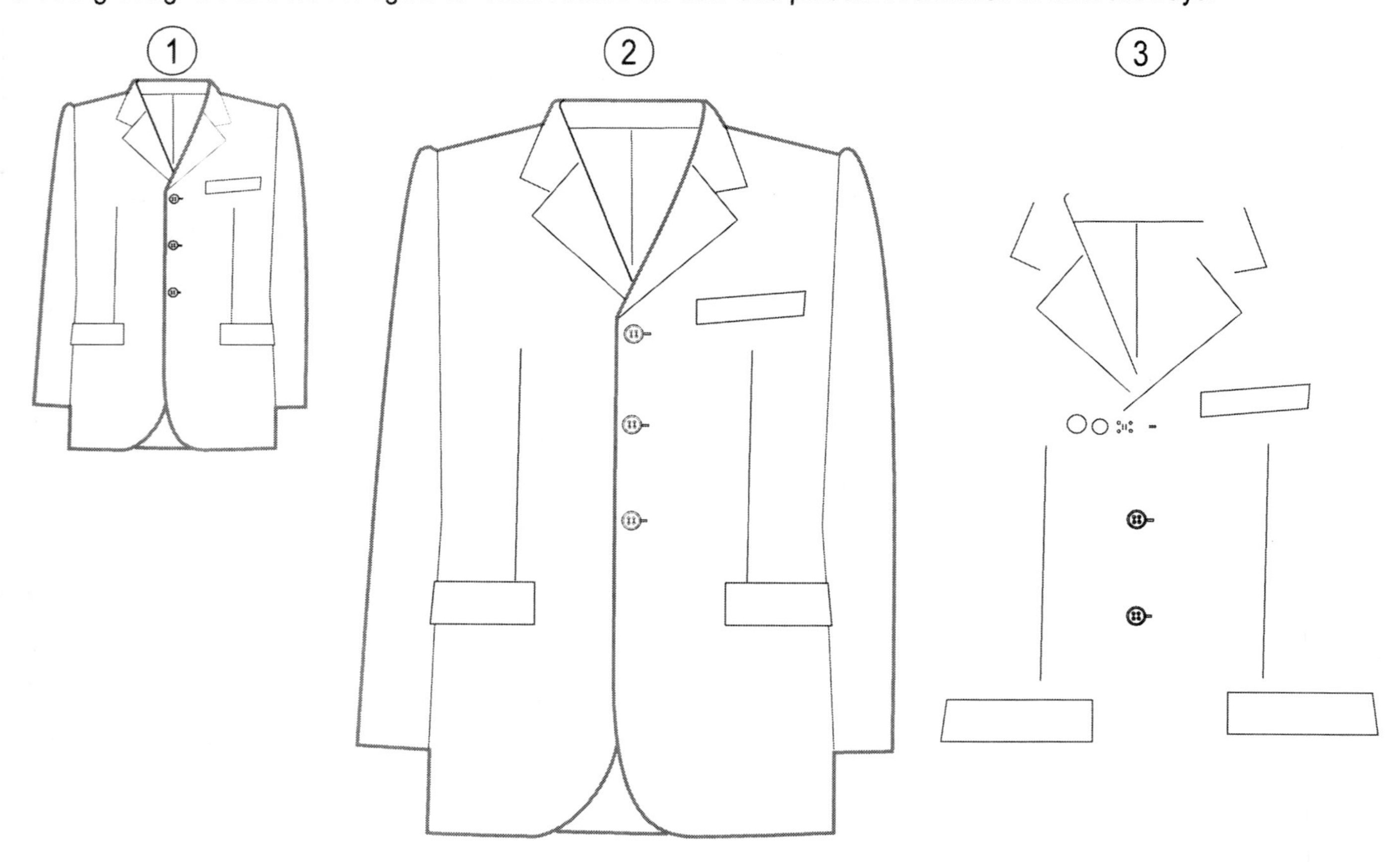

Using CAD I start with the same outline used for the cardboard cut outs and added the detail for the pockets darts, waist shaping, collar, lapel and buttons. Illustration 1 is now my first template, 2 demonstrates how the size of the drawing can be increased keeping exactly the same proportions freeing the illustrator of restrictions on the size of the drawing and the limitations of using a standard box to put the drawing in. The only limitation being the size of the page. Illustration 3 is a break down of the simple lines that make up the style features.

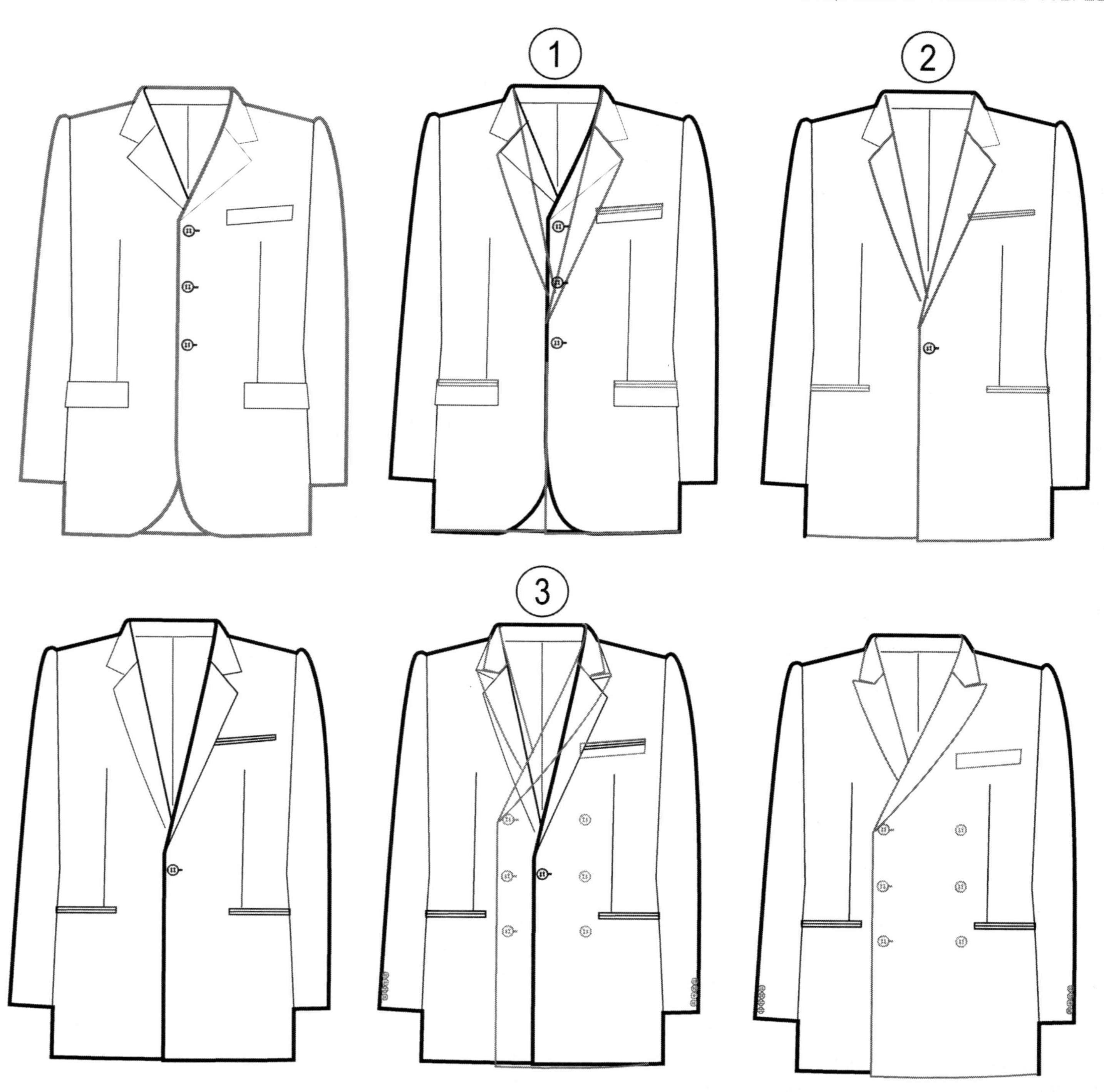

This page demonstrates how simple it is using your first jacket template to create style variations. Illustration 1 is changing the jacket to a one button fastening, square fronts with 3 jetted pockets using the first style as a guide and template to draw in new style details. When satisfied with the results select and delete the old style lines. If, as with this drawing the front edge is part of the outline, select and use the eraser tool to delete the part you don't want leaving the new shapes as illustration 2. Our next style 3 is derived from illustration 2 and is created in the same way as the first style. There are now three styles very quickly added to our library and many style variations can be derived from these first drawings.

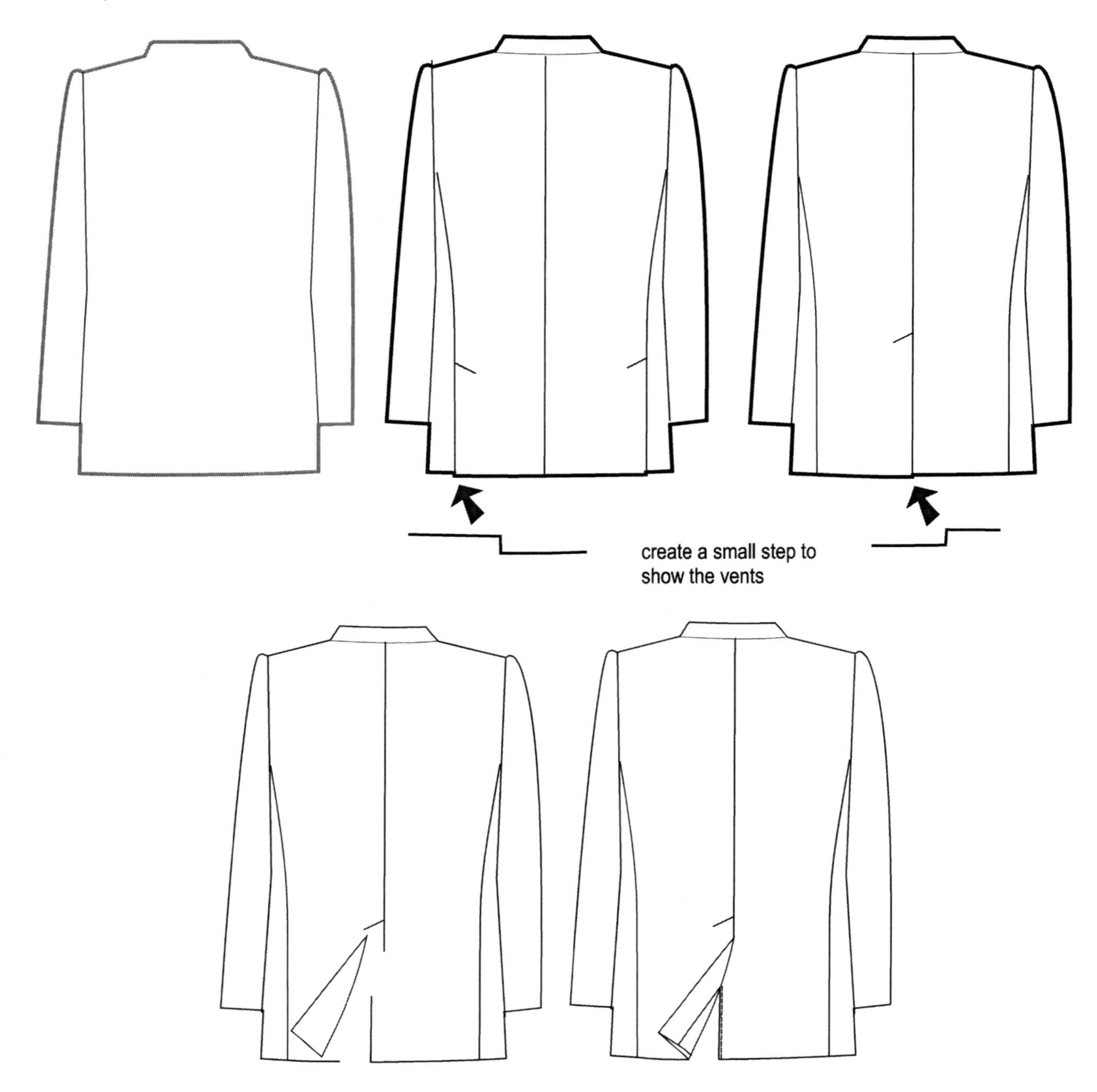

The back view should not be overlooked, although usually there is not as much detail as the front, it is equally as important to show the style. The outline will be the same as the front, all that is needed is detail of the seam positions and on a jacket if applicable show centre or side vents. Some illustrators like to show the vent open.

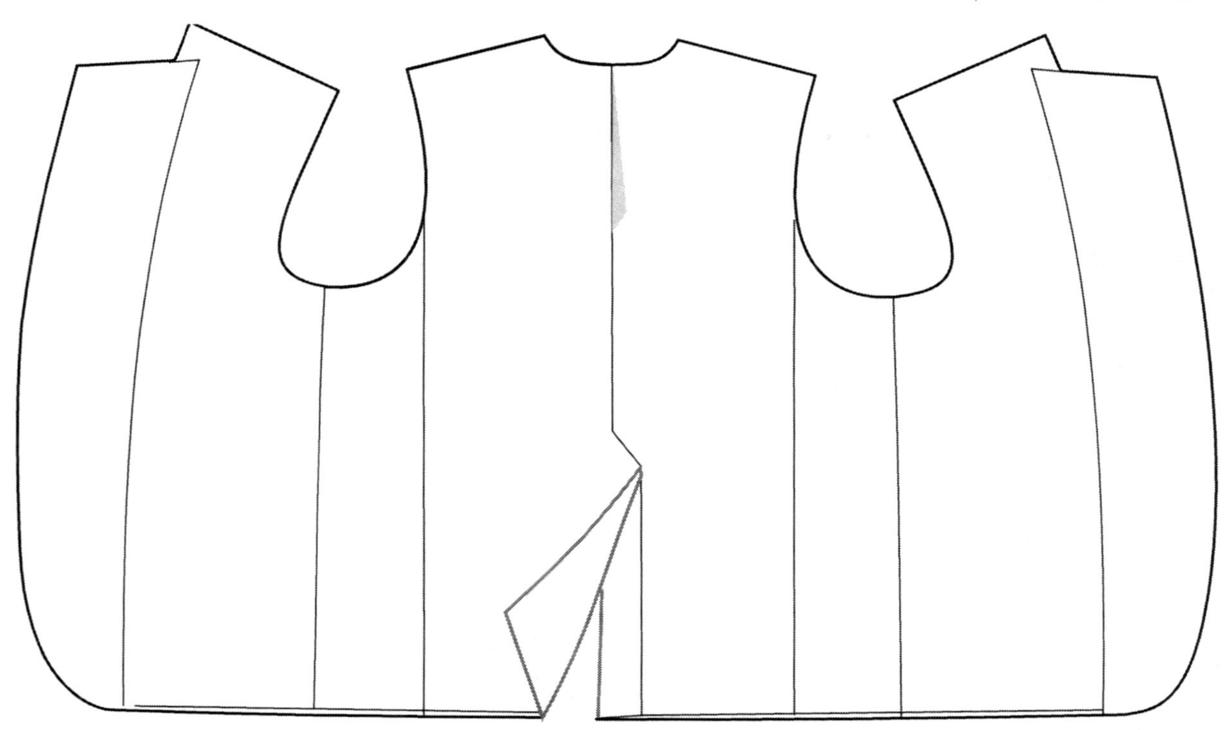

The inside

Once proficient at using CAD you will want to see how creative you can be adding new dimensions to your specifications. In the overcoat chapter I show the inside of the coat and this was very important to illustrate because of all the detail. I have used this method of showing the coat open before the shoulders are joined now for several years and the same outline with slight amendments can be used for many men's and ladies jackets and coat styles to great effect. This type of illustration is of great assistance especially to machinists as all the details are laid out like a map. It can also be used to illustrate the outside. See the next pages for examples of both.

This is another more simplified way of specifying a coat compared to the more detailed overcoat specification featured in the overcoat chapter, one outline is used for both outer and inner. I would use this method when working with a jacket factory who you already have an established relationship with. You may have many styles you want them to sample in a short time and this method saves you time but don't forget to highlight the key style details inside and out.

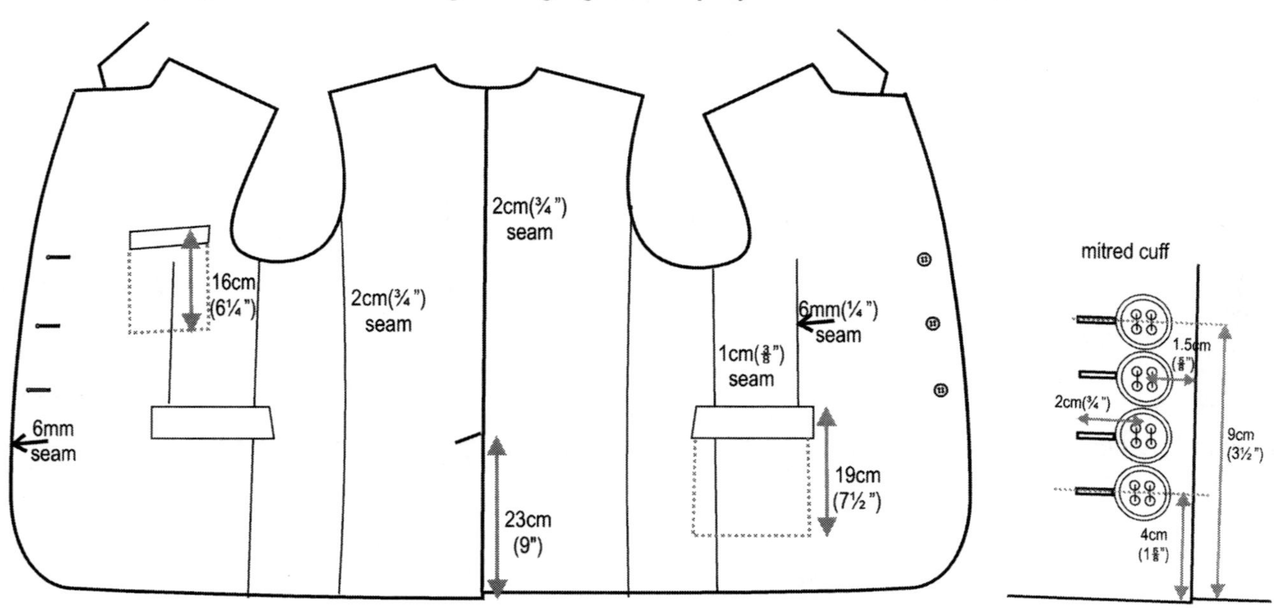

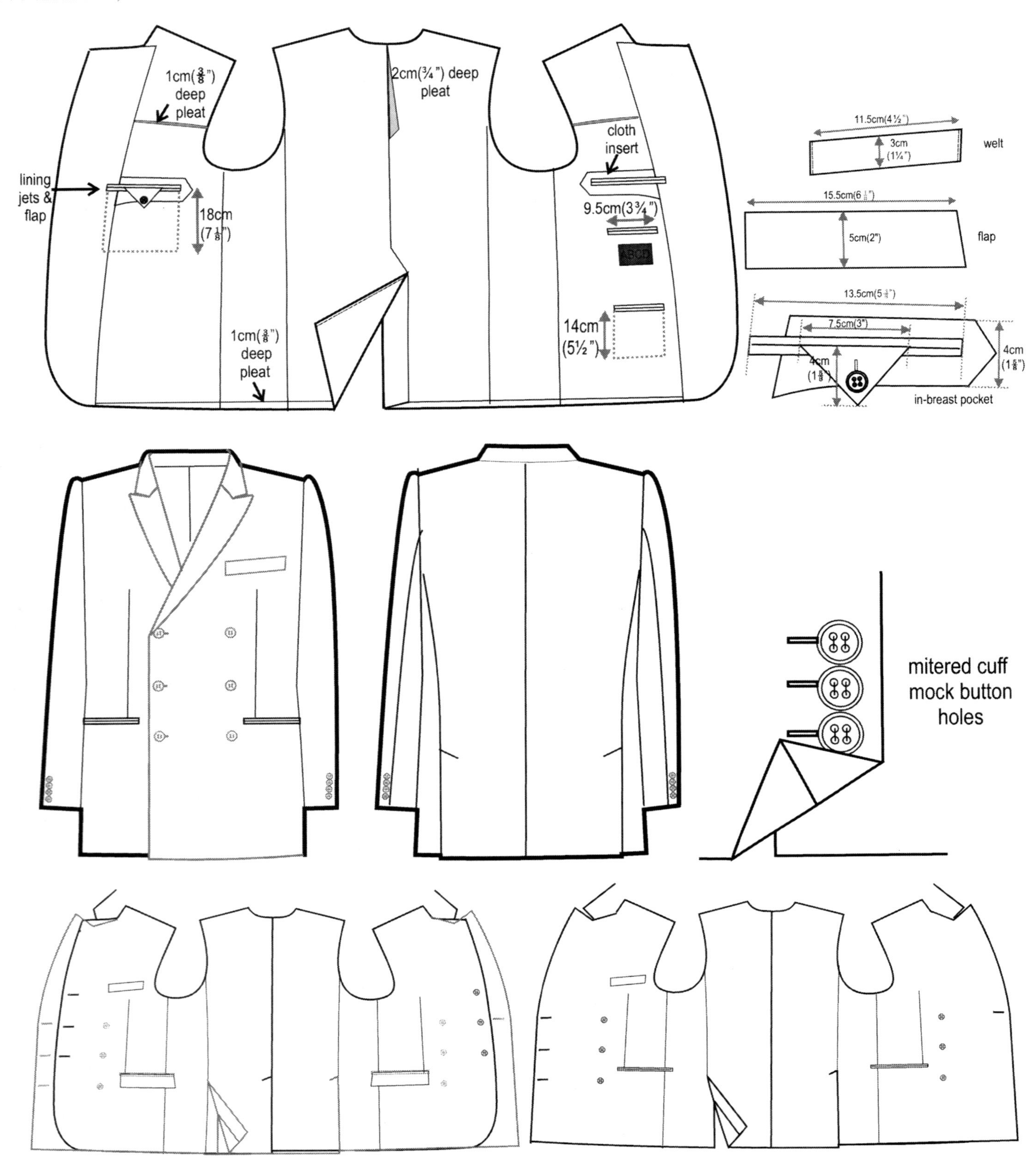

This shows the double breasted open jacket illustration created from the single breasted jacket.

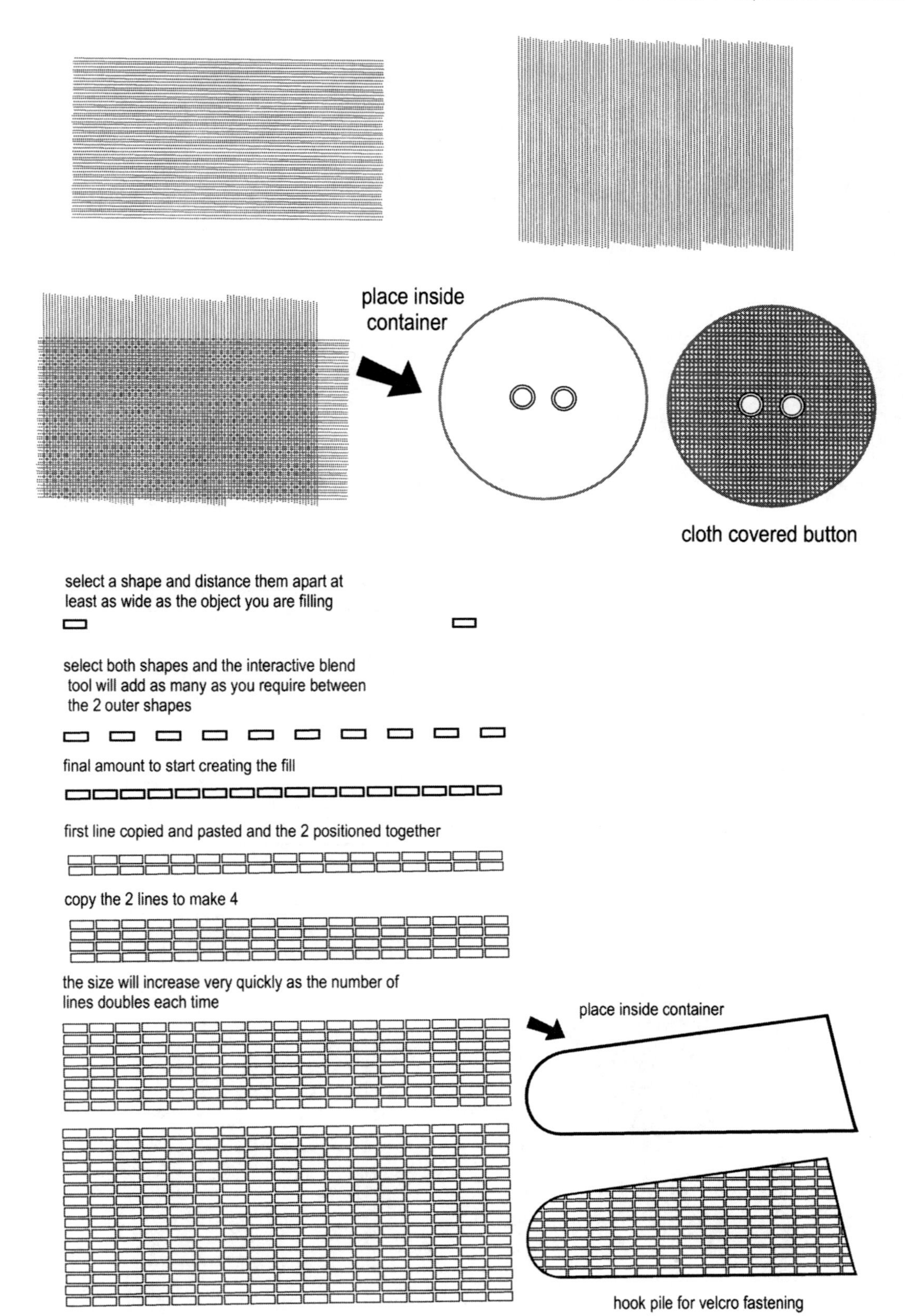

Creating your own fills

At times you may want or need to illustrate a material that has a textured appearance rather than a flat surface. Computer aided design packages usually have a library already set up, but not always with what you want, so you can create your own. They are not difficult to create and then saved to be used again. The designs are repetitive and easy to construct.

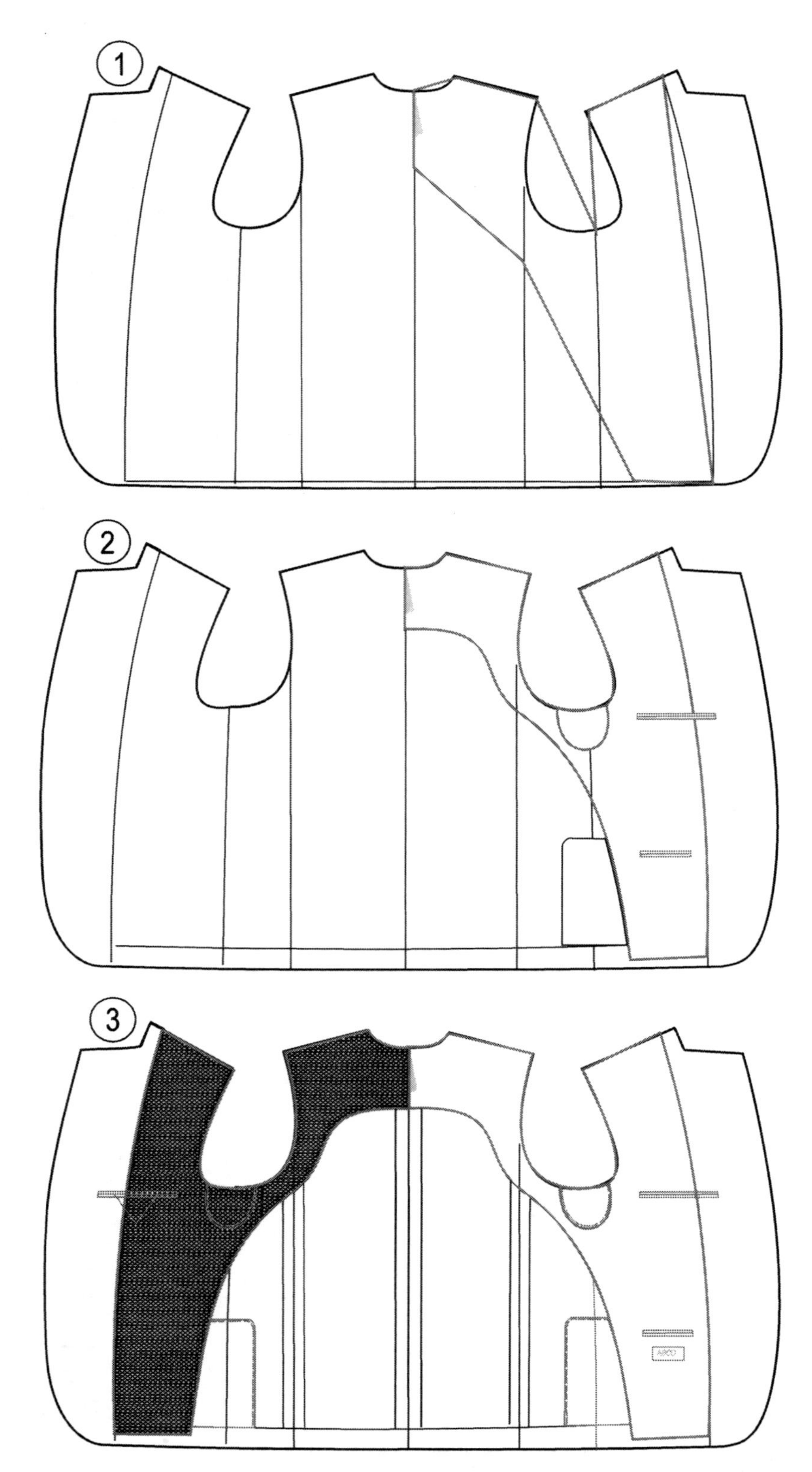

The inside of this jacket is usually described as buggy or half lined and the lining is a mesh fabric. The best way to convey this to a factory is by illustration and I have used the mesh lining design from the anorak chapter as the fill to show the mesh. Using the template outline from the previous jacket, illustration 1 shows joining straight lines for the area covered by the lining. Illustration 2 are the lines curved to the required shape. With illustration 3 the finished shape has been copied, pasted and mirror imaged. When joined together the mesh fill is transferred to the shape with the power clip tool and the remainder of the style detail added. In this example I have used an existing outline as a template and created a new template for a buggy lined jacket.

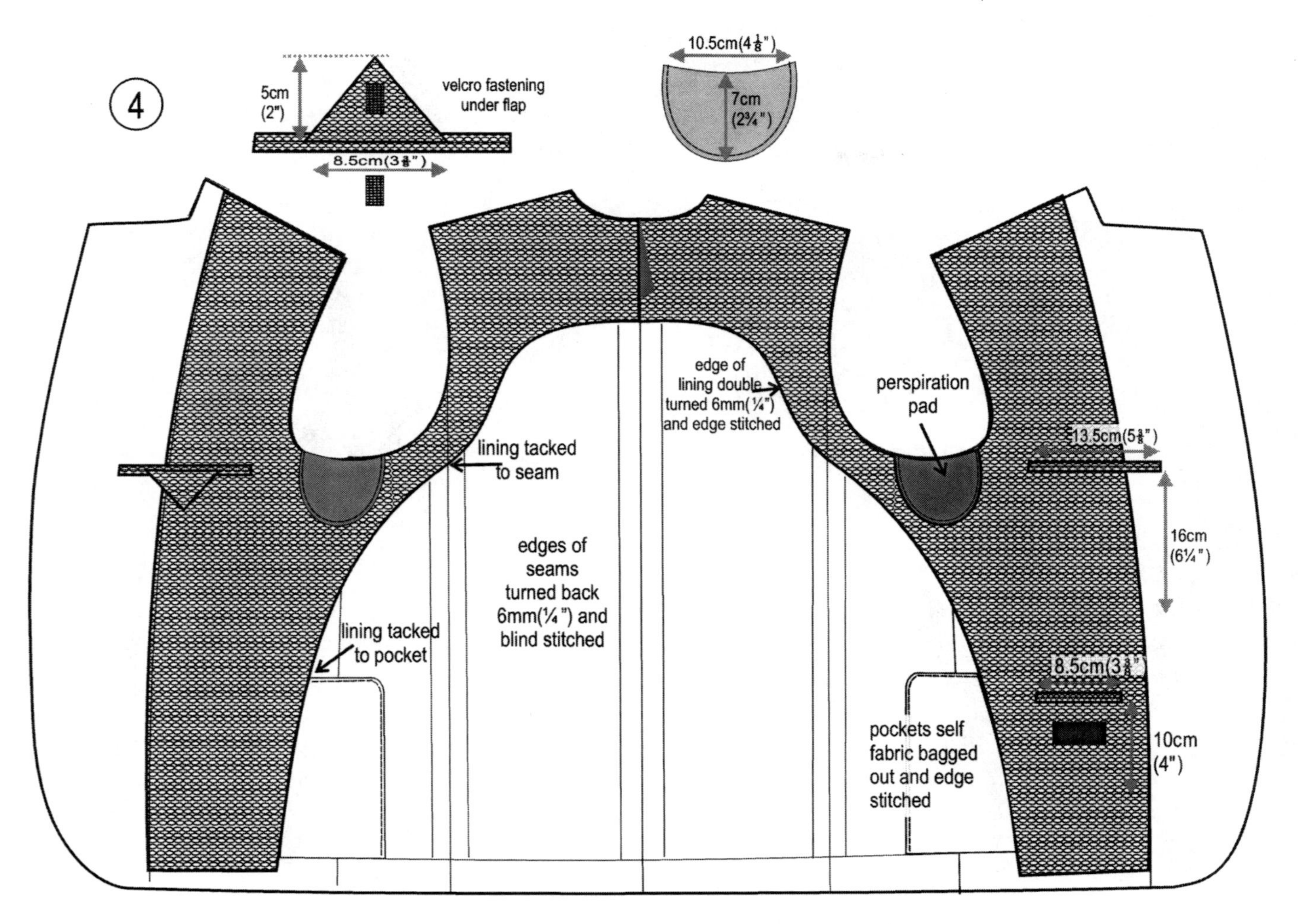

Illustration 4 is the completed inside, also taking the opportunity to add more detail. The pocket sizes are always important. Sometimes customers specify the pocket openings and depths but if they don't, it should not be overlooked and it should be added to the specification rather than leave it to the factory to decide. Add detail of the inner pocket flap and perspiration pads plus other details help to insure that the factory make the samples correctly.

CHAPTER 3

MOTOR BIKE

My introduction to CAD and how I got started... I was motivated to find a drawing package when working as a pattern cutter for a company making Motor bike clothing. Many of the garments were made of different colored panels to make the riders stand out and be noticed. The company owner designed the jackets and I cut the patterns. When the pieces were cut out ready for sewing they looked like parts of a jigsaw and it was difficult to recognize which parts fitted together and their color. A sample was always made first to make sure that the new design looked right, but they quickly disappeared, taken by the agents to show customers, so often there was no visual reference for the factory. Either the owner or his wife (who was the sample machinist) were on site if the machinists had a problem, but this was not the best solution. As the style developed, I wanted to keep a visual record for myself and the sewing room. It was impossible for me to draw these by hand and I discovered that the company had Corel Draw software but no one knew how to use it. This then was the beginning for me and I taught myself to use the software.

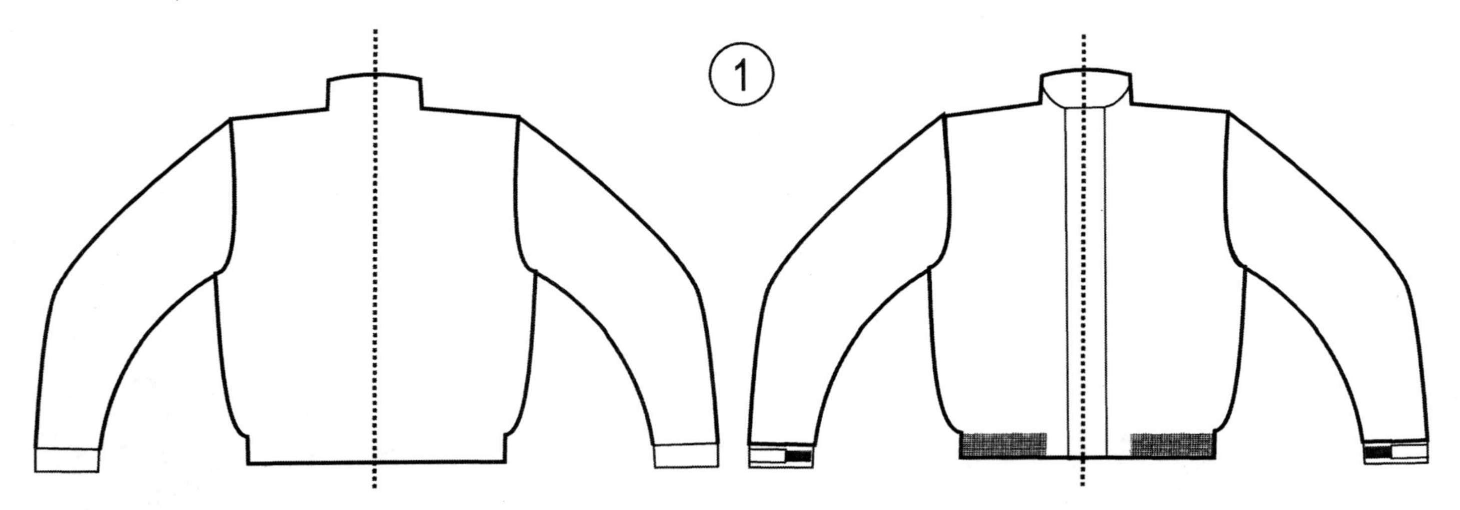

Creating the outline.

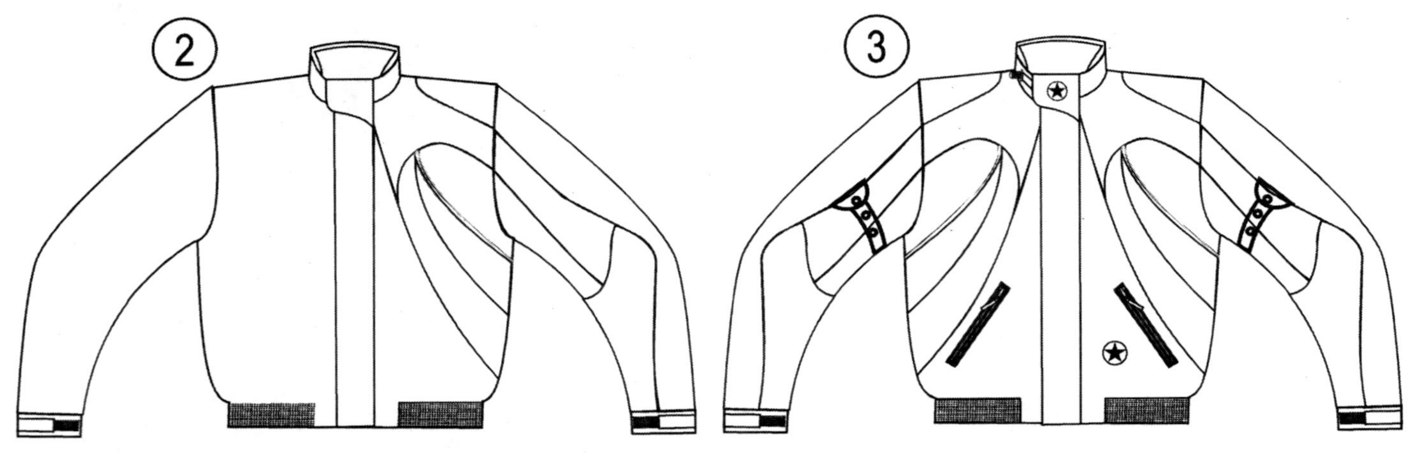

2. Add the panels first on one front and sleeve 3. Once happy with the result copy, paste and mirror image the outline of the panels to the other front and sleeve and add the remaining style details.

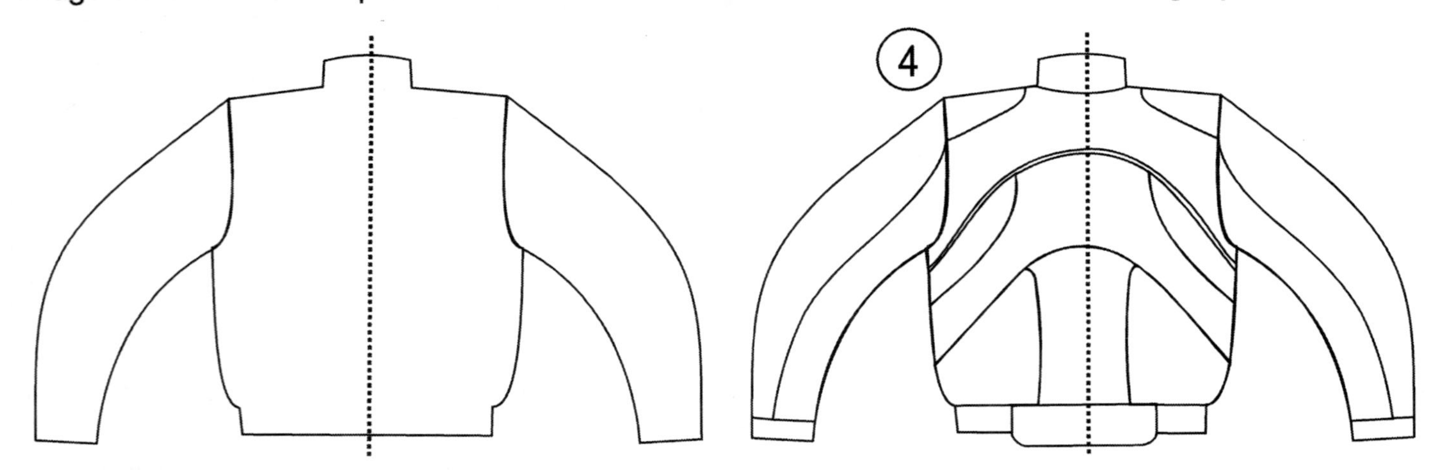

(The 2 halves of the jacket must be exactly the same)
4. Using the same outline, create the back panels.

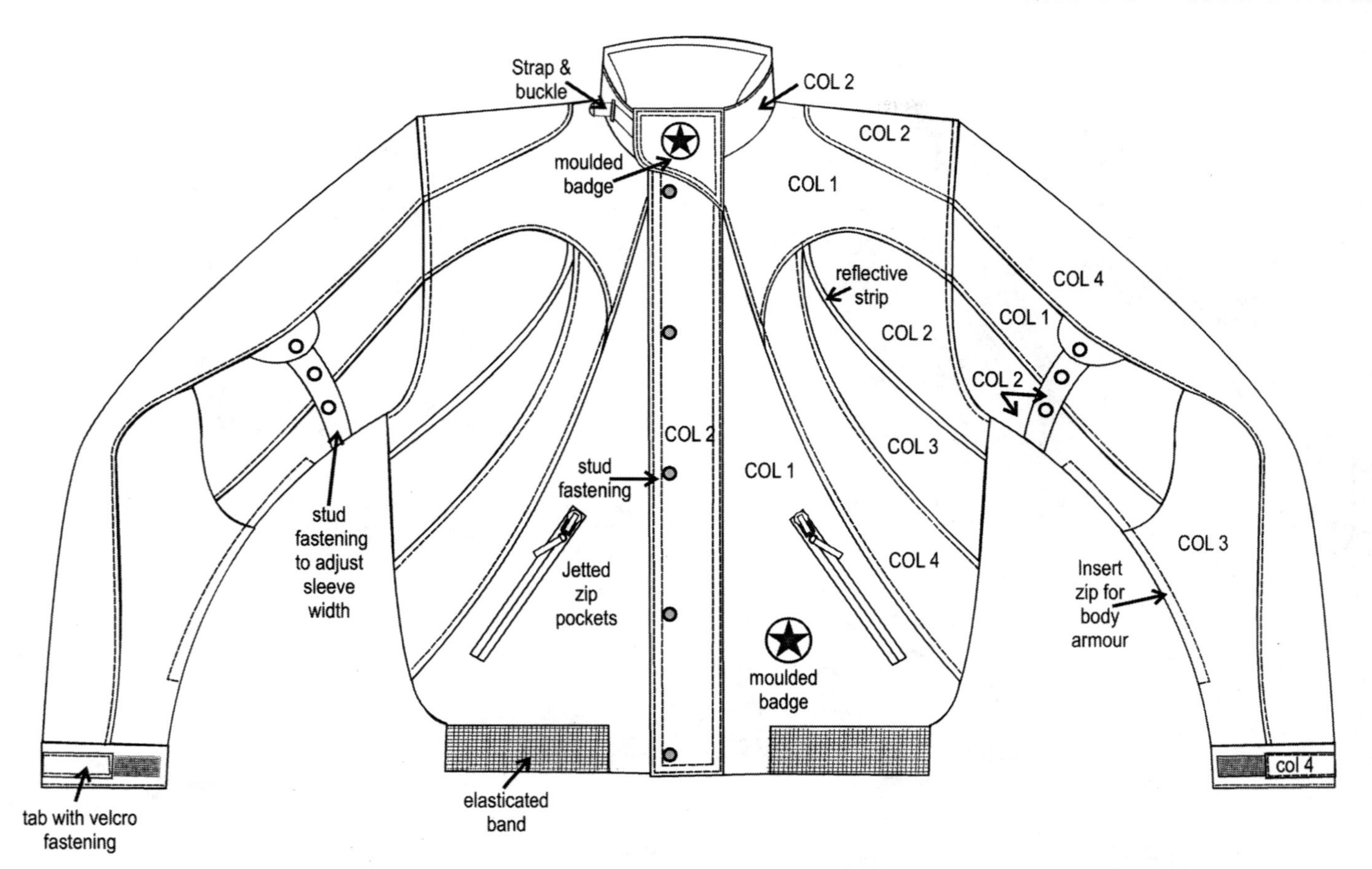

Illustrate the front & back of the jacket in more detail, showing which panels have top stitching and the color of the panels. Shows colored panels with coding.

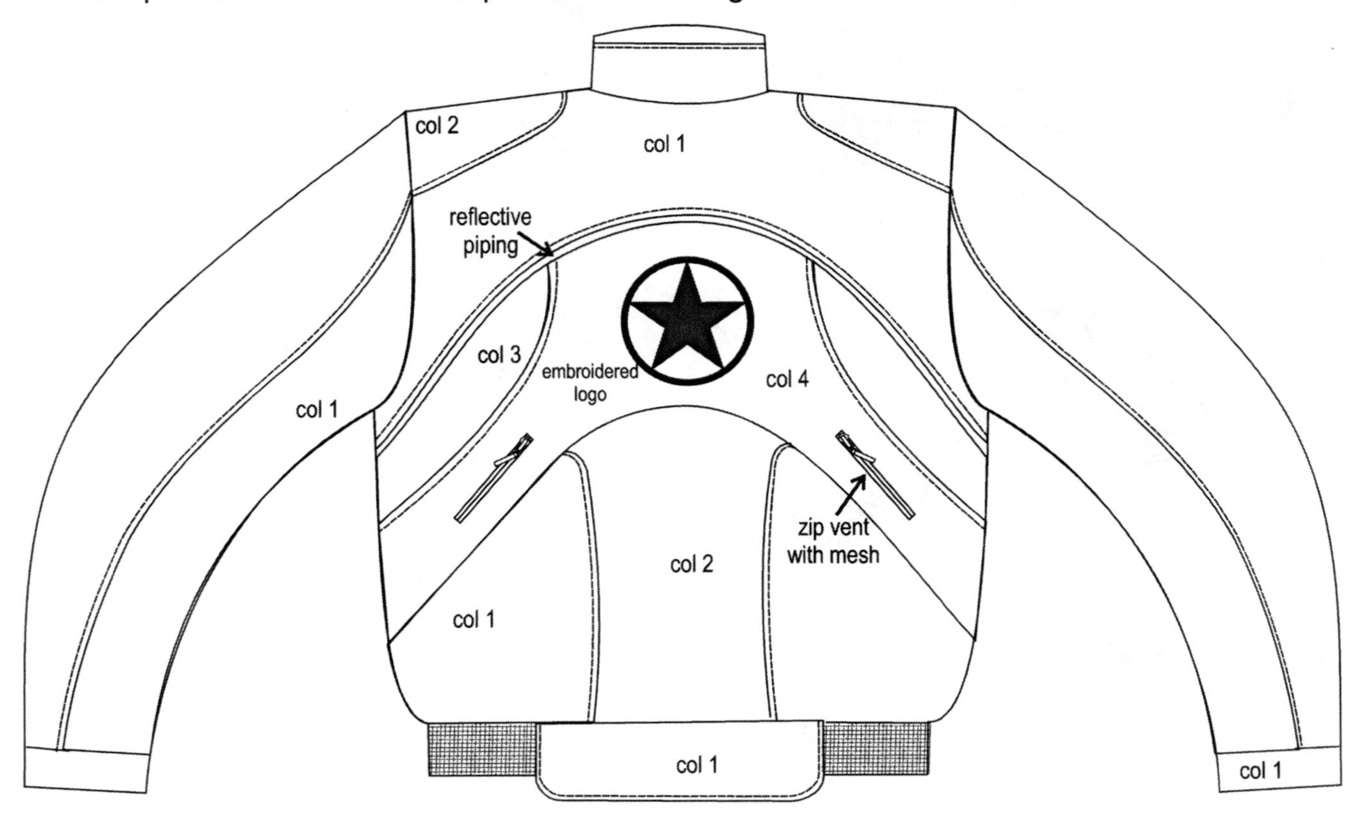

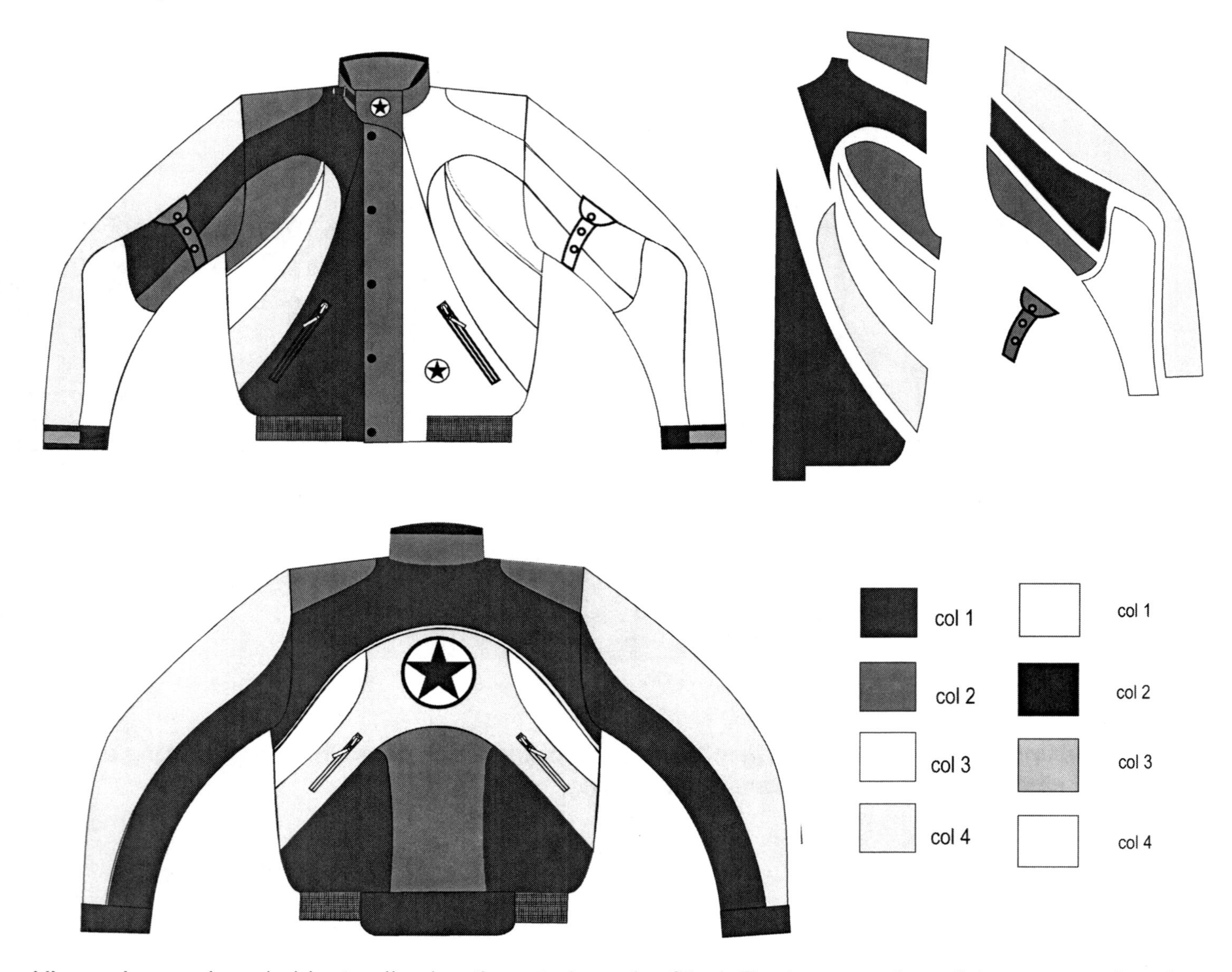

All panels are closed objects allowing them to be color filled. To change color, click on a panel and then choose a new color.

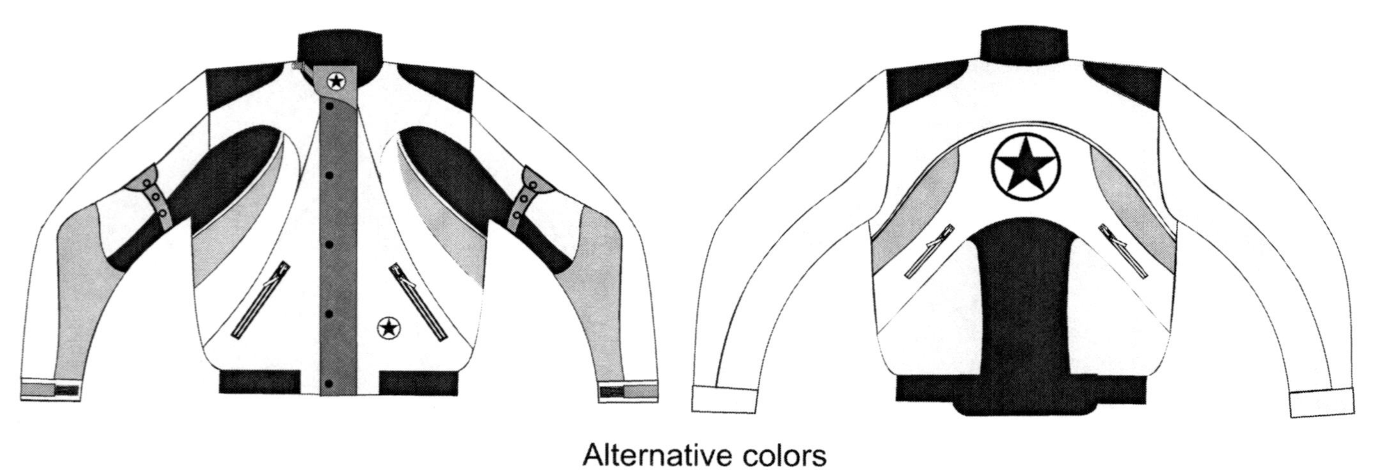

Alternative colors

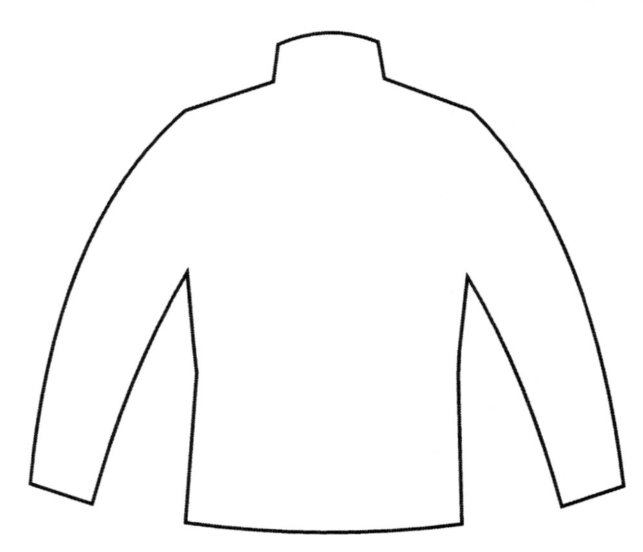

These motor bike jackets as the previous style, feature different colored panels. This is also common with outdoor jackets, performance and sports wear. When doing specifications for these type of garments you will find that you will only need a few basic outlines. As an example the motor bike jackets are either a short racing jacket style or the longer touring style, but there are endless options for changing the style and color combinations. So first, establishing a good outline is very important, which can be tweaked if necessary. Your outline is a blank canvass to create a new style. Panel colors can be changed in seconds.

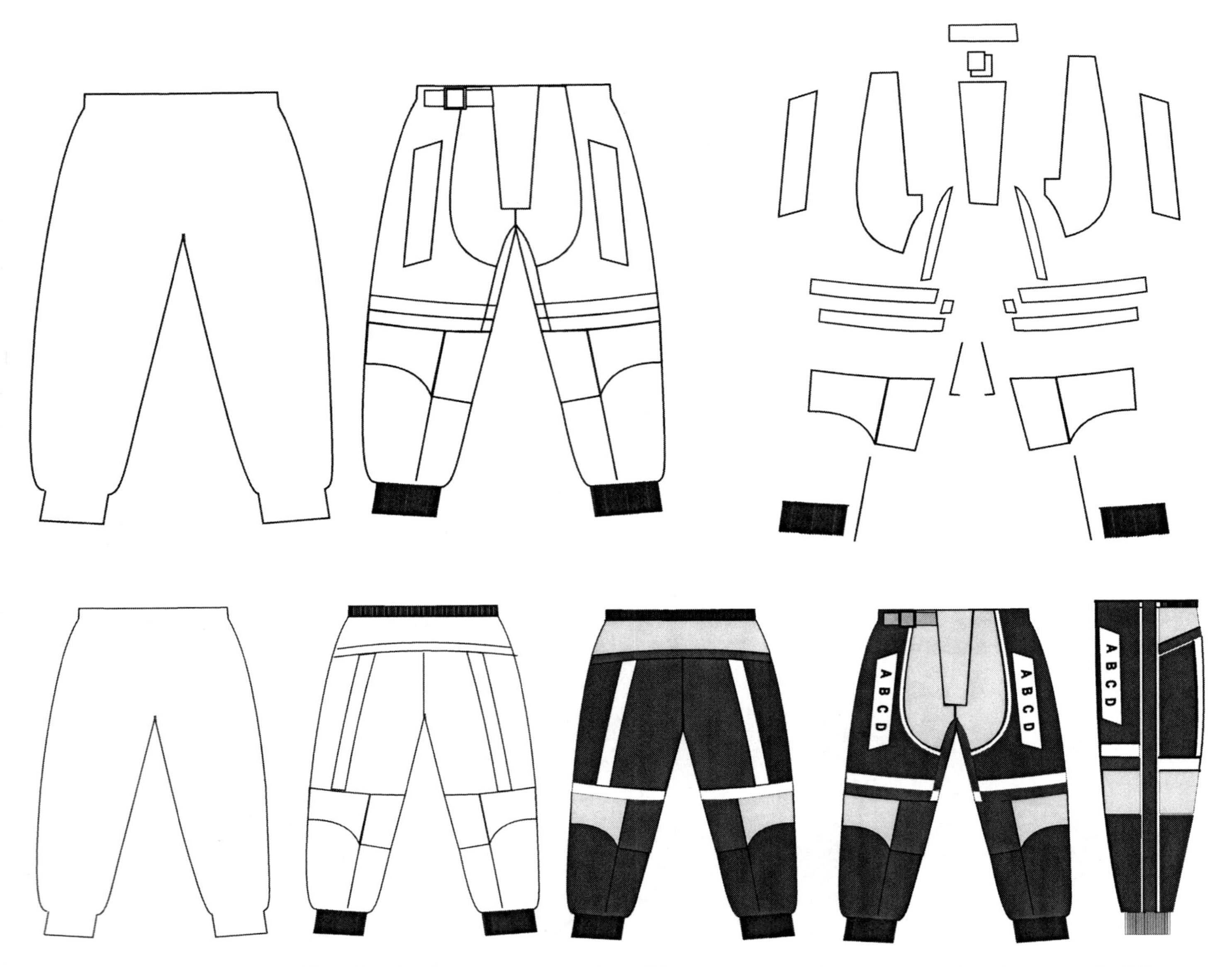

Motor cross trousers, like the jackets, are made with many panels in several colors and different fabrics. They have Kevlar to protect the inner leg, knitted banding at the side seam, cuff, waist band and across the back stretching for comfort when the rider is on the bike. The exploded version shows most of the pieces are drawn as the jacket as closed objects so that color can be added. Motor bike wear never looks very comfortable when you see the garment on the rail or flat on a table, but they are designed for comfort and protection when riding.

CHAPTER 4

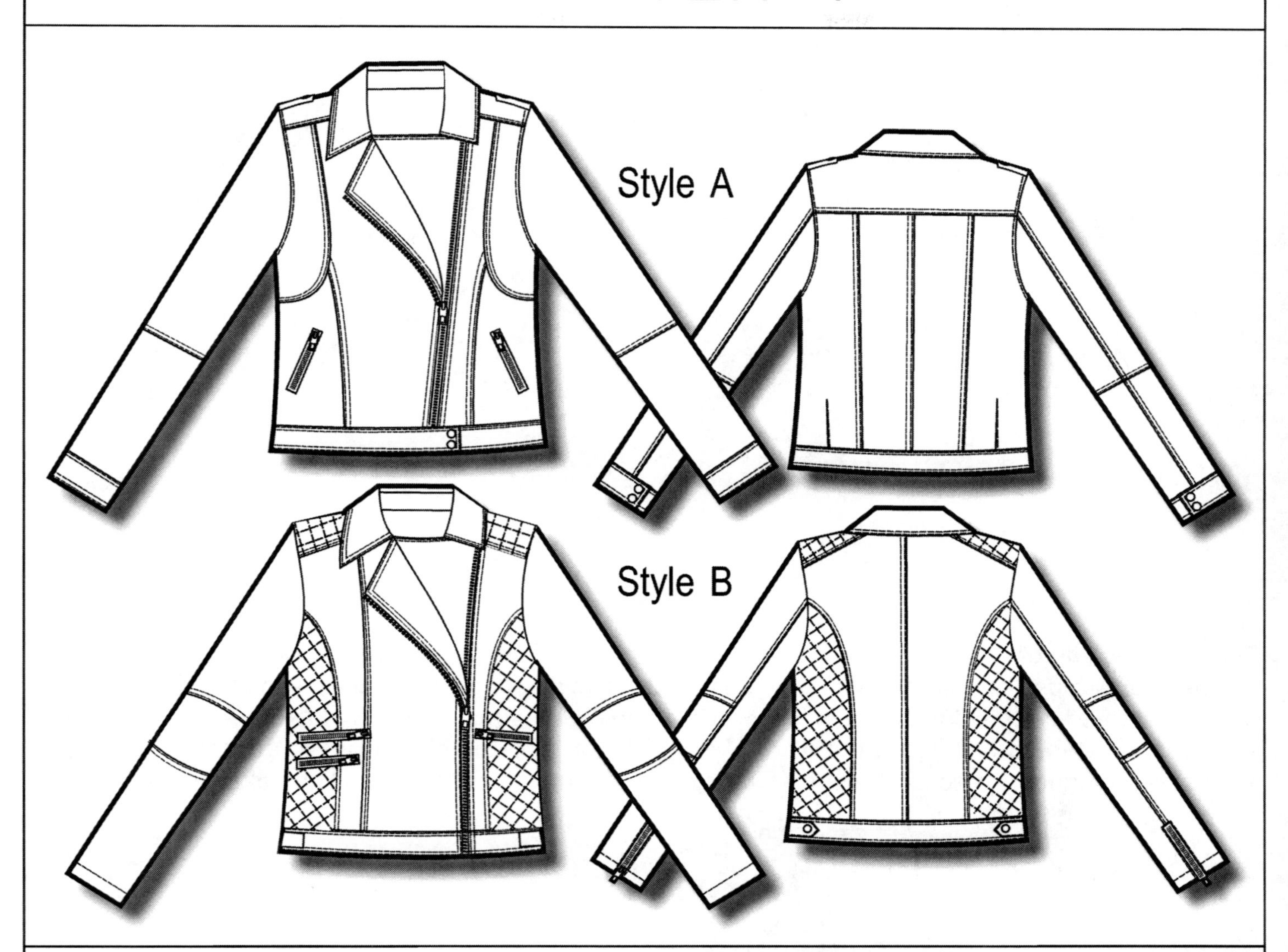

LADIES FASHION BIKE JACKET

The previous chapter on motor bike clothing dealt with items that were designed specifically for wearing when riding a bike, but no one would wear these jackets on a bike as they wouldn't give any protection. Bike styles have always been popular and glamorized in many films such as Easy Rider, projecting a rebellious image. Designers often feature them in their ranges worn with t-shirts and jeans. Popular with men and women, the jacket can mix well with many different items. The genuine bike jackets in this style are made from high quality leather and could have wadding, for warmth and protection. These 2 jackets are made from PVC and will be a fraction of the cost of the genuine jackets.

The following specification for the 2 styles shows the development of style A and style B. These jackets are the same shape and measurements, only the style details are different. I have used the short biker jacket from the last chapter as a template to start off the new styles and to show the differences between a genuine biker jacket and the fashion versions.

I have made these specifications as visual as possible concentrating on the design features, with the minimum of text. The style features can be interchangeable between the two jackets.

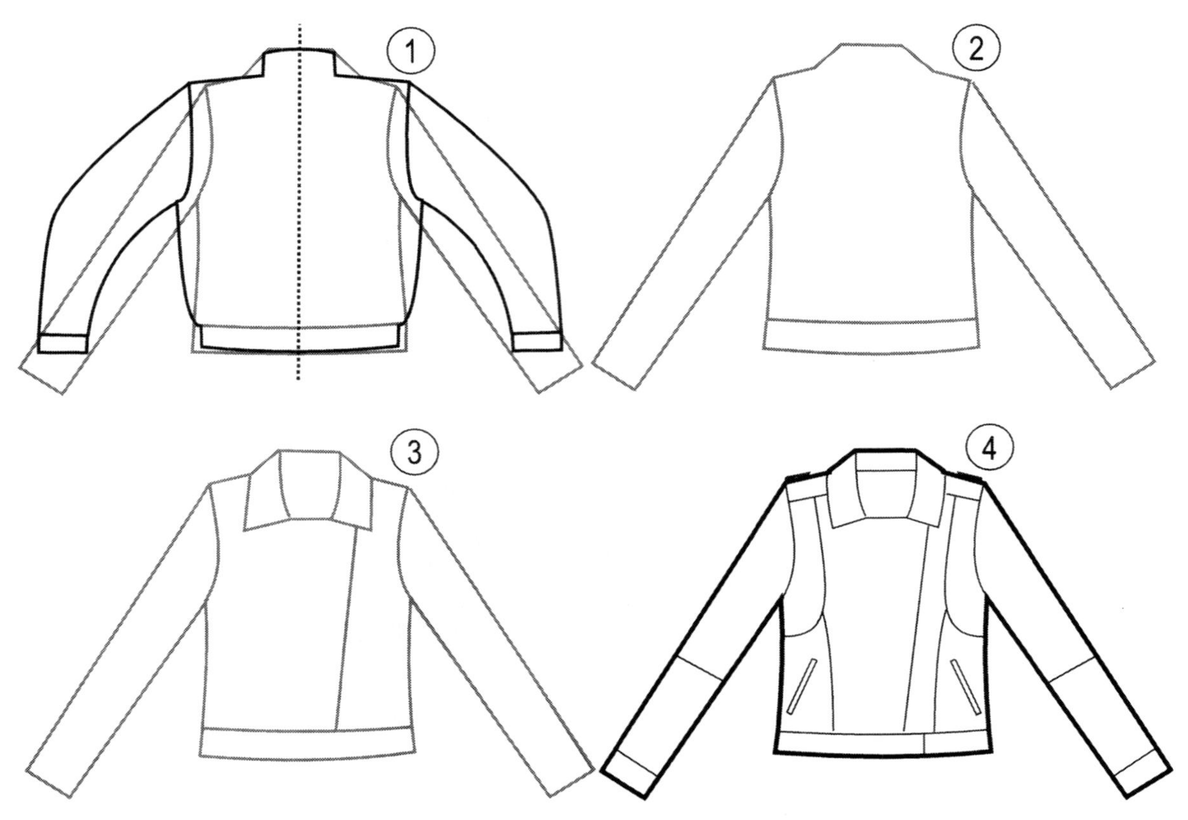

The black outline of drawing 1 shows the short bike jacket featured in the previous chapter. The new outline in drawings 1 & 2 are for both fashion jackets. The most noticeable difference between the true biker jacket and the fashion jacket is the shape of the sleeves (as shown on the black outline), which are cut for comfort when riding the bike. The true biker jacket is also wider to accommodate body armor and filling for protection & warmth. Drawing 3 & 4 are creating the outlines of style A.

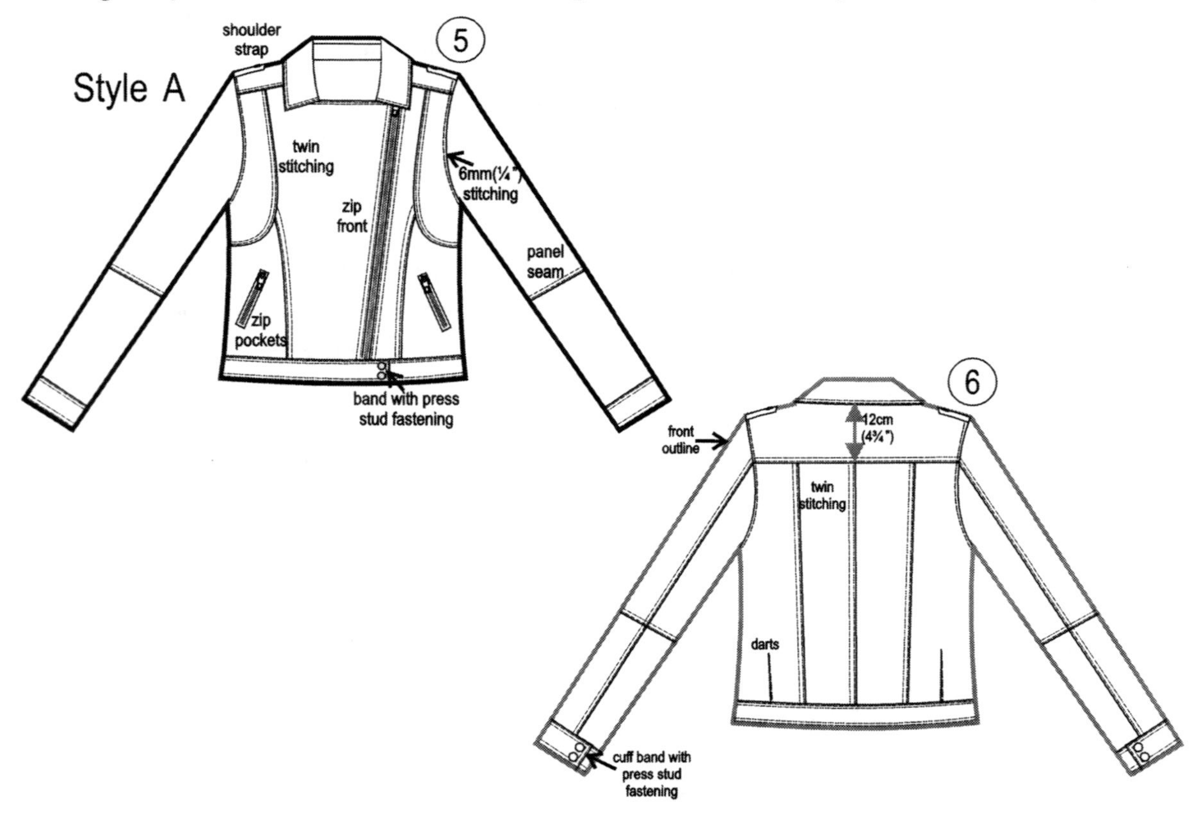

Drawing 5 & 6 are the finished front & back. The back outline is exactly the same as the front

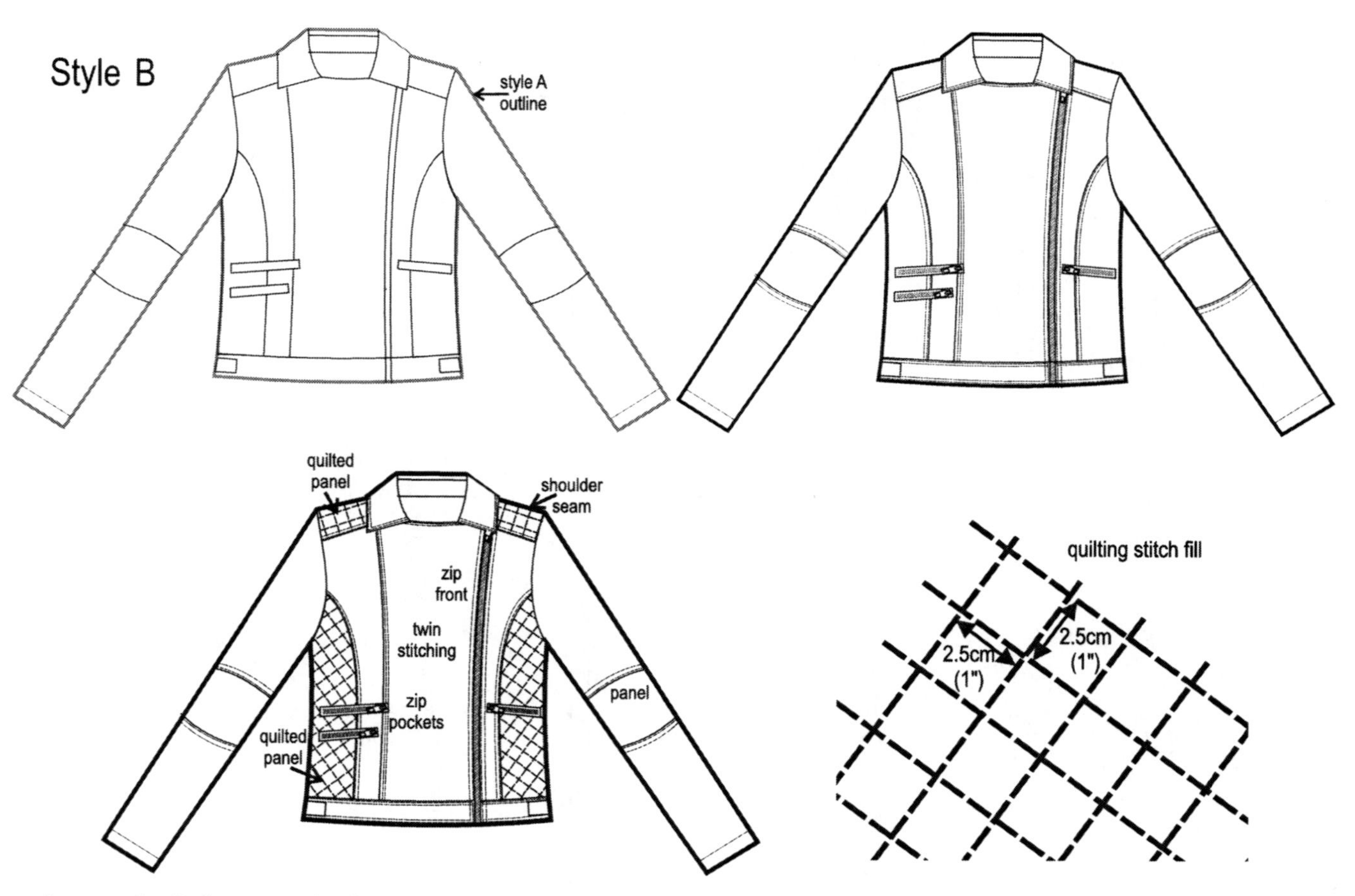

Creating style B from style A, adding each layer of detail.

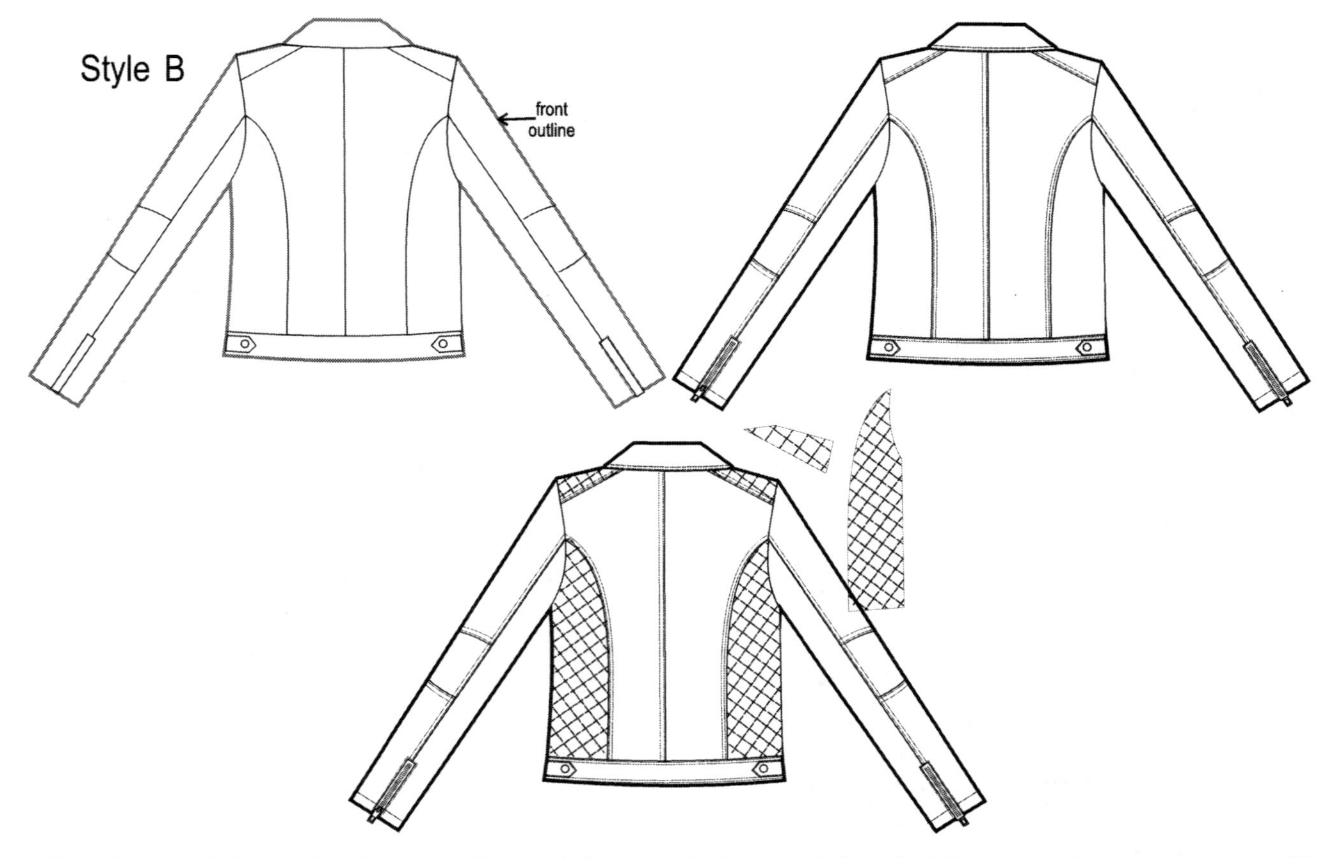

Creating the back from the front outline adding each layer of detail. After creating the quilting fill, add to the panels, which are enclosed objects with the power clip tool.

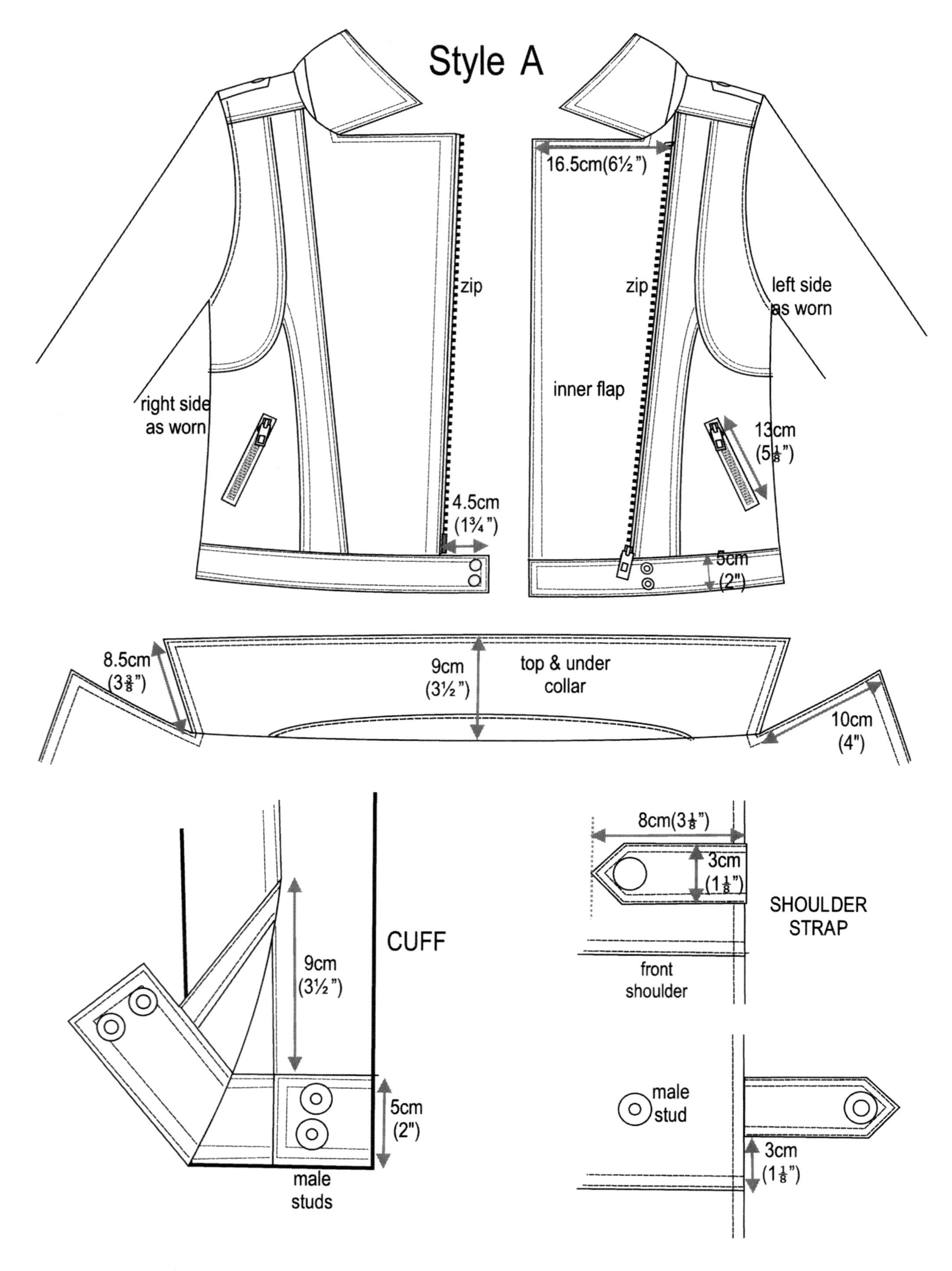
Style A
16.5cm(6½")
zip
zip
left side
as worn
inner flap
right side
as worn
13cm
(5⅛")
4.5cm
(1¾")
5cm
(2")
8.5cm
(3⅜")
9cm
(3½")
top & under
collar
10cm
(4")
8cm(3⅛")
3cm
(1⅛")
SHOULDER
STRAP
9cm
(3½")
CUFF
front
shoulder
male
stud
5cm
(2")
male
studs
3cm
(1⅛")

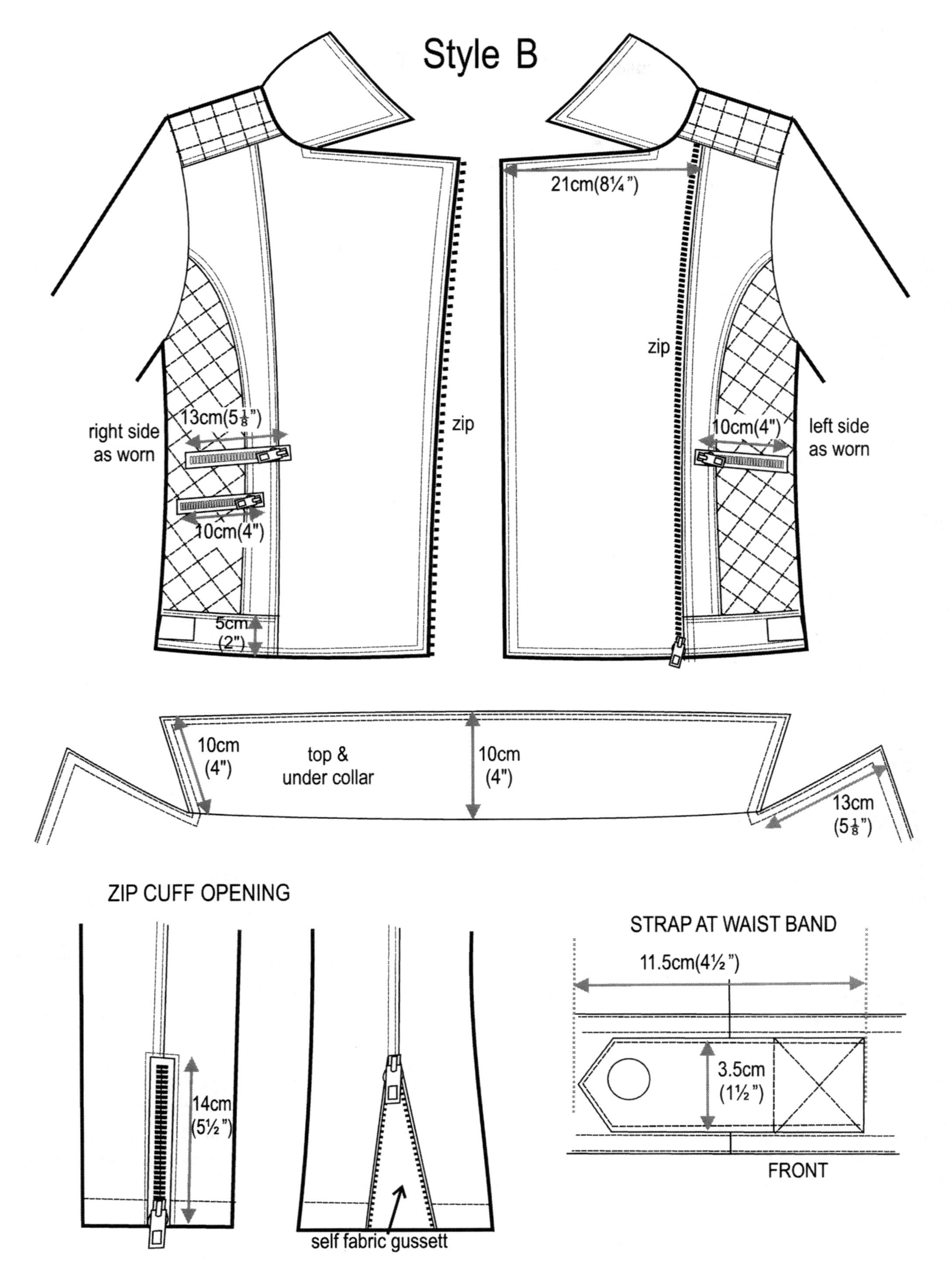
Style B
21cm(8¼")
zip
right side as worn
13cm(5⅛")
10cm(4")
zip
10cm(4")
left side as worn
5cm (2")
10cm (4")
top & under collar
10cm (4")
13cm (5⅛")
ZIP CUFF OPENING
14cm (5½")
self fabric gussett
STRAP AT WAIST BAND
11.5cm(4½")
3.5cm (1½")
FRONT

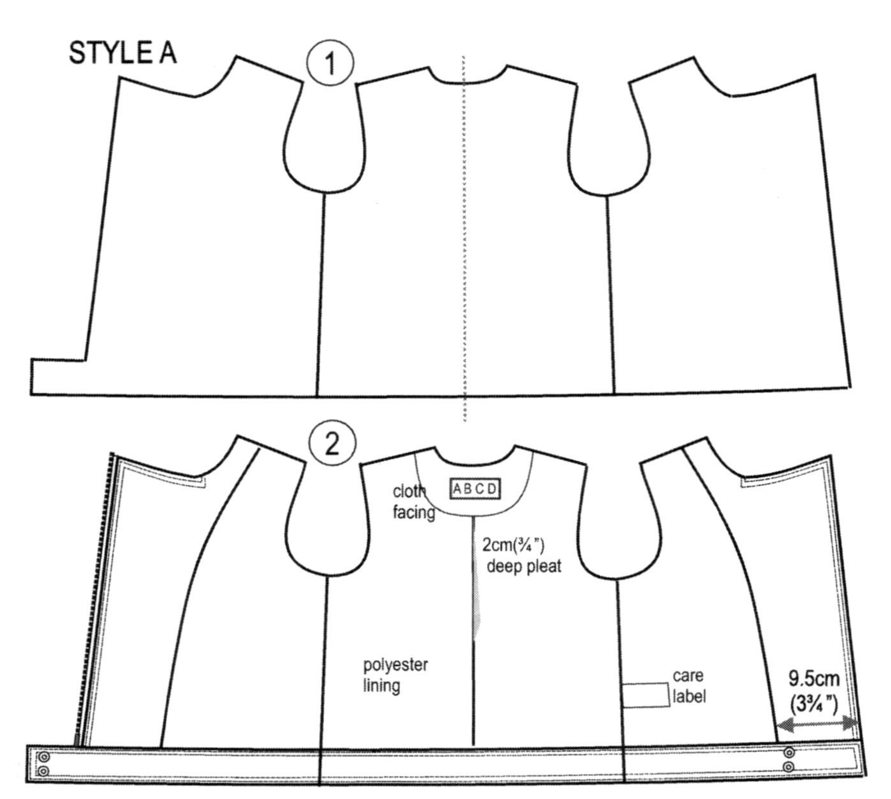

Drawing 1 is the basic outline for style A lining opened out.

Do the outline in 2 halves as shown in the chapter on templates, and when satisfied the proportions are correct combine the 2 halves together.

Drawing 2 is the inside with the finished detail completed.

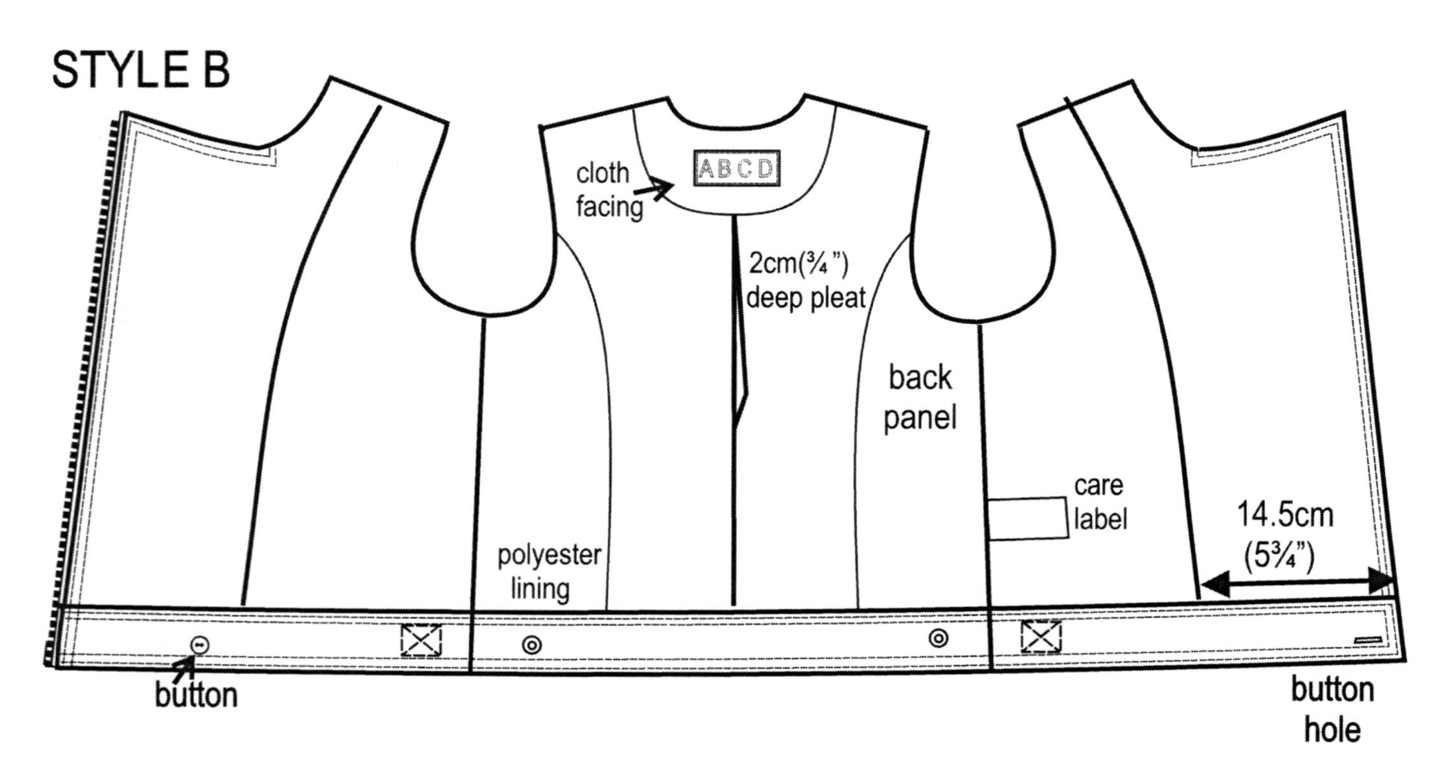

Style B is adapted from style A lining. Often using existing shapes is quicker and easier than creating a new drawing.

Style B lining differs slightly from Style A: there is a back panel in the lining and the inner facings are wider. The other difference between the two styles is the detail on the bottom bands of the jackets. The inside of the jackets do not have too much detail, but including them in your specification is always helpful for the factory.

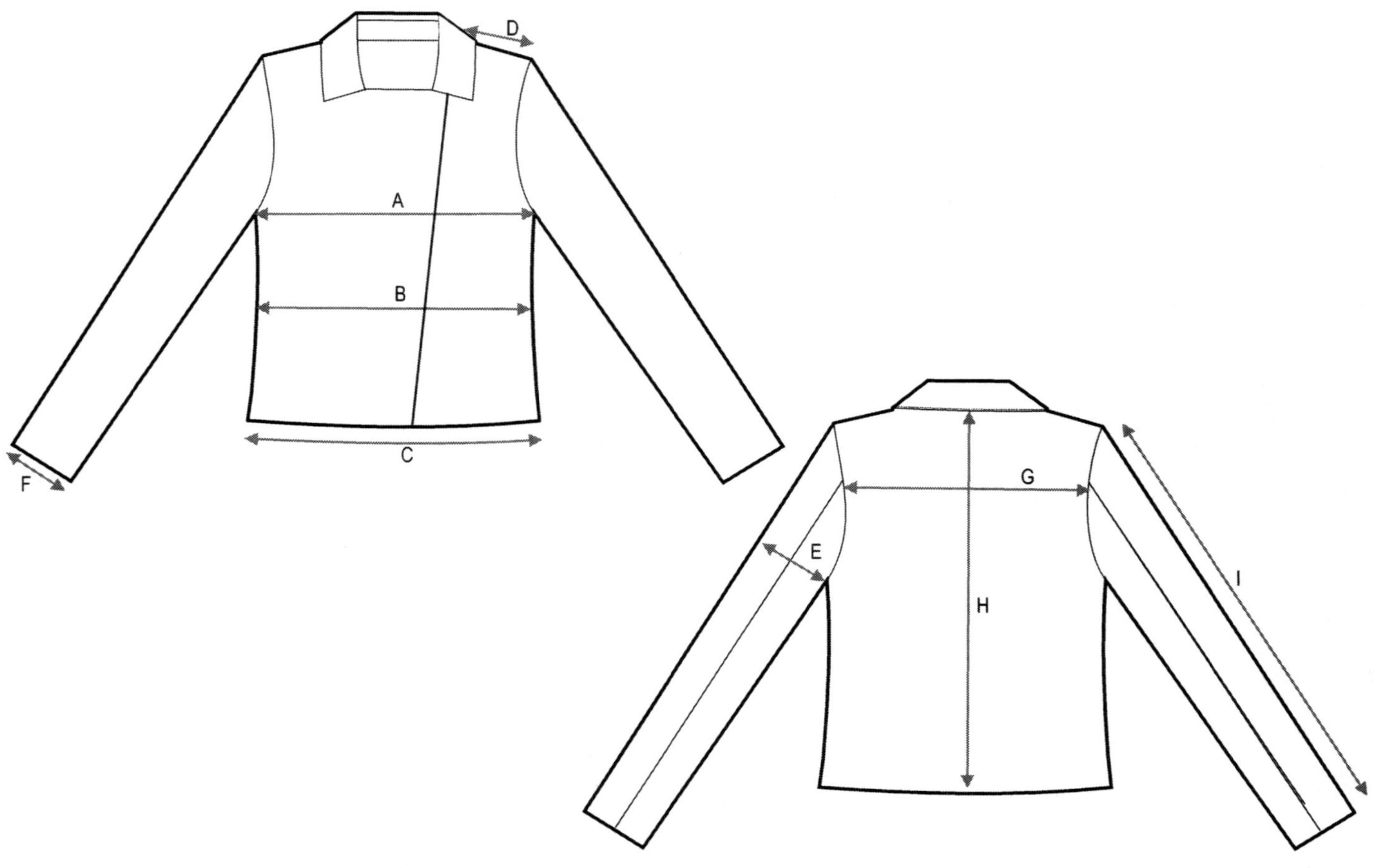

As the measurements are the same for both jackets I have created one size chart. The drawings showing the measuring points are basic outlines, and do not show style details, but this is sufficient to show the critical measurements.

SIZE	UK 12	
	cms	Inches
A. Bust at base of armhole	100	39⅜"
B. Waist	88	34⅝"
C. Hem	92	36¼"
D. Shoulder, measured on the natural shoulder line	11	4⅜"
E. Biceps	37	14½"
F. Cuff fastened	24	9½"
G. Back width	37	14½"
H. Full length from neck seam including bottom band	56	22"
I. Sleeve crown to bottom edge of the cuff including any bands	64	25¼"

CHAPTER 5

DENIM JACKET

This jacket never seems to go out of fashion, which was a good reason to include it in the book. But I realized that the outline and measurements were the same as the fashion bike jackets. I suspect that originally it was popular with cowboys for the same reason bikers like this style, because being short and fitted it's comfortable when riding. The shape is classic and a good addition to your library.

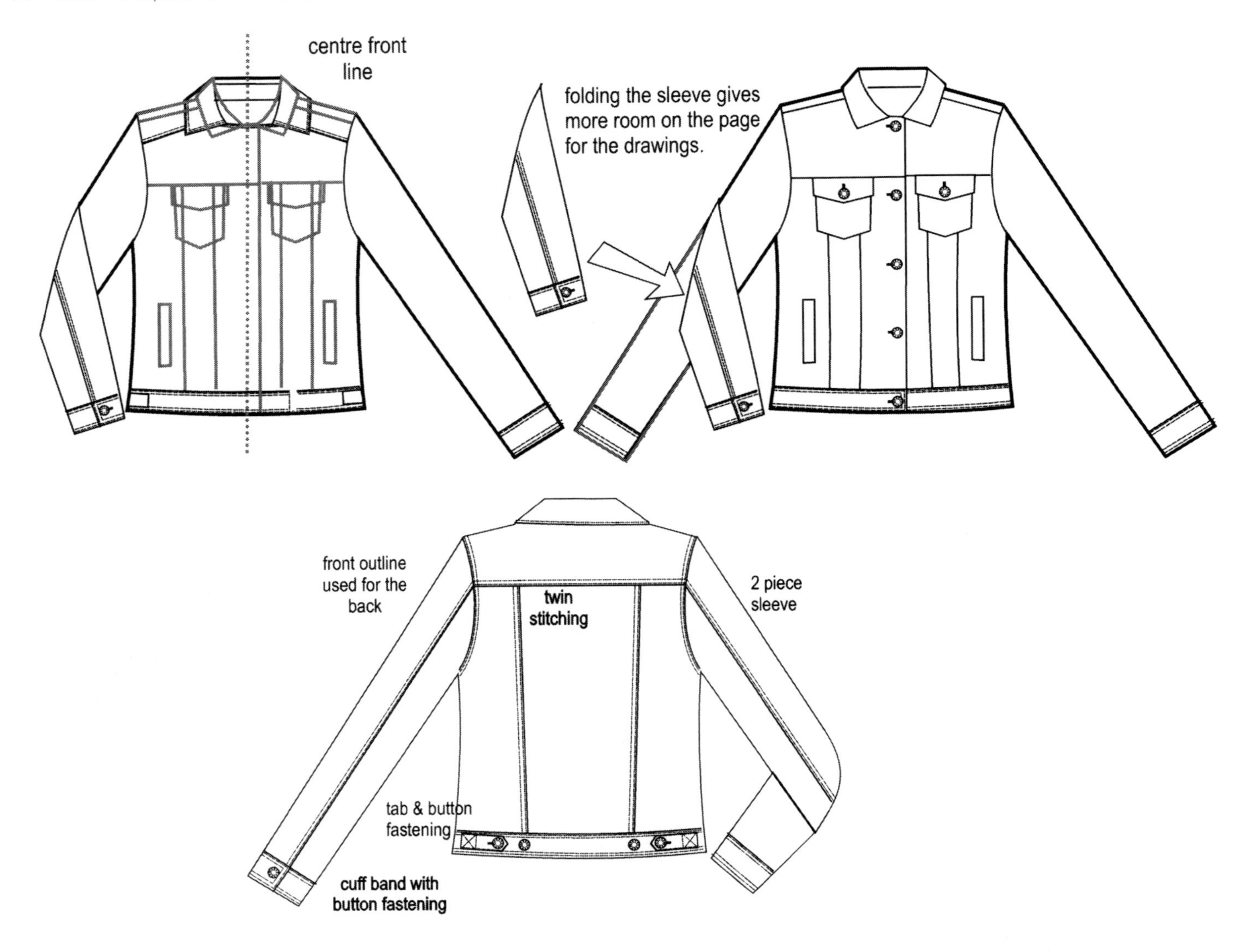

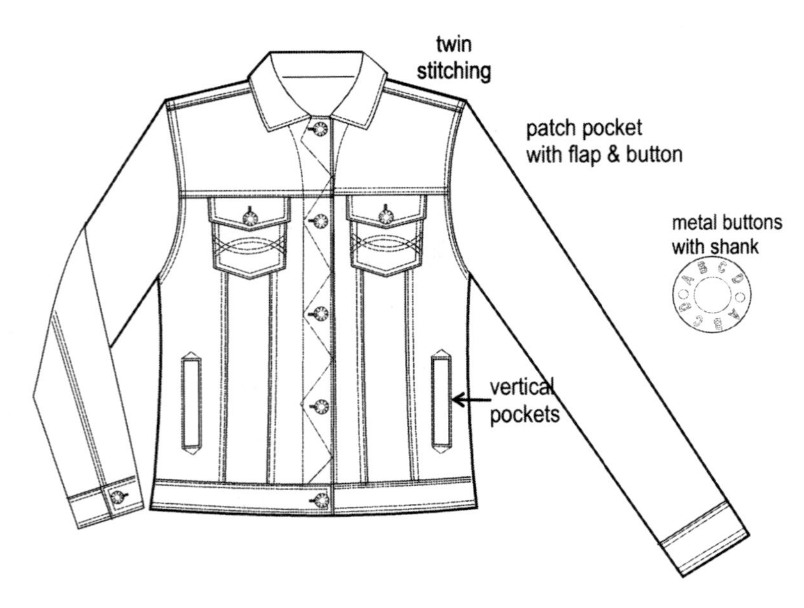

For the front I have used style B bike jacket and removed the panel seams and zip, but left the collar and shoulder seam as a guide for drawing the new collar and shoulder position. I copied the cuff details from style A and added the center front line for the position of the buttons. Finally I sketched the outline of the pockets and front panel seams. Style A was used for the back with the center back seam deleted and the side straps added to the back waist band. At this stage be sure that the first draft is correct before you start adding all the stitch detail to the final drawings.

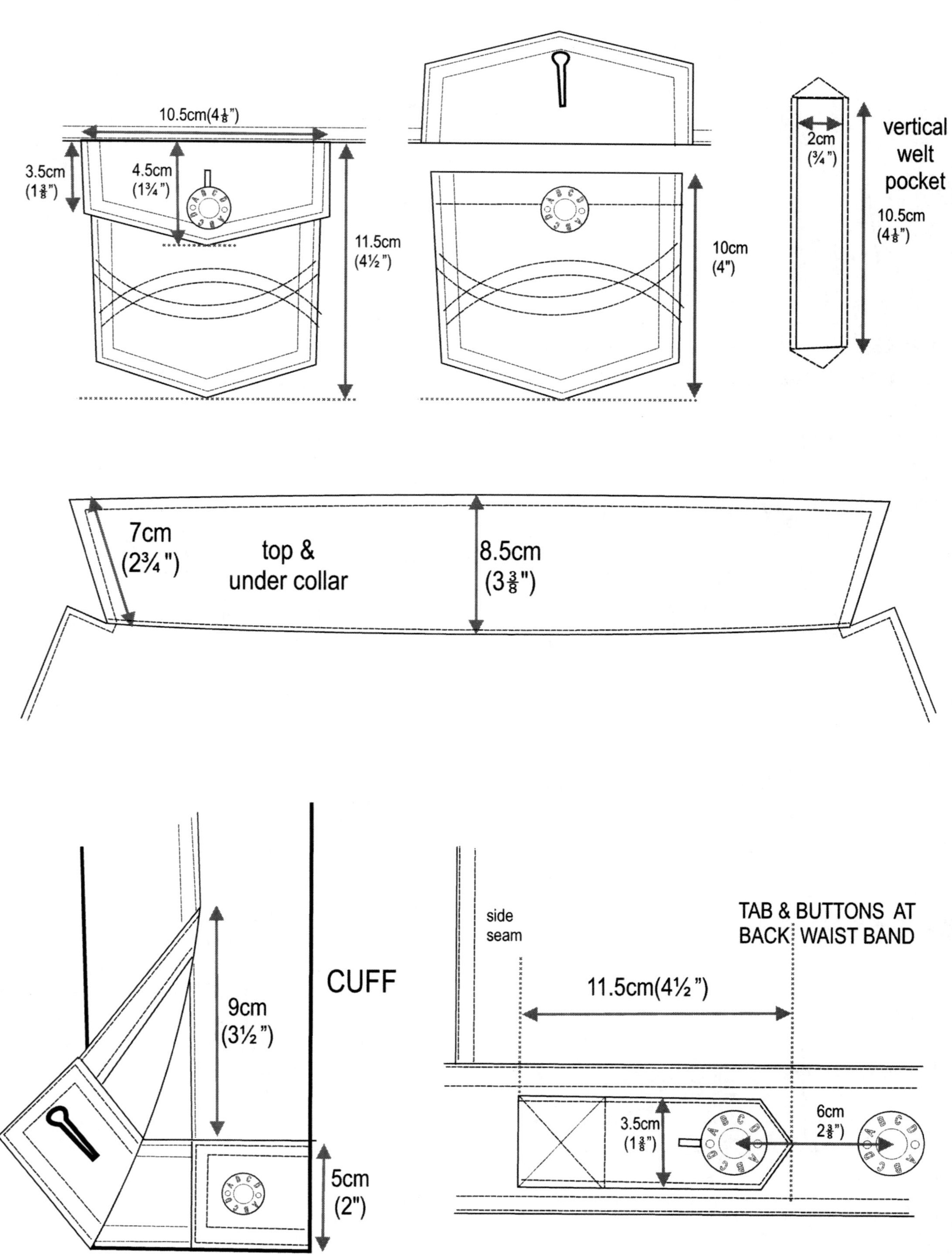
10.5cm(4⅛")
3.5cm (1⅜")
4.5cm (1¾")
11.5cm (4½")
10cm (4")
2cm (¾")
vertical welt pocket
10.5cm (4⅛")
7cm (2¾")
top & under collar
8.5cm (3⅜")
CUFF
9cm (3½")
5cm (2")
side seam
TAB & BUTTONS AT BACK WAIST BAND
11.5cm(4½")
3.5cm (1⅜")
6cm 2⅜")

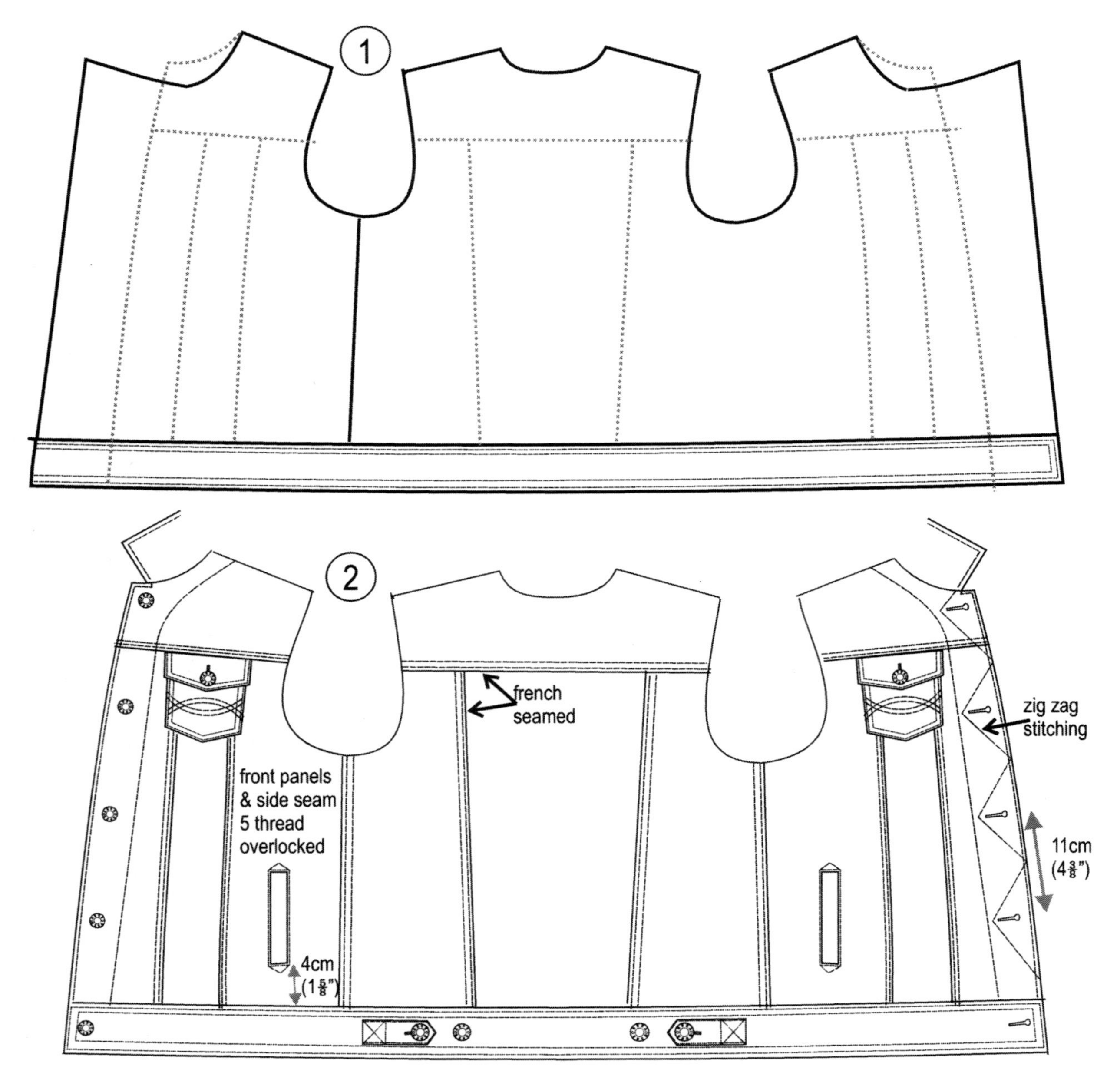

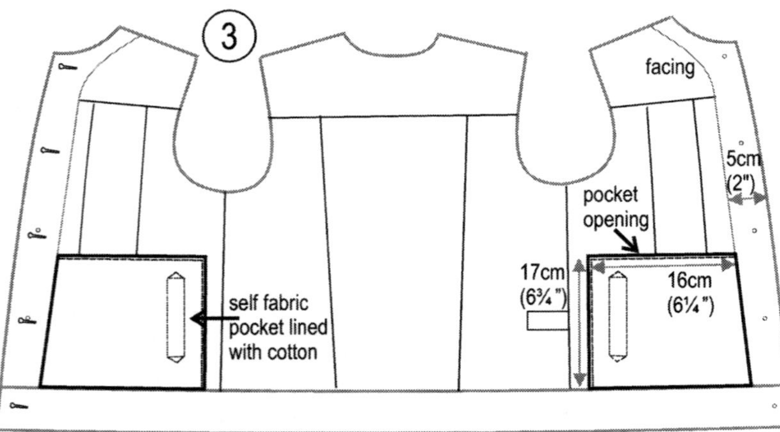

Drawing 1 is the outline of biker jacket A. The details of the denim jacket are shown with a dotted line. Drawing 2 is the completed opened out jacket. Drawing 3 is the inside. It is not necessary to show all the inside detail except the inner pockets and the width of the inner band. The jacket seams are either 5–thread over–locked or french–seamed and this is indicated on the drawing.

SIZE	UK 12	
	cms	Inches
A. Bust at base of armhole.	100	39⅜"
B. Waist	88	34⅝"
C. Hem.	92	36¼"
D. Shoulder, measured on the natural shoulder line.	11	4⅜"
E. Biceps.	37	14½"
F. Cuff fastened.	24	9½"
G. Back width.	37	14½"
H. Full length from neck seam including bottom band.	56	22"
I. Sleeve crown to bottom edge of the cuff including any bands.	64	25¼"

CHAPTER 6

OVERCOAT

This is a classic modern shape that can be updated with a lot of interesting detail. The first step is to create a style drawing of the front and back. More frequently today, customers are turning to their suppliers for new ideas. Once the first style is created, the drawings can be used as a basis for a design brief by using the flat drawing and showing different options. If you feel particularly creative, find a suitable figure to scan into your PC, trace around the figure and superimpose the overcoat on to it showing each figure with different style details. Add lines to show movement. Corel has an application called mesh fill where you can mix other colors, showing light and dark areas creating a more interesting presentation. I do not consider myself very proficient at this, but it does impress customers if you make the effort to provide a design package as part of the overall product development procedure.

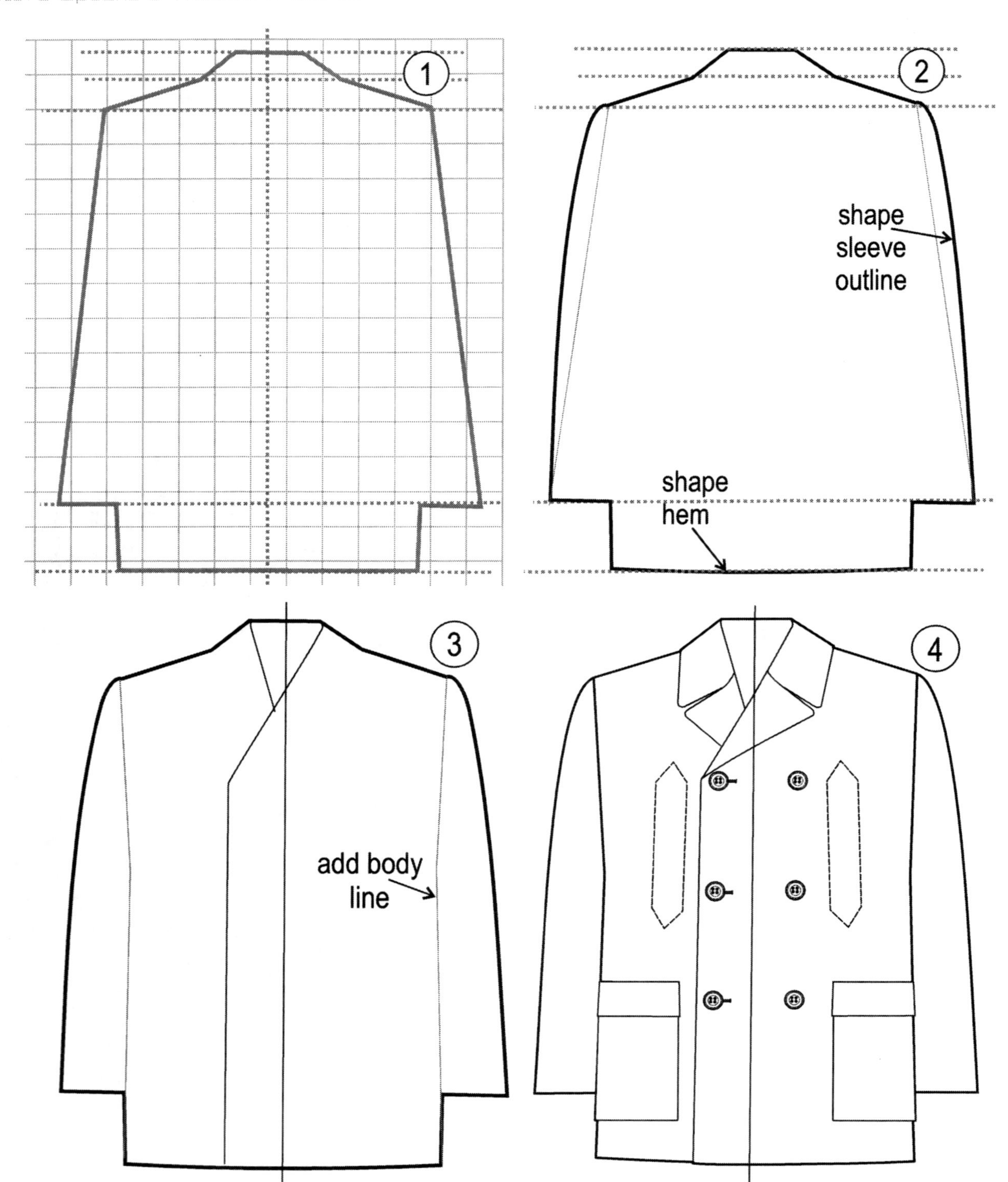

This first drawing is the most important because the key to drawing an accurate shape is to achieve the right proportions in the width and the height of the garment. Figure 1 is formed by connecting straight lines from the collar crease to the outer edge of the collar, to the shoulder point, the bottom of the sleeve and to the bottom of the coat hem as shown by the horizontal lines. I check that both sides of the coat are an equal distance apart by adding the vertical center front line, as the buttons will need to be centered equally either side of the line. Working with a grid helps you ensure that the left and right sides of the garment are level. Figure 2 shows a small amount of curve added to the sleeve and hem to complete the outline. You can only be sure that your drawing is accurate when you add the front edge, body line, buttons and the outline of the pockets as in figure 3 & 4. Figure 5 completes the front.

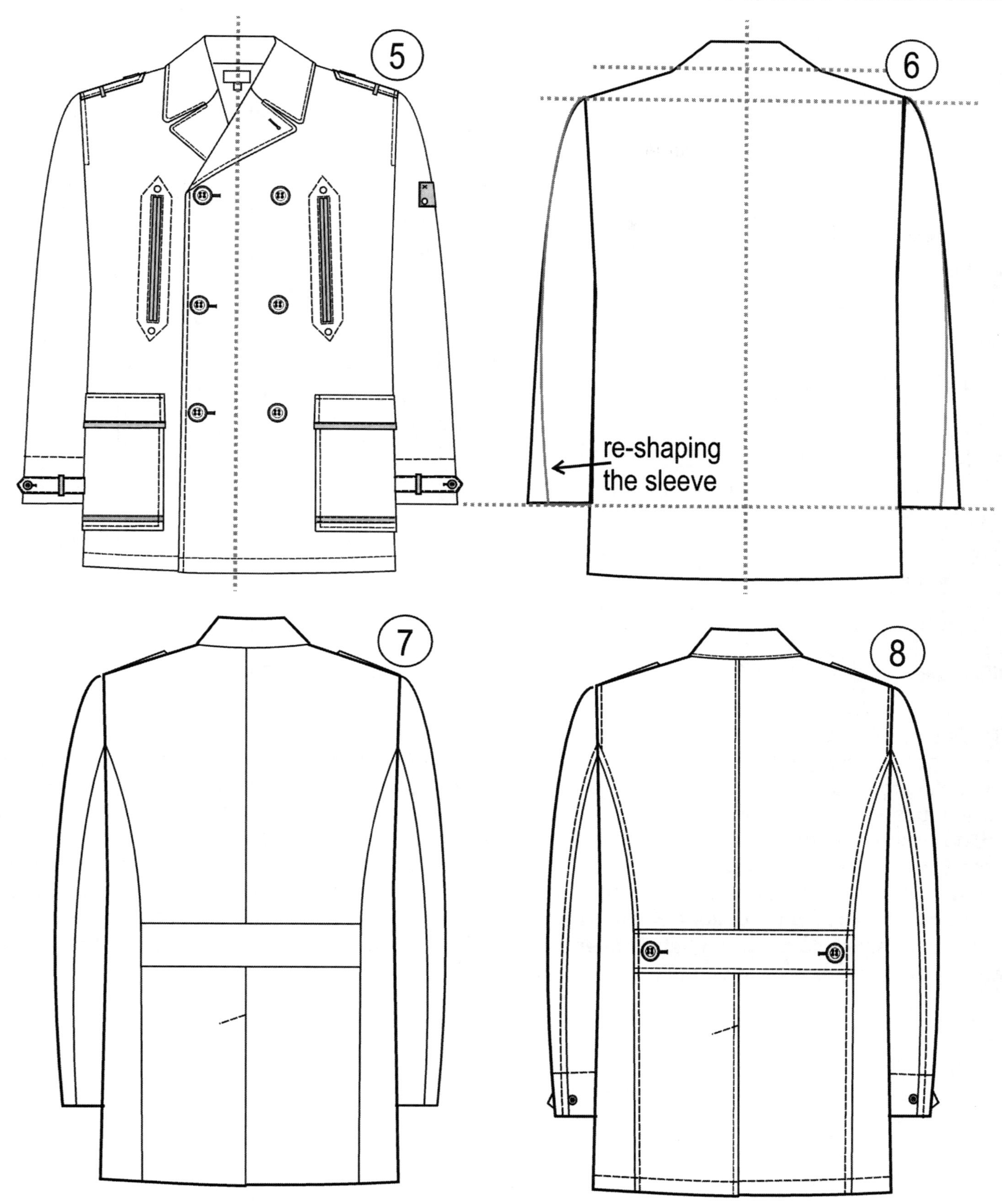

From this point onwards the rest of the style detail will fit into place. The back outline is exactly the same as the front except I have narrowed the cuff and tapered in the sleeve slightly. Figures 6 to 8 show the completion of the back. With a little bit of adjustment these outlines can be re-used for many jackets and coats styles. See chapter on templates.

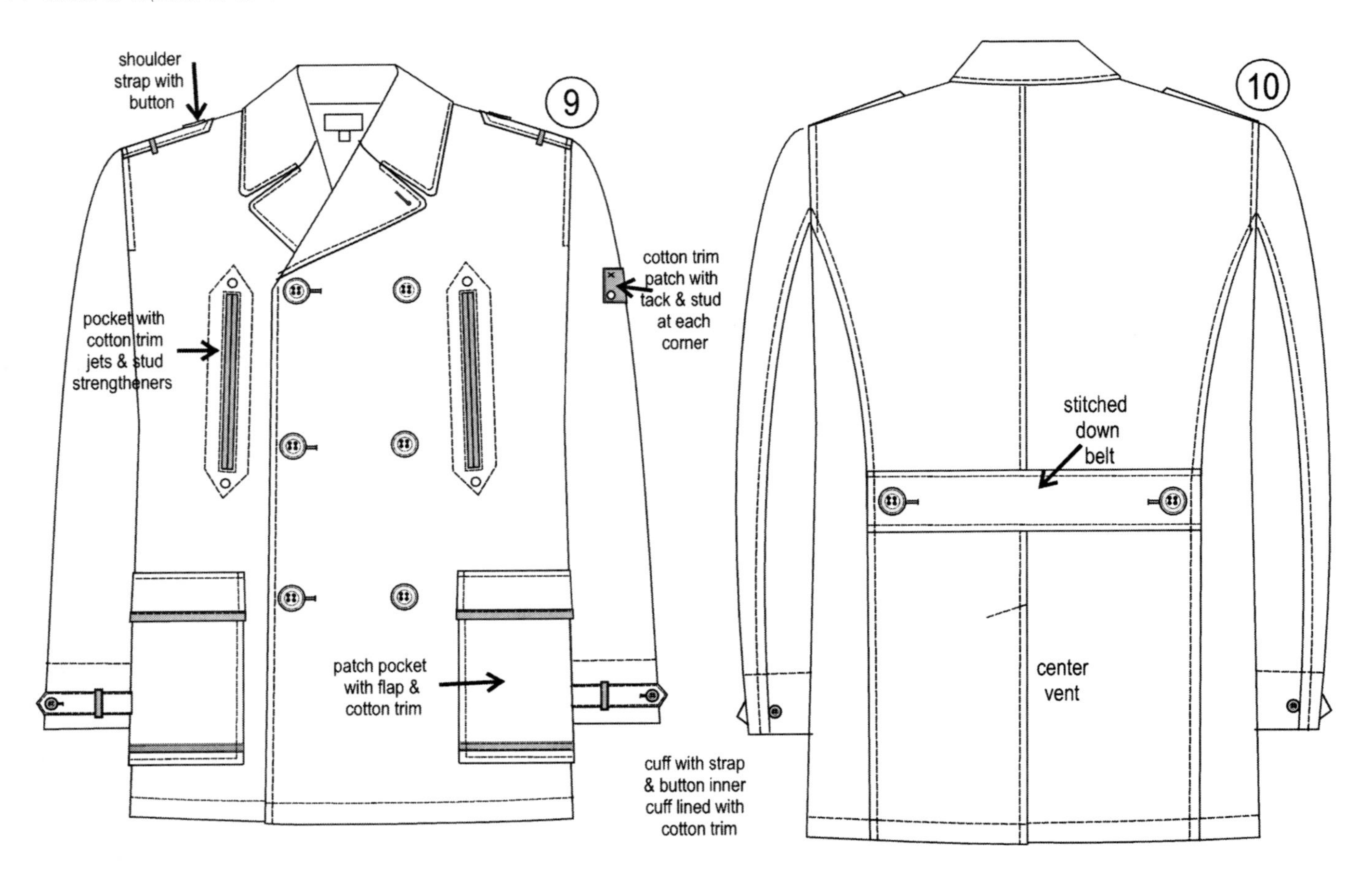

Illustrations 9 & 10 show the outside of the coat with text describing the style detail.

LININGS/INSIDE Illustration 11

The inside of a garment is as important as the outside whether it is fully–lined, half–lined, buggy–lined or unlined. Designers have gone to a lot of trouble to make the detail of the inside interesting and appealing to the customer. I've heard it said that men use a jacket or coat like a bag, especially those who refuse to carry a "man bag". The outside of this coat is well equipped with pockets and so is the inside; I usually carry a phone, cigarettes, lighter, pen and sometimes a camera with me at the same time so this was a good reason for me to buy this coat. Companies definitely pay more attention to the detail inside of a garment, and brands and labels like to add their own "signature" to the inside as a way of making it look different. The lining in this coat has many features, and I considered them important enough to show the details over 3 illustrations. Firstly, the overall appearance of the lining and each of the pockets separately.

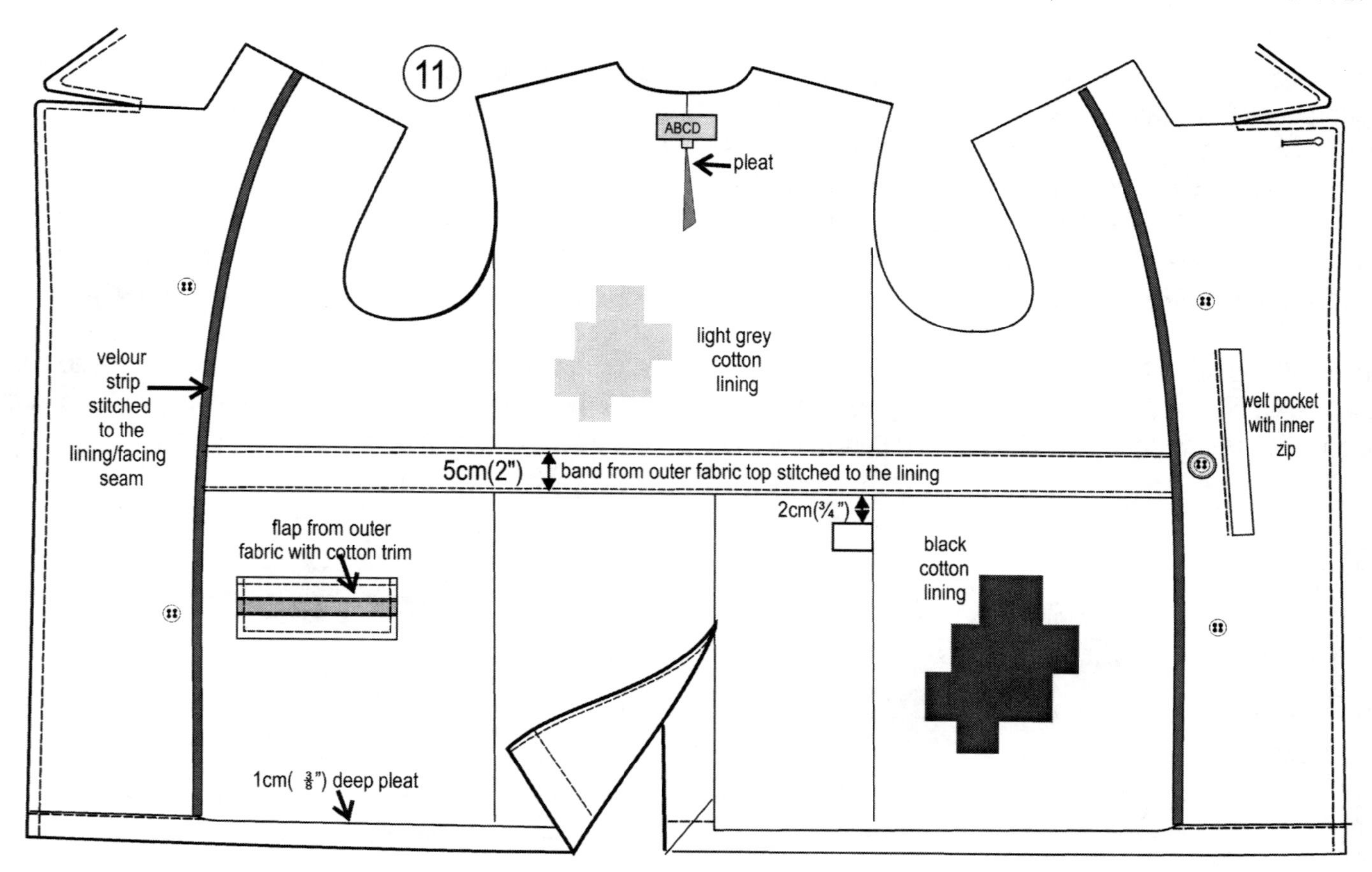

Lining

- All lining seams 5–thread over–locked.
- 5cm(2") wide outer fabric waist band.
- Upper body light grey cotton lining.
- Lower body black cotton lining.
- Lining 5–thread over–locked to the waist band.
- Band, edge stitched on both edges.
- 2cm (¾") pleat at the center back neck.
- Pleat stitched closed to below the brand label.
- 1cm (⅜") pleat at the hem.
- Vertical welt pocket with zip left facing as worn.
- Flap pocket lower forepart lining right side as worn.

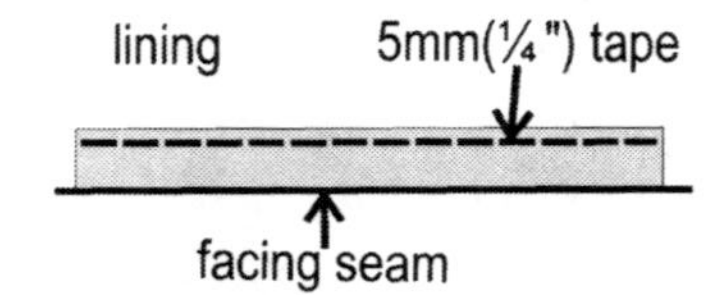

Labels

- Brand label sewn at center back neck 2.5cm(1") below the neck seam.
- Size tab stitched centrally under the bottom edge of the brand label.
- Care/identification label sewn in to the side seam, left side as worn
- Top edge of the label 2cm (¾") below the waist band.

Hem

- 4cm (1⅝") hem top stitched 2.5cm(1") from the folded edge.

Facing

- Velour tape stitched in to the facing/ lining seam and edge stitched to the lining, finished width of the tape 5mm(3/16")

INTERLININGS

Interlinings, although never seen in the finished garment are very important in the manufacturing process and to the finished appearance of the garment. Most garments need some parts fused with interlining, either to improve their appearance or strengthen areas such as button holes, pockets and to prevent distortion when sewing. It should not be left to the factories' discretion as to what quality of interlining is used and which parts are fused, however the factory may suggest changes that would benefit the product. This should always be followed up and if you are in agreement amend the specification. (This applies to every aspect of the specification and the factory should be encouraged to give input wherever they think necessary, but once a final specification is agreed upon they must not make any further changes without your approval.)

The interlining specification achieves two aims: first to specify which interlinings are used where, and second, to serve as a visual guide and check for the fusing press operative. The style below has many parts that need interlining, and the specification clearly shows all the parts and how many there are. An added help is to color code each part.

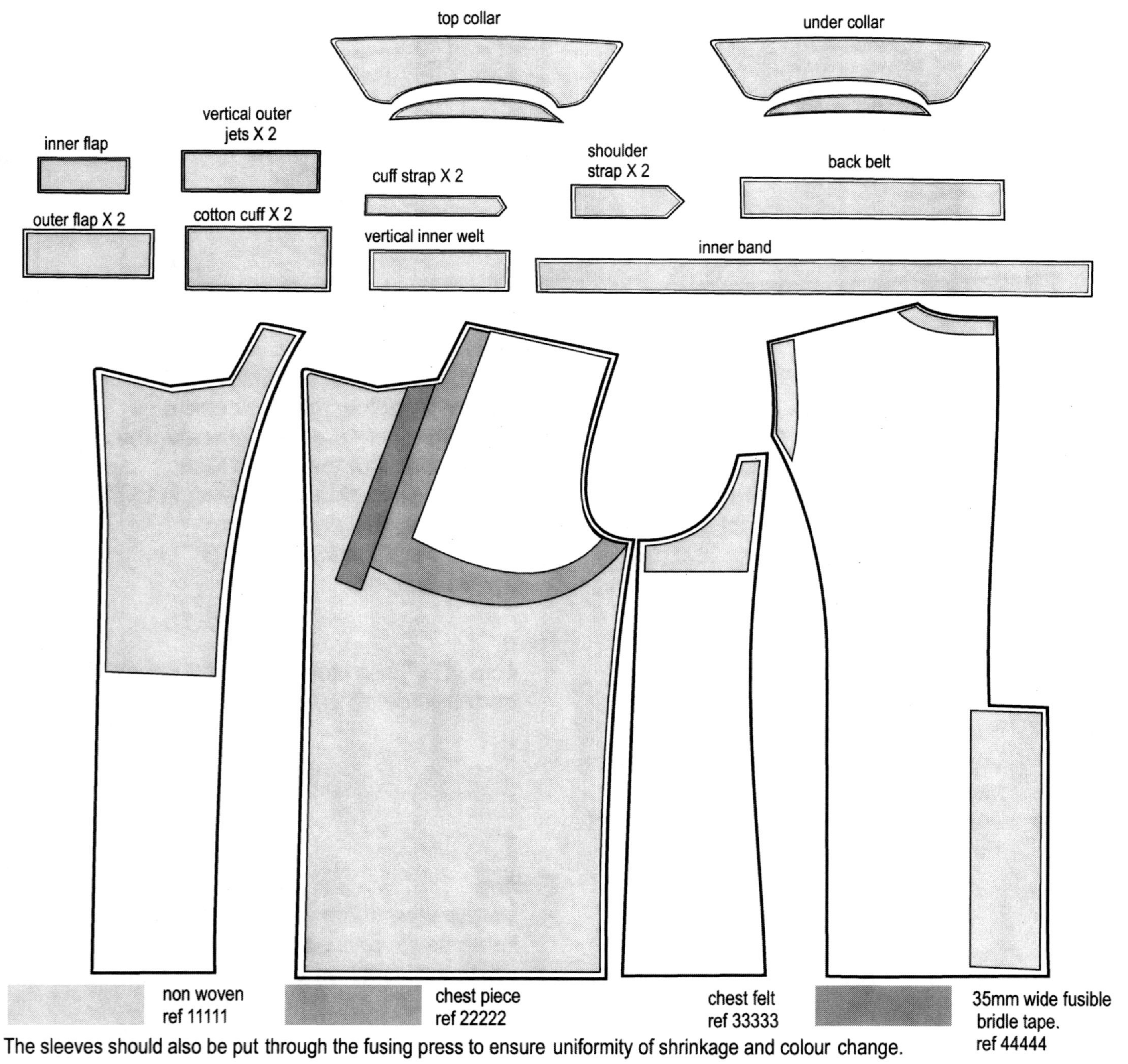

The sleeves should also be put through the fusing press to ensure uniformity of shrinkage and colour change.

After the panel seams are sewn, the pockets are assembled and attached to the front. I have not graded the pocket sizes, so we can show the position of the pockets. If the pockets need to be graded then the positions can be finalized when size sets are approved. (Usually the smallest, middle and largest sizes are sent).

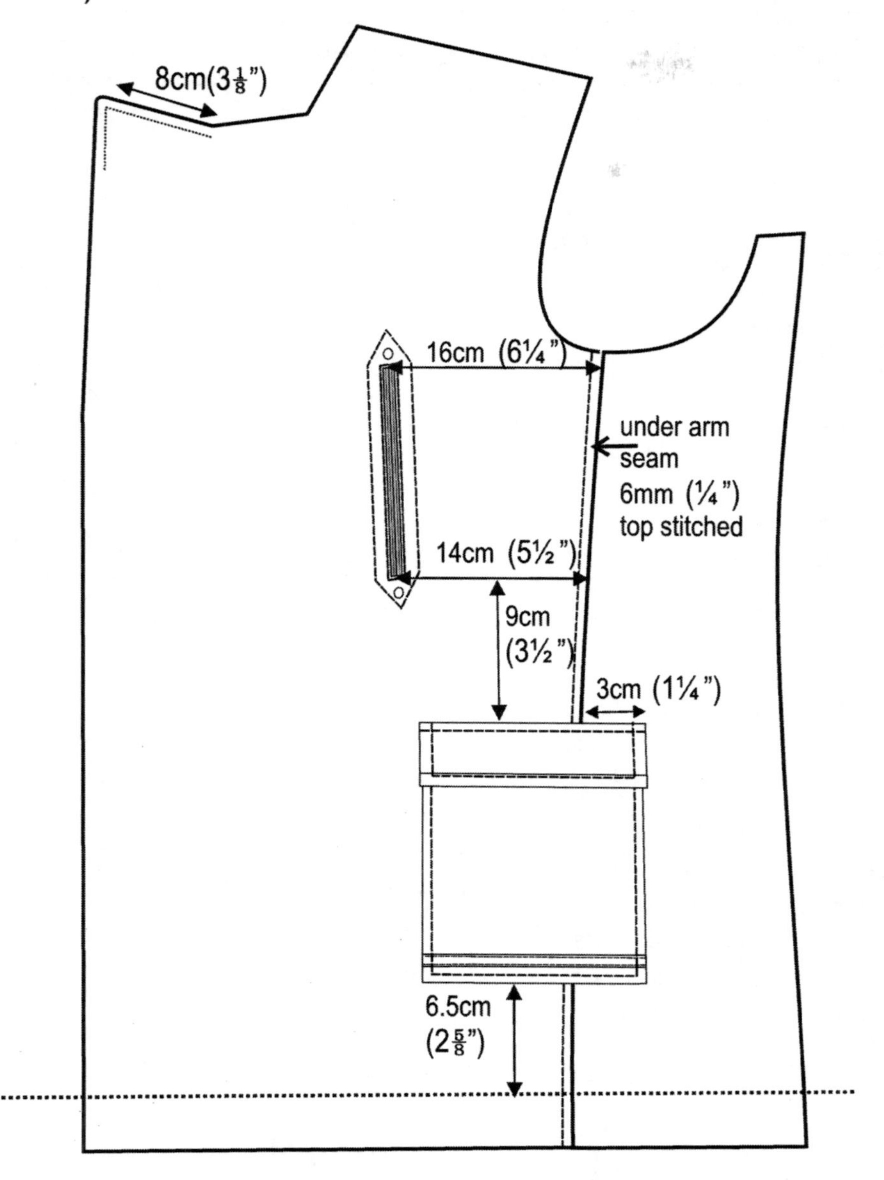

Fronts

- 2 panel front
- All seams 1cm (⅜")
- Under arm and side seam raised and top stitched 6mm (¼")
- Shoulder seam pressed open
- Lapel step to finish 8cm (3⅛")
- Fronts, collar and lapel top stitched 6mm (¼")

Patch pocket

- With flap on each front
- Bottom edge of the patch 6.5cm (2⅝") from the finished hem
- Back edge of the flap positioned 3cm (1¼") past the underarm seam
- Vertical jetted pocket on each front.
- Bottom corner of the pocket opening 9cm (3½") from the top edge of the flap &14cm (5½") from the under arm seam.
- Top corner of the pocket opening 16cm (6¼") from the under arm seam at the base of the armhole.

OUTER POCKETS

When writing specification for pockets it is necessary to add as much detail as possible, not only because pockets are functional but also to ensure the style detail is correct. If, as in this example, the pockets are the same dimensions for all sizes, the measurements can be added to the drawing. I use the same format for all flap pockets, showing the flap down and then folded back to show the pocket opening underneath. The vertical front pocket is an important style feature of the coat; I have covered the positioning of it and then concentrated on the style detail. There is symmetry between the opening, the stud position and the top stitching. The stitching and stud are not only decorative but add strength to the pocket, which is needed because the wearer will be constantly pushing their hands in the pockets and the corners can start to weaken and tear if not strengthened. Also note that the pocket bag is double stitched.

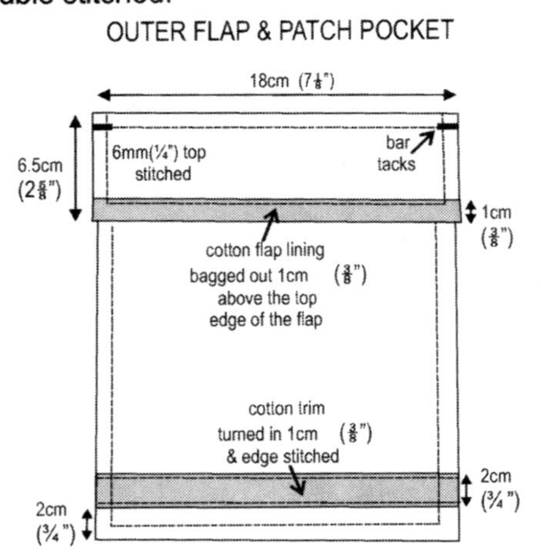

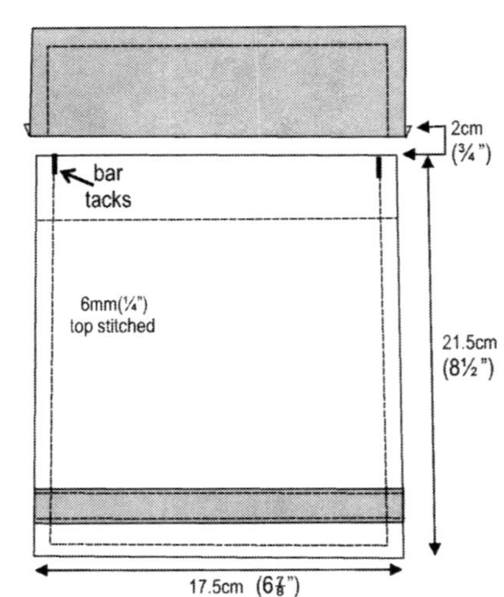

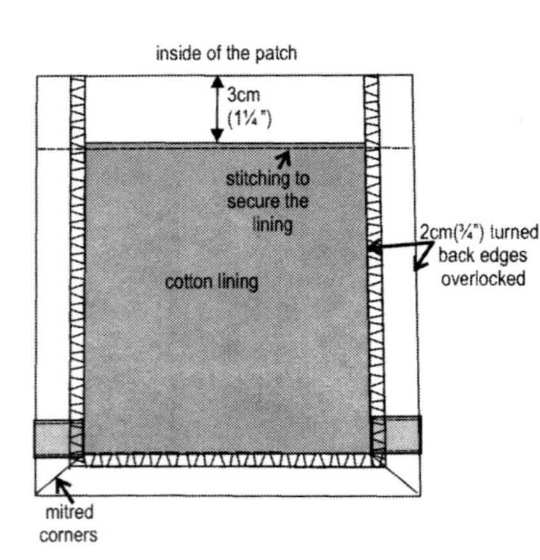

Patch pocket

- Black cotton trim edges turned in 1cm (⅜") & edge stitched to the patch pocket, trim to finish 2cm (¾") wide & 2cm (¾") from the bottom edge of the patch.
- Patch lined with black cotton lining
- 3cm (1¼") turn back at the top of the pocket
- Lining sewn to the turn back & edge stitched
- Edges of patch & lining over locked together
- Corners of patch mitred
- Patch 6mm (¼") top stitched to the forepart
- Vertical bar tack at the pocket corners.
- Patch to finish 21.5cm (8½") deep X 17.5cm (6⅞") wide

VERTICAL FRONT POCKET

black cotton pocket bag
16cm(6¼")
2 rows of stitching 1cm(⅜") between each row
pocket bearer
8cm (3¼")
3cm (1¼")
metal stud
black cotton pkt jets top stitched down the center
pocket edge stitched
outline stitching 6mm(¼") from the pocket seam
16cm (6¼")
1cm(⅜")

Flap

- Outer fabric flap fused
- Lined with black cotton lining.
- Lining is folded back and edge stitched to the front edge of the flap.
- Flap & lining are bagged out with 1cm (⅜") deep cotton piping showing at the front of the flap.
- Top edge of the flap is stitched to the forepart 2cm (¾") above the top edge of the patch, folded over and top stitched 6mm (¼").
- Flap to finish 18cm (7⅛") wide X 6.5cm (2⅝") deep.
- Horizontal bar tack at each corner of the flap

Vertical front pockets

- Black cotton jetted pockets
- Line of stitching down the center of each jet
- Pocket seam edge stitched
- Effective pocket opening
- Self fabric back pocket bearer to finish 4cm deep bottom edge turned in 1cm (⅜") and edge stitched
- Black cotton pocket bag 16cm wide from the edge of the pocket opening X 8cm (3¼") deep from the bottom of the pocket opening.
- Pocket bag stitched with 2 rows of stitching 1cm apart.
- 6mm (¼") wide black metal stud positioned centrally at the top & bottom of the pocket.
- Center of the stud 1cm (⅜") from the edge of the pocket.
- Out line stitching 6mm (¼") from the pocket seam on each side of the pocket opening, stitching finishing at a point centrally 3cm (1¼") from the top & bottom opening of the pocket.

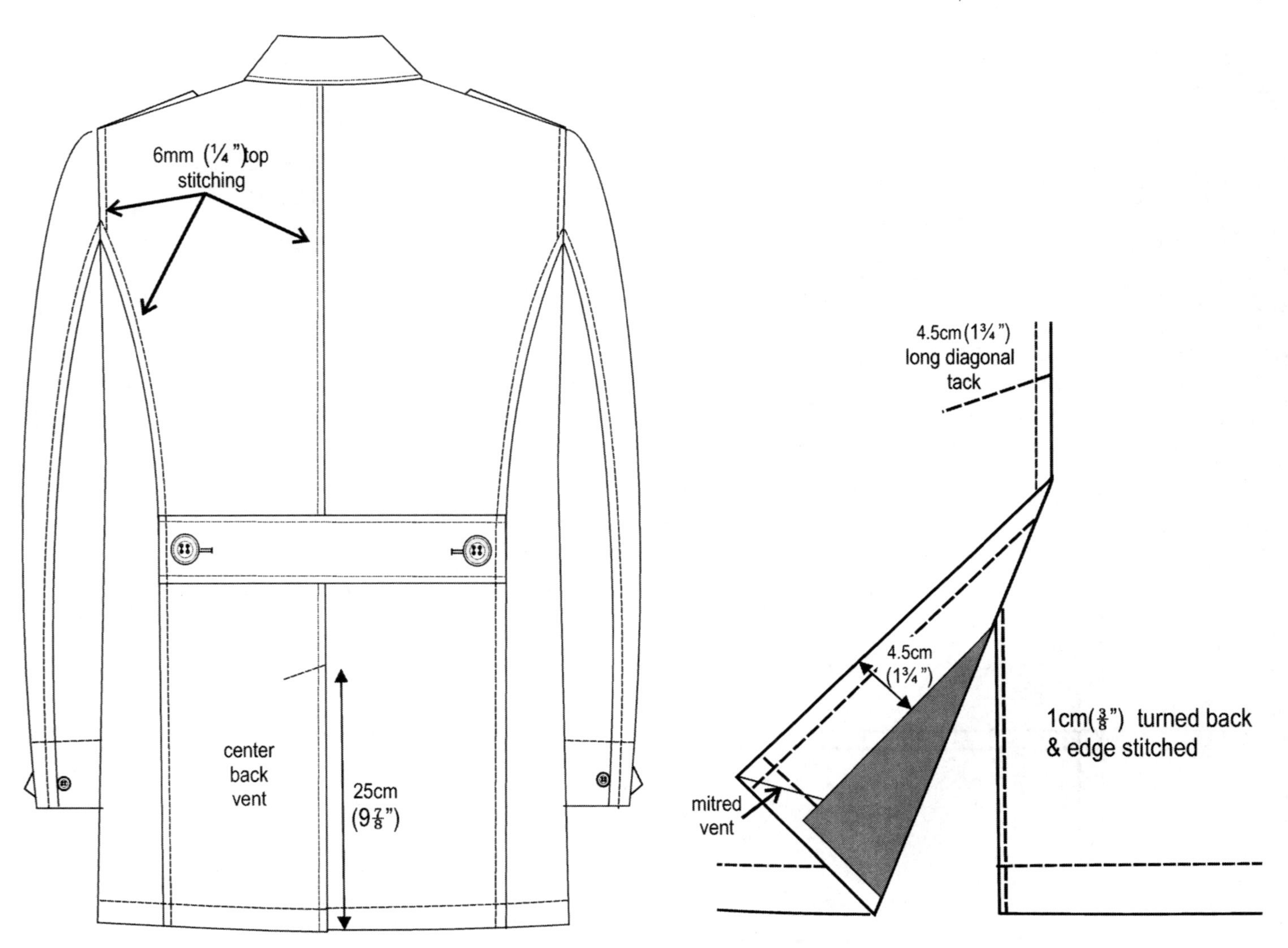

Back

- 2 panel back.
- 1cm (⅜") seams.
- Center back & side seams raised & top stitched 6mm (1/4").
- 25cm (9⅞") long centre vent with mitre.
- Top vent turned back to finish 4.5cm (1¾").
- Underneath vent turned back 1cm (⅜") & edge stitched.
- 4.5cm (1¾") diagonal tack at the top of the vent to show on the right side.

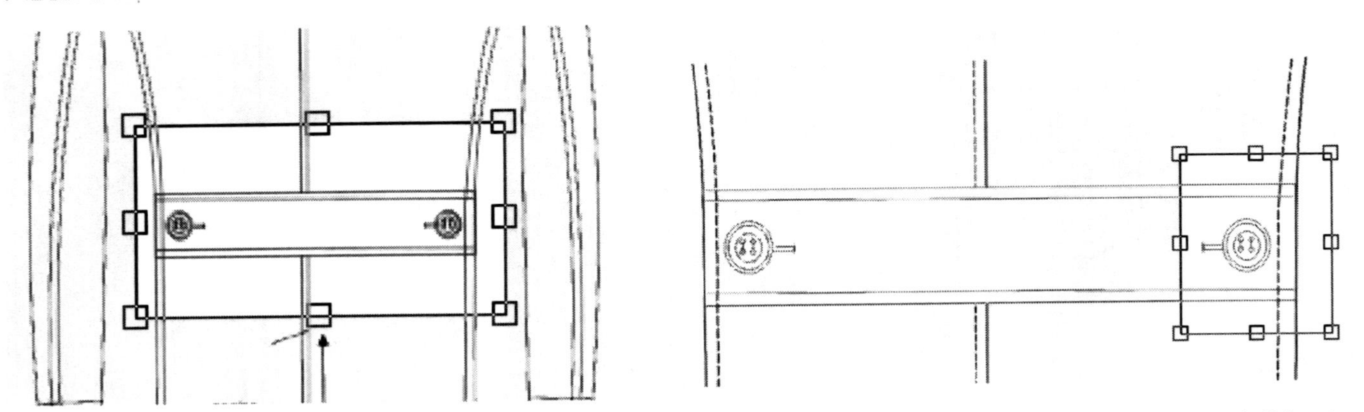

BELT The following pages are examples of how CAD can save time by re-using one drawing several times. I did not want to put too many points in to one drawing, which could cause details to be overlooked. Using the cropping tool I first selected the complete belt, then the button hole and button of the belt (see drawings below)

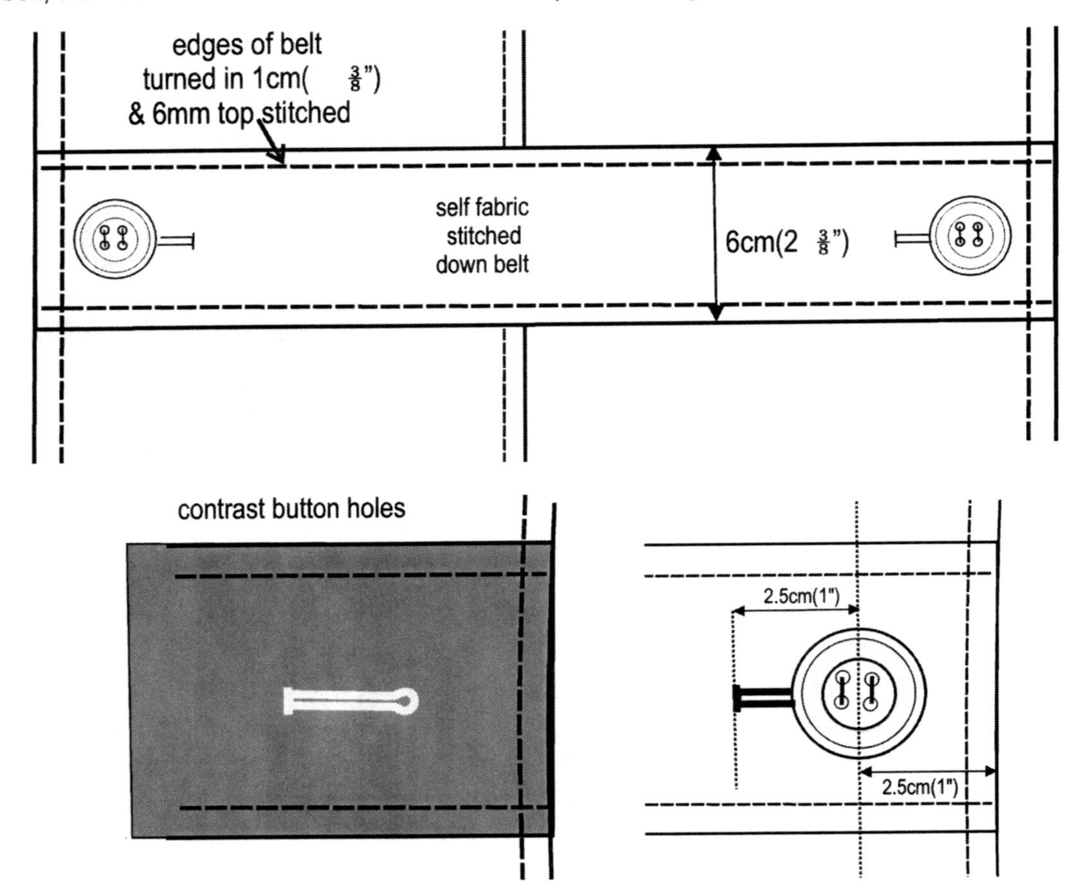

Half belt

- Belt fused with interlining.
- Stitched to the back panel and sewn in when closing the side seams.
- Uncut key hole button hole with bar tack. Stitched in contrasting thread.
- Positioned centrally each side of the belt.
- Button hole length 2.5cm (1").
- Eye of the button hole to the side seam 2.5cm (1").
- 40 ligne 4 hole buttons stitched through the button hole.

SLEEVE, CUFF AND SHOULDER STRAP

These pages are examples of breaking down the information about component parts and showing different views of the sections. Designers will consider each important as they go to make up the whole design. A strap too wide or too short will spoil the overall appearance. The patch on the sleeve has to balance with the rest of the design. Giving the finished measurements even to the detail of the size and position of the stud and bar tacks ensures that the finished effect is what you require.

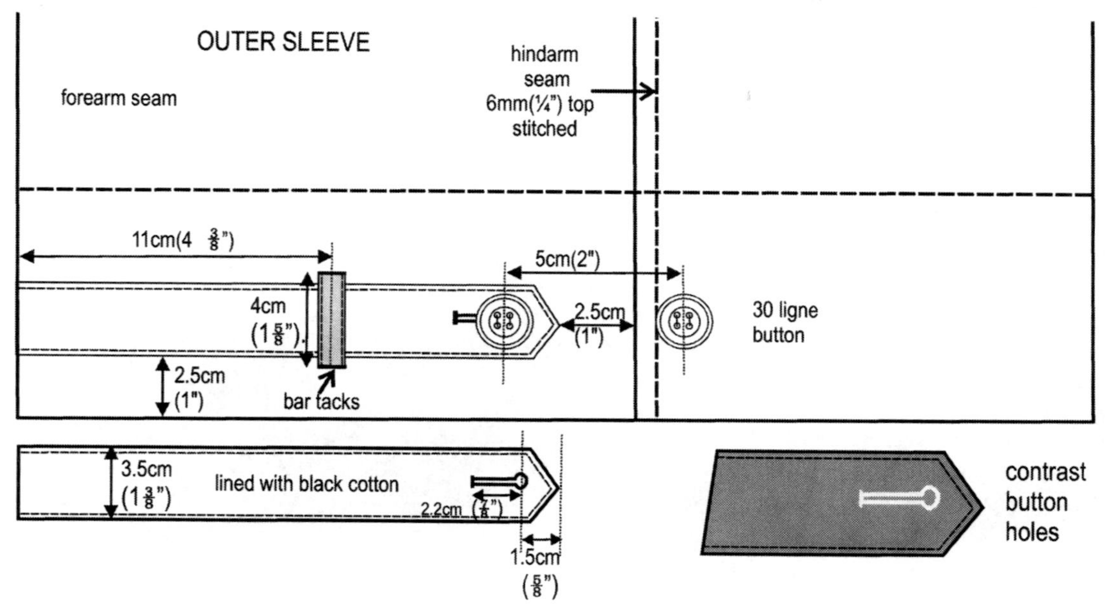

Sleeve

- 2 piece sleeve.
- 1cm (⅜") seams.
- Forearm pressed open.
- Hind arm seam raised & 6mm (¼") top stitched.
- Inner cuff lined with single ply black cotton stitched into the forearm seam to finish 9.5cm (3¾") deep.
- Cuff lining fused.
- Top edge of the inner cotton cuff sewn to the polyester sleeve lining.
- Shoulder pad stitched to the armhole.
- Sleeve head role stitched from the front sleeve pitch to the back hind arm seam.

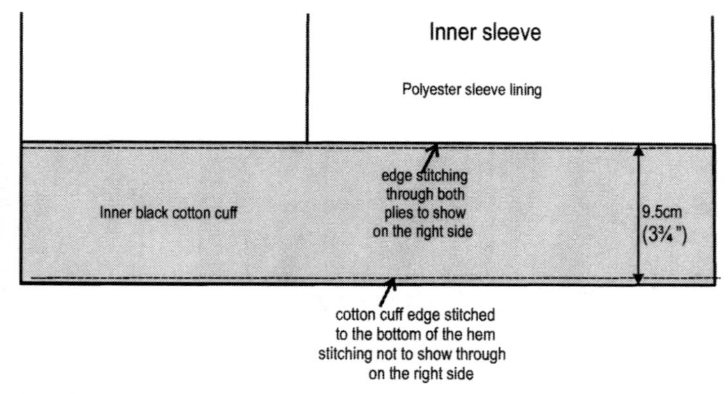

Cuff strap

- Self fabric pointed strap 3.5cm (1⅜") wide lined with black cotton & edge stitched.
- Strap stitched in to the forearm seam.
- Point of strap to finish 2.5cm(1") from the hind arm seam'
- The bottom edge of the strap to finish 2.5cm from the finished edge of the cuff.
- Key hole button hole with bar tack stitched in contrast cotton and positioned centrally at the pointed end of the strap.
- Eye of the button hole 1.5cm (⅝") from the point of the strap
- Button hole effective opening 2.2cm (⅞")
- 1cm (⅜") wide edge stitched cotton loop bar tacked at both edges to the top sleeve.
- Effective loop opening 4cm (1⅝").
- Two 30 ligne 4 hole button fastening
- First button sewn through the button hole, centre of the 1st button to the centre of the 2nd button 5cm(2").

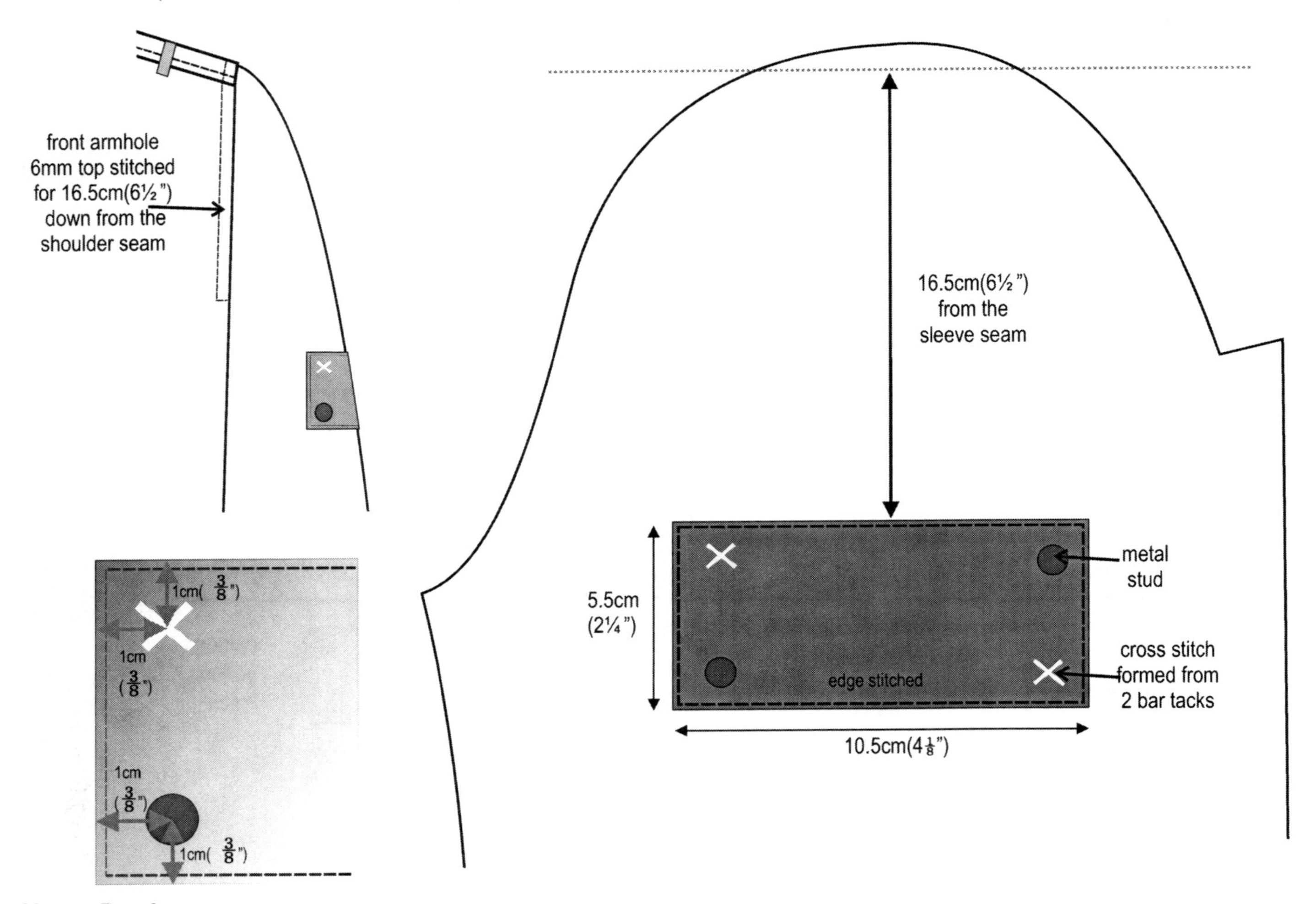

Sleeve Patch

- Black cotton patch to finish 10.5cm (4⅛") wide X 5.5cm (2¼") deep.
- Edges of the patch turned in 1cm (⅜") and edge stitched to the top sleeve left side as worn.
- Patch positioned centrally on the top sleeve.
- Top edge of the patch 16.5cm (6½") down from the sleeve seam at the shoulder.
- Stud and stitched bar tack detail at patch corners.
- Center of bar tack and stud 1cm (⅜") from both edges of the patch.
- Bar tacks 1cm long, stud 6mm (¼") wide (⅜").

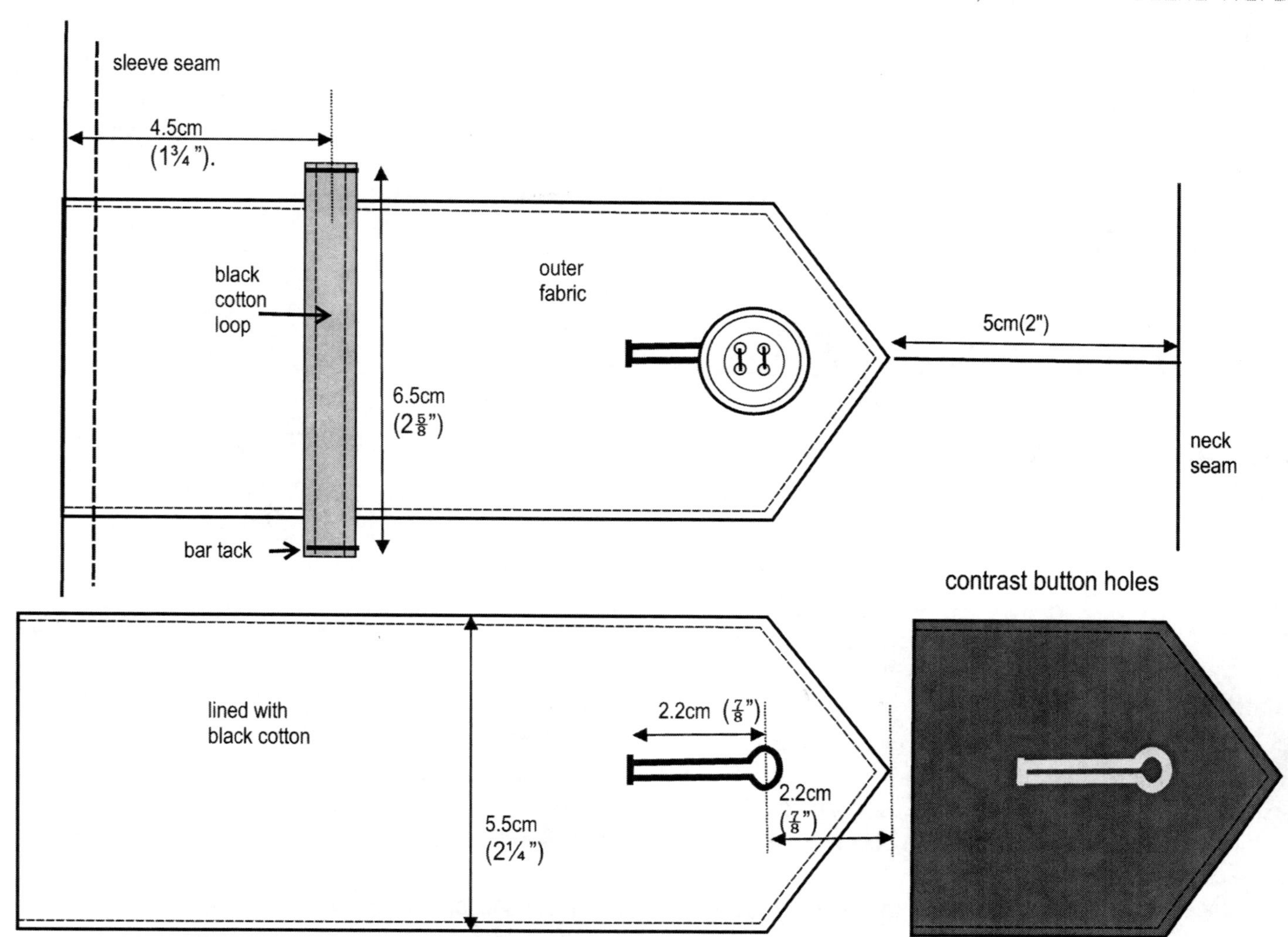

Shoulder straps

- Pointed strap 5.5cm (2¼") wide, lined with black cotton & edge stitched.
- Strap positioned centrally on the shoulder seam & stitched into the sleeve seam.
- Point of strap to finish 5cm(2") from the neck seam.
- Key hole button hole with bar tack stitched in contrast thread & positioned centrally at the pointed end of the strap.
- Eye of the button hole positioned 2.2cm (⅞") from the point.
- Effective opening of the button hole 2.2cm (⅞").

Loop

- 1cm (⅜") wide edge stitched cotton loop, bar tacked at both ends to the front & back shoulder, effective loop opening 6.5cm (2⅝").
- Centre of loop to the sleeve seam 4.5cm (1¾").

Buttons

- One 30 ligne 4 hole button sewn through the button hole.

COLLARS

Collar construction is decided by the style, fabric, and finished appearance, therefore it is important to specify this in detail. To achieve a better fit round the neck, both or one of the collars can have a separate stand and fall. The collar specification like all the other specifications not only explains to the factory how the collar should be made but shows the pattern cutter the construction and measurements required.

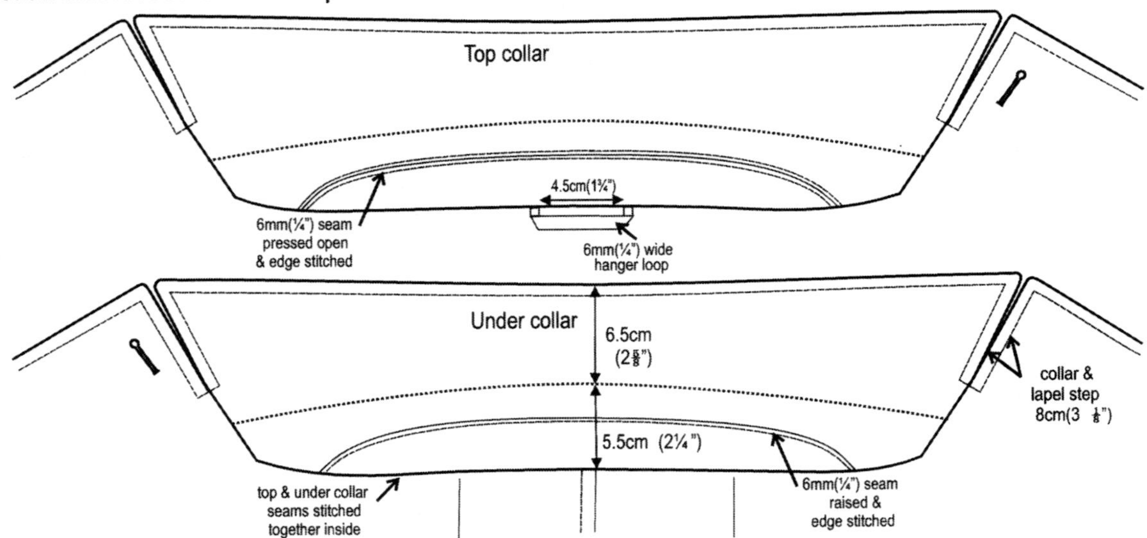

Collars

- 2 piece self fabric under collar & top collar.
- Both collars fused.
- Top collar stand to fall 6mm (¼") seam pressed open & seams edge stitched on both sides of the seam.
- Under collar stand to the fall seam 6mm (¼") seam, raised & edge stitched.
- All other seams 1cm (⅜").
- Collar fall, collar edge to crease 6.5cm (2⅝").
- Collar stand, neck seam to collar crease 5.5cm (2¼").
- All other seams 1cm (⅜").
- Collars bagged out at neck seams.
- Collar & lapel step 8cm (3⅛").

Hanger

- Black cotton loop 6mm (¼") wide, edge stitched & sewn into the neck seam centrally at the center back neck seam.

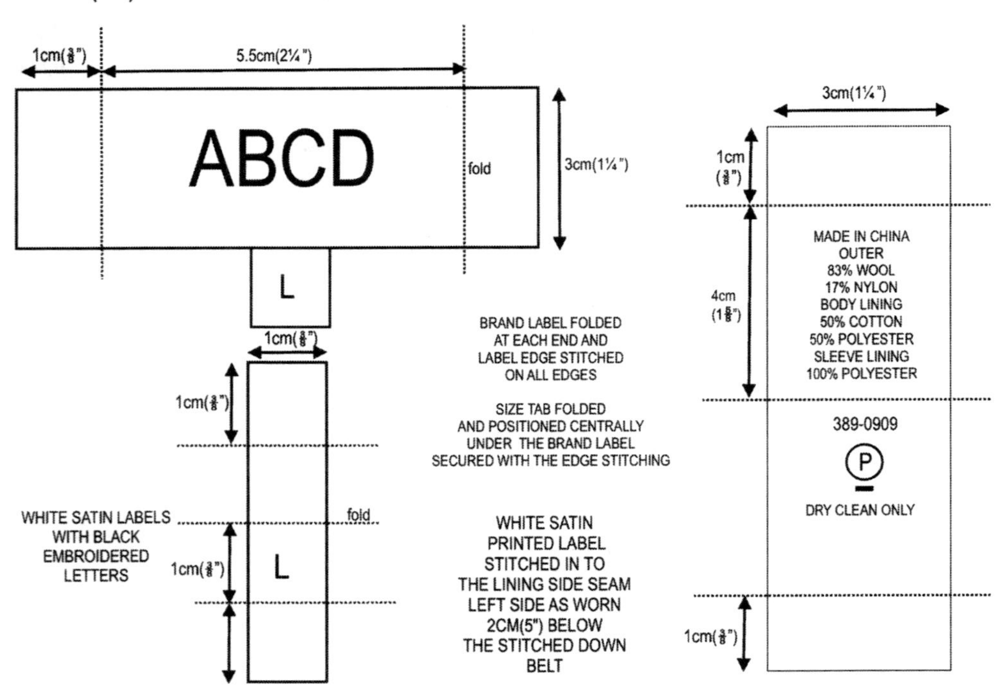

Example of a labeling specification. Most factories will have the labels printed locally and it is necessary to specify the size, position, wording and show symbols very clearly, then ask for labels to be sent to you for final approval for quality.

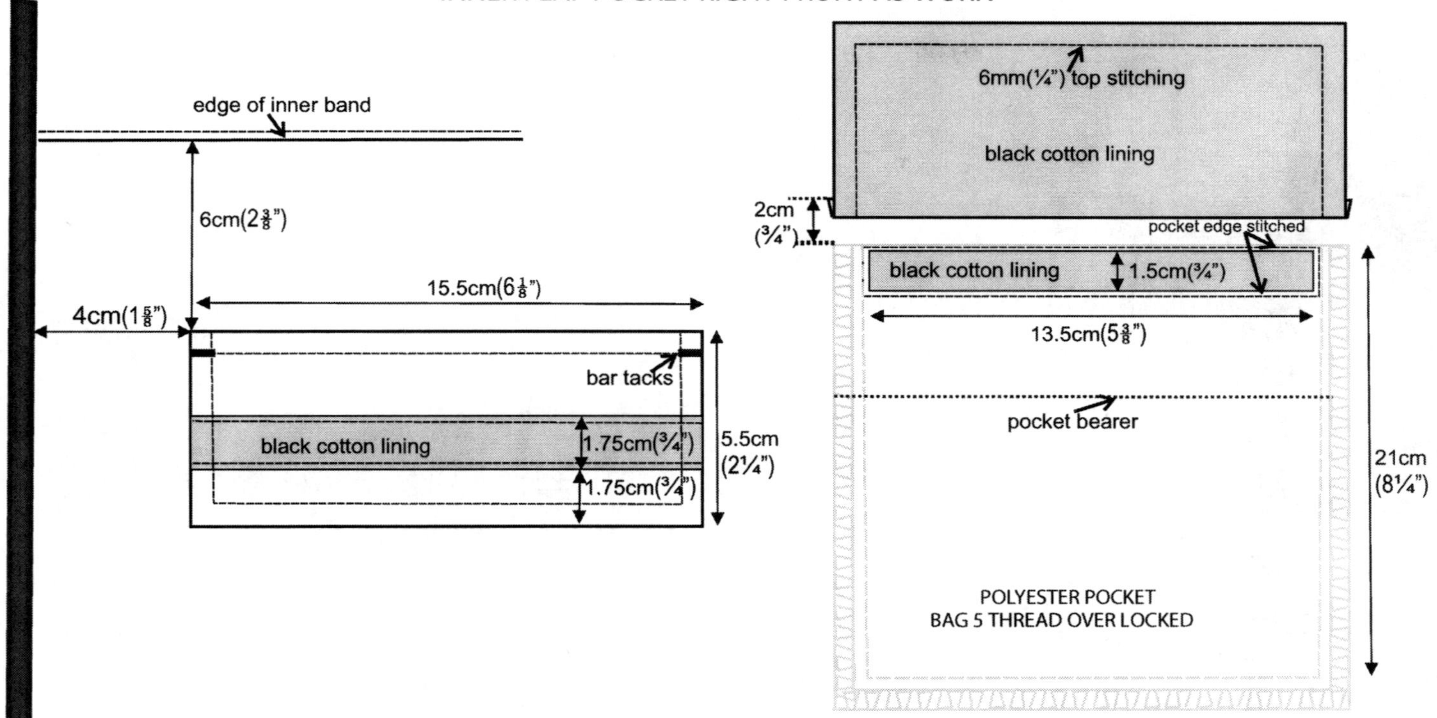

Flap

- Self fabric square flap, lined with black cotton.
- Top ply fused with interlining.
- Flap 15.5cm(6 wide X 5.5cm(2") deep.
- Black cotton trim 1.75cm (¾") wide edge stitched to the outer flap, only 1.75cm (¾") up from the bottom edge of the flap.
- Front edge of the flap 4cm (1⅝") from velour strip at the facing seam.
- Top edge of the flap 6cm (2⅜") from the bottom edge of the band at the waist.

Welt pocket

- Black cotton welt pocket 1.5cm (⅝") wide set into the lining.
- Positioned centrally under the flap and 2cm (¾") below the top edge of the flap.
- Effective pocket opening 13.5cm (5⅜").
- Polyester lining pocket bag 5 thread over locked effective depth from the top of the welt 21cm (8¼").
- Black cotton pocket bearer, edge turned in 1cm (⅜") & edge stitched.
- Pocket outline edge stitched.

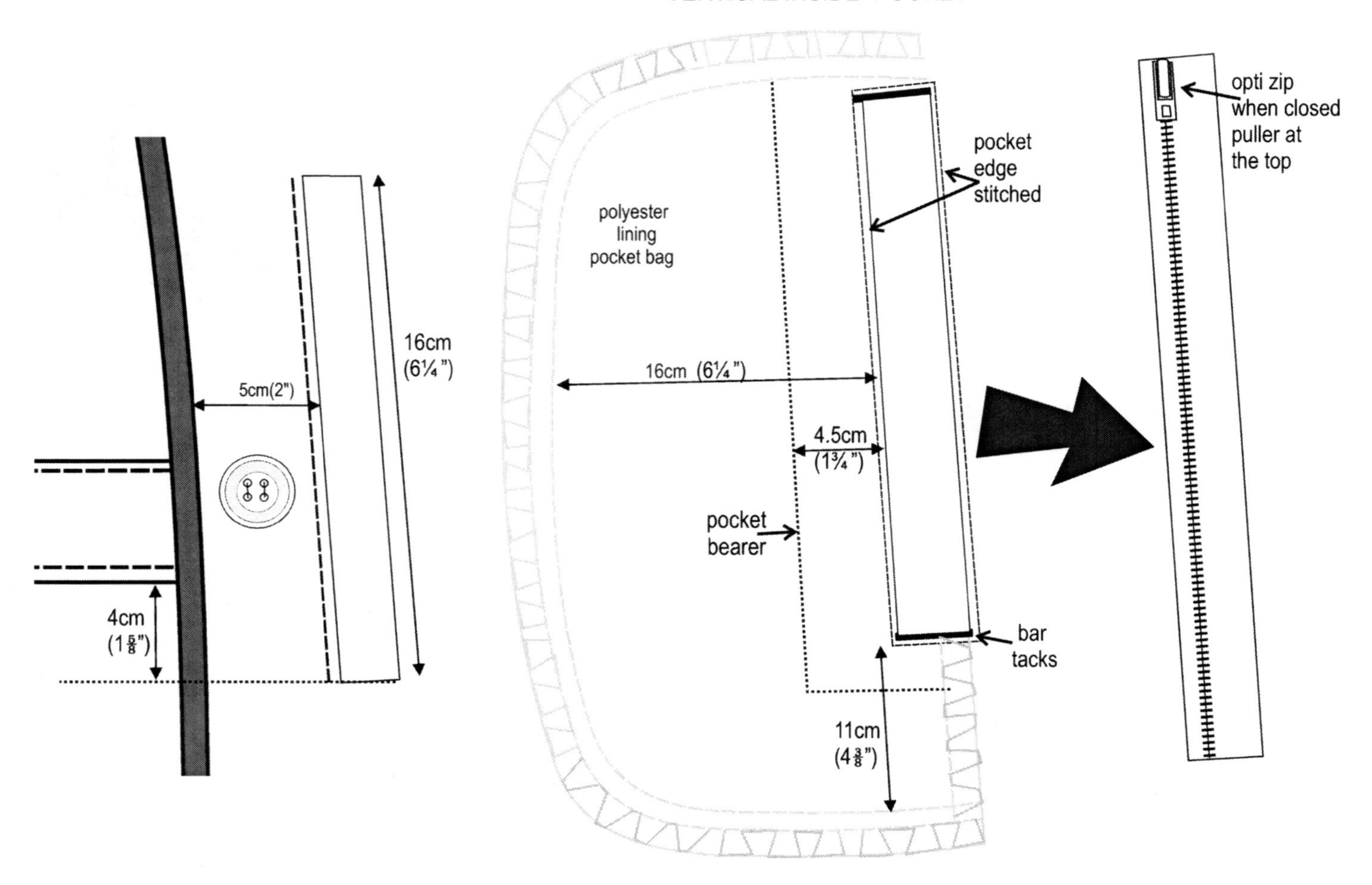

Inner zip pocket left side as worn

- 1.5cm (⅝") wide self fabric welt with zip fastener.
- 16cm (6¼") effective opening.
- Welt fused.
- Pocket positioned 5cm (2") from the facing velour strip.
- Bottom edge of pocket 4cm (1⅝") below bottom edge of the waist band.
- Polyester lining pocket bag 5–thread over–locked.
- Self fabric back pocket bearer to finish 4.5cm (1¾") deep.
- Pocket bag width from edge of the welt 16cm (6¼").
- Pocket bag depth from bottom of the pocket 11cm (4⅜").
- Pocket seam edge stitched.
- Pocket corners bar tacked.

Front fastening

Button holes and buttons are one of the last sewing operations. Many garments have been ruined by button holes being the wrong size or in the wrong position. Extra care should be taken with any operation that involves cutting into the cloth panel; mistakes can be very costly. A factory should have detailed instructions on the type, position and size of the button holes and buttons. Fastening buttons usually need a shank formed from the thread they are sewn on with so that they can pass through the button hole easily; a show button needs to be sewn flat to the front. Show buttons with a metal shank are usually plugged, which means sunk into the front so that they don't stand away from the front and look untidy.

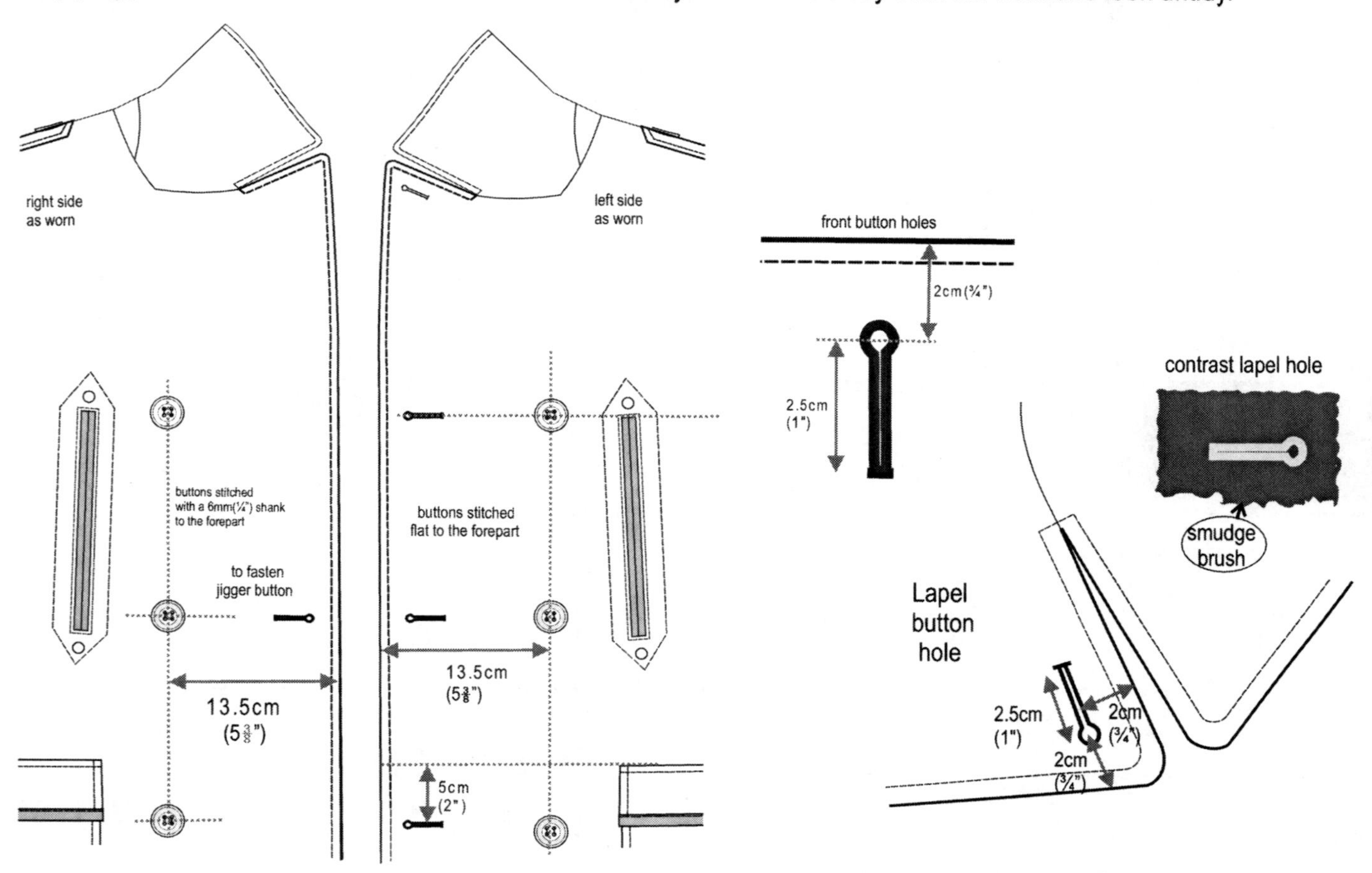

Left side as worn

- 3 front key hole button holes with bar tacks stitched in color matching thread.
- Top button hole at the lapel break level with the top of the vertical pocket.
- Bottom button hole 5cm (2") below the top edge of the flap.
- The middle fastening button is positioned centrally between the top and bottom button.
- Eye of the button hole 2cm (¾") from the front edge.
- Lapel button hole stitched in contrasting thread. (See Measurements). Please note the lapel button hole is stitched on the facing side.
- Eye of the button holes 2cm (¾") from the front edge.
- Three 40 ligne 4 hole show buttons sewn flat to the forepart level with the button holes.
- 40 ligne 4 hole jigger button sewn on the inside behind the middle button.
- **Jigger button sewn through the facing only not through the inner pocket.**
- 20 ligne 4 hole backing buttons stitched behind the 1st & 3rd buttons up from the hem.

Right side as worn

- One color matching key hole button hole with bar tack for the jigger button level with the 2nd button up from the hem, effective opening 2.5cm (1").
- Center of the eye of the button hole 2cm from the front edge.
- Three 40 ligne buttons stitched with a 6mm (¼") shank to the forepart.
- Center of buttons to the front edge 13.5cm (5⅜") buttons to correspond with the button holes on the left forepart.
- 20 ligne 4 hole backing buttons stitched behind the 1st and 3rd buttons up from the hem.

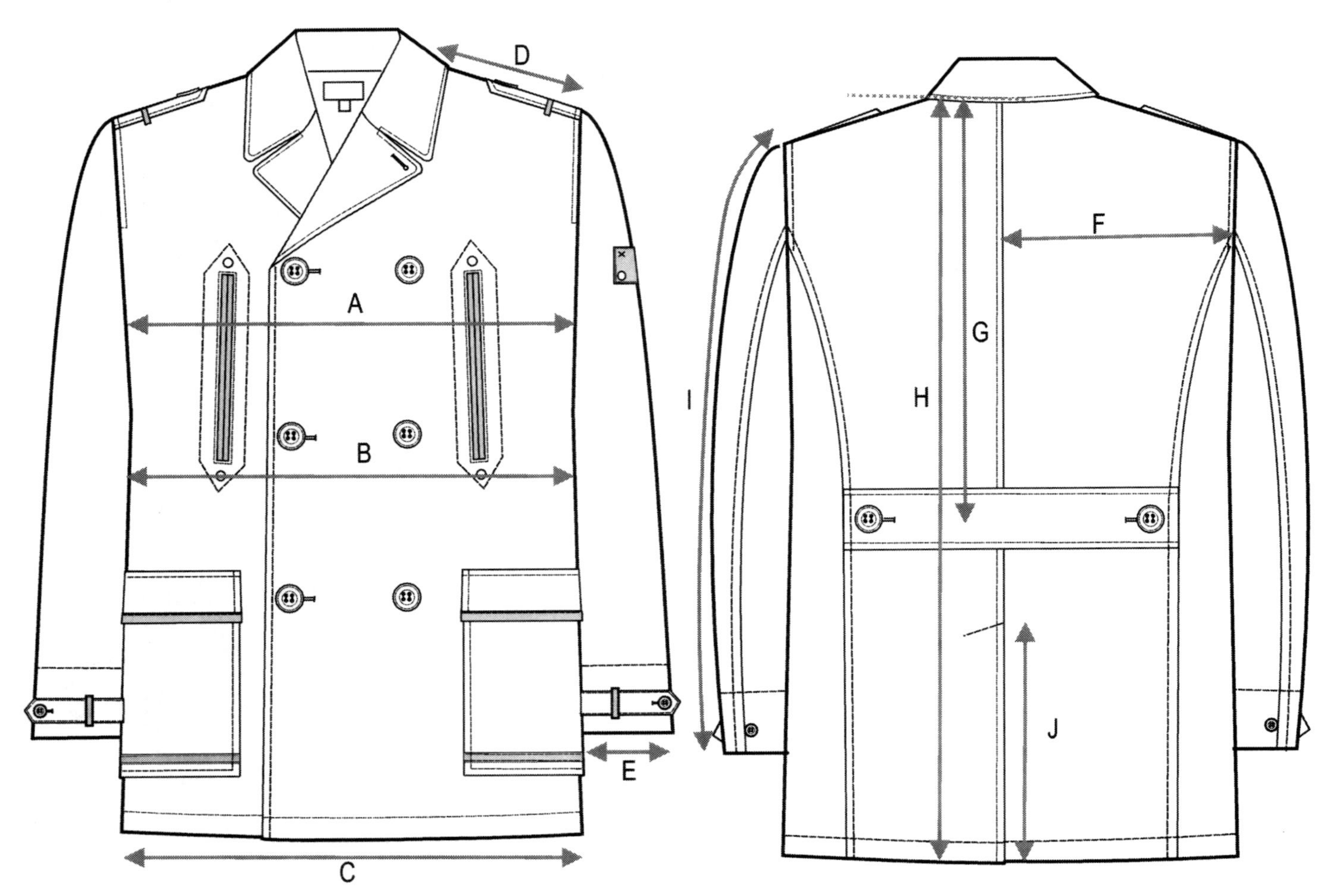

SIZE	S		M		L		XL		XXL	
	cm	inches	cms	inches	cms	inches	cms	inches	cms	inches
A. Chest at base of armhole coat fastened half measurement	53	20¾"	58	22¾"	63	24¾"	68	26¾"	73	28¾"
B. Waist coat fastened half measurement	48	19"	53	21"	58	23"	63	25"	68	27"
C. Hem coat fastened half measurement	51	20"	56	22"	61	24"	66	26"	71	28"
D. Shoulder Sleeve seam to neck seam	16.1	6⅜"	16.4	6½"	16.7	6⅝"	17	6¾"	17.3	6⅞"
E. Cuff half measurement	14	5½"	15	5⅞"	16	6¼"	17	6⅝"	18	7"
F. Half back width	22.6	8⅞"	23.9	9⅜"	25.2	9⅞"	26.5	10⅜"	27.8	10⅞"
G. Neck seam to waist	47	18½"	47	18½"	47	18½"	47.5	18¾"	47.5	18¾"
H. Full length from neck seam	86	33⅞"	86	33⅞"	86	33⅞"	87	34¼"	87	34¼"
I. Sleeve crown to cuff	67	26⅜"	67	26⅜"	67	26⅜"	68	26¾"	68	26¾"
J. Center vent	26	10¼"	26	10¼"	26	10¼"	26	10¼"	26	10¼"

Packaging

The final section of the specification should relate to packaging. Re-processing is expensive so the information should be detailed. Hanging or boxed. Quality of the bag and how they are sealed. Bag and box labels and their positioning. Swing tickets & bar codes. If you are buying for your own stores then packaging and labeling should be standard for each product category, then you should consider compiling a packaging/company manual.

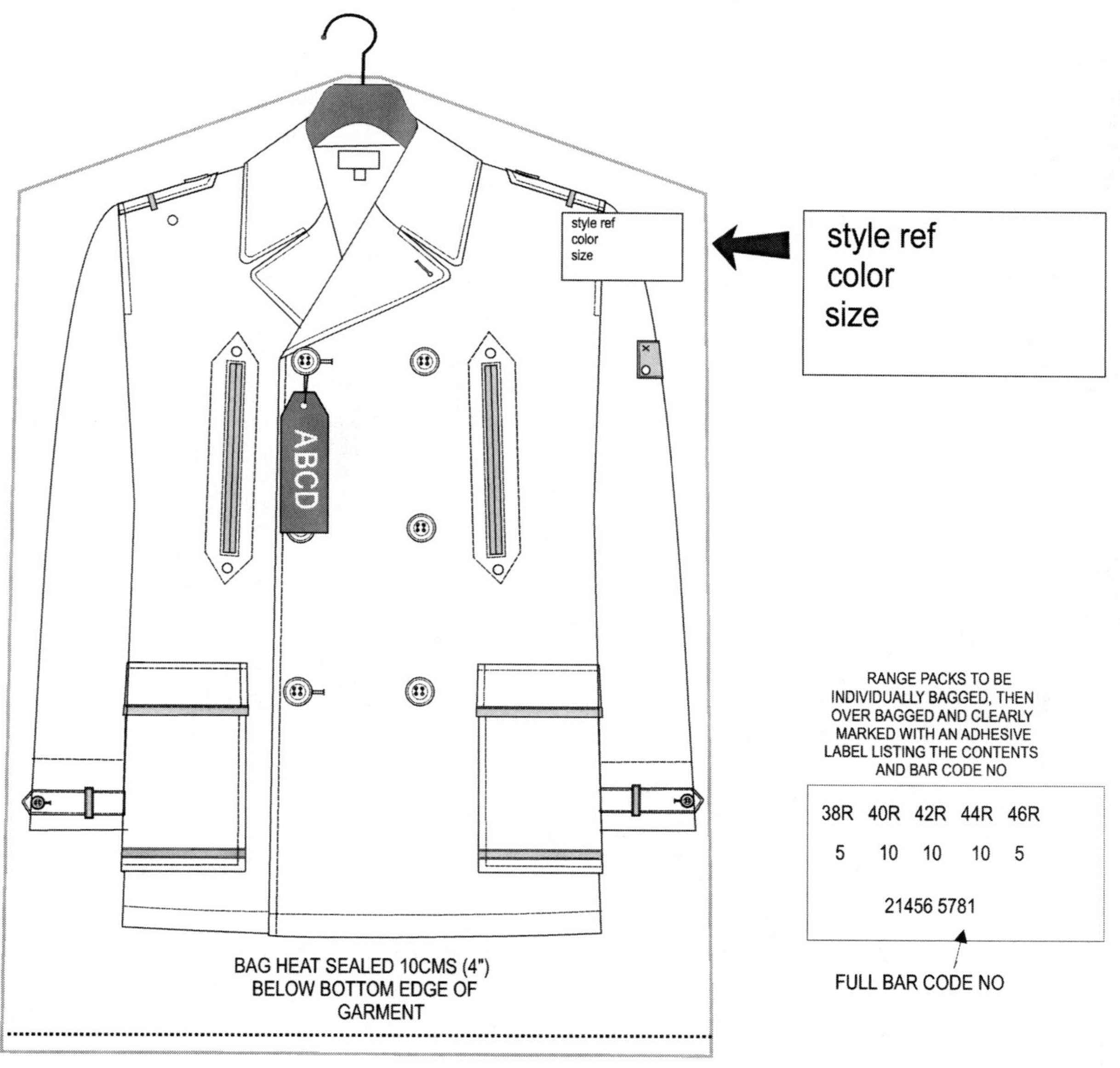

Packaging & labeling

- Delivered on hangers
- Polythene bag

CHAPTER 7

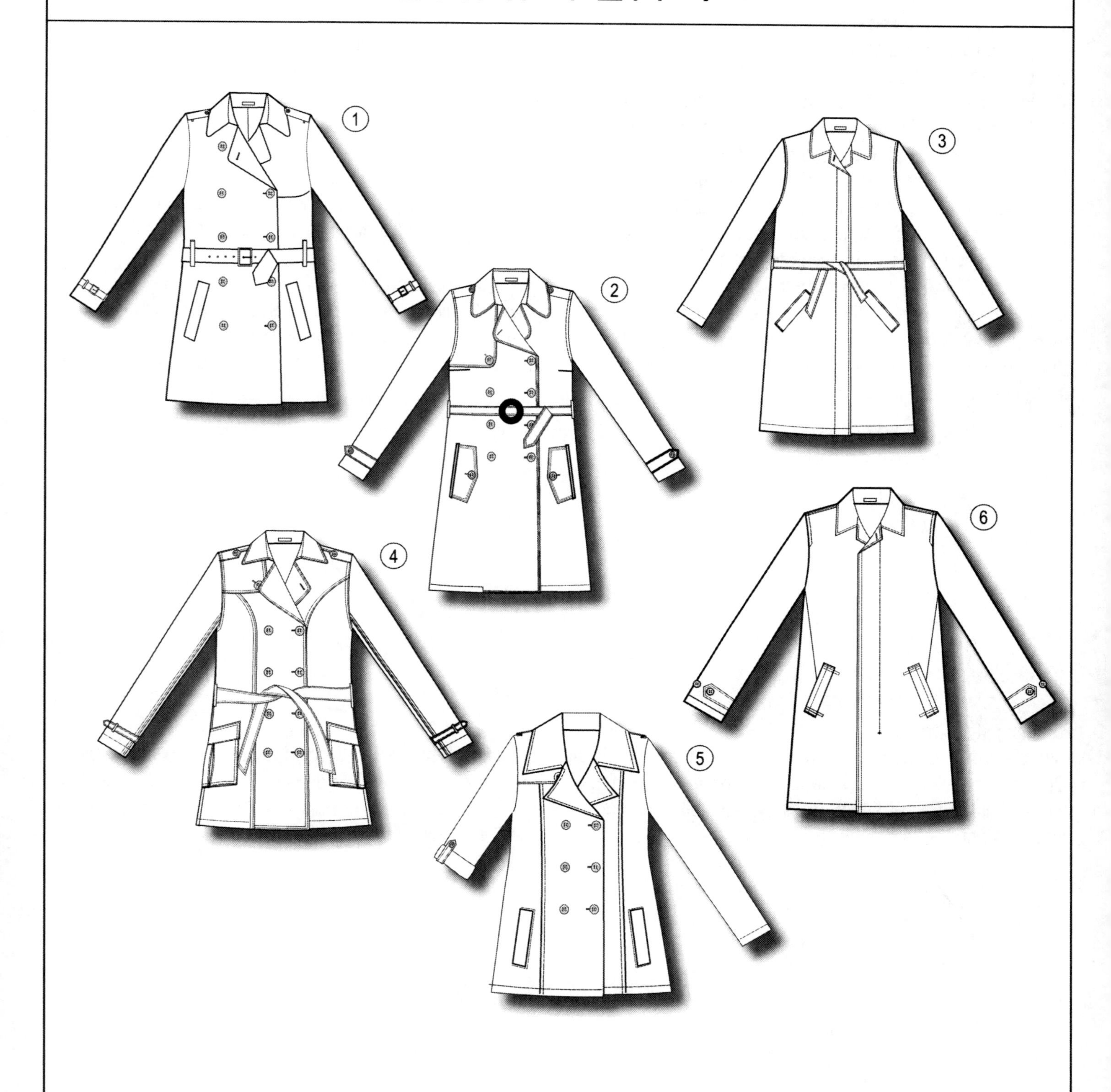

RAINCOAT

The following pages show specifications for 6 rain coats, 5 ladies' and 1 men's. I have created templates for the first style and adapted them for the other 5 styles. These specifications have fewer pages and less text than, for example, the waterproof anorak and overcoat chapter. In this development we need to send information quickly for all 6 coats to several factories to agree upon a price and make samples.

Each specification consists of the following:

1. Style specification ---front and back buttoned.
2. Open view of the coat, inside and out. I find this added view very helpful to the factory as it shows the outer and inner positioning of seams, pockets and buttons more clearly than the style drawing of the jacket fastened.
3. Detailed specification of components such as collar, pockets, cuff and shoulder straps. I have also shown examples of label information -- although not essential at this stage it can affect the costing and become an issue at a later stage.
4. The garment size chart completes the specification. Please note the outlines for the style drawings on both the fastened and open illustrations are a back drop for the style features of the coats and they do not have to be lengthened or shortened in accordance to the measurements in the size chart. Changes to the outline are at your discretion and you should interpret the "look" of the garment and the size chart measurements to see that they are the actual physical dimensions. The more detail that we can send at the beginning the easier it is for the manufacturer to interpret what you want and make an accurate first sample.
5. For each style, I have shown the steps to create that style from a previous one.

As you progress and add more styles to your library, creating specifications becomes easier and faster. Our goal as technologists is to produce clear, accurate, easily understood information quickly for the factories to produce first samples that are correct or need very little alteration to meet the customer's deadlines. Details of fabric colors and quality can be added to the spec or sent separately.

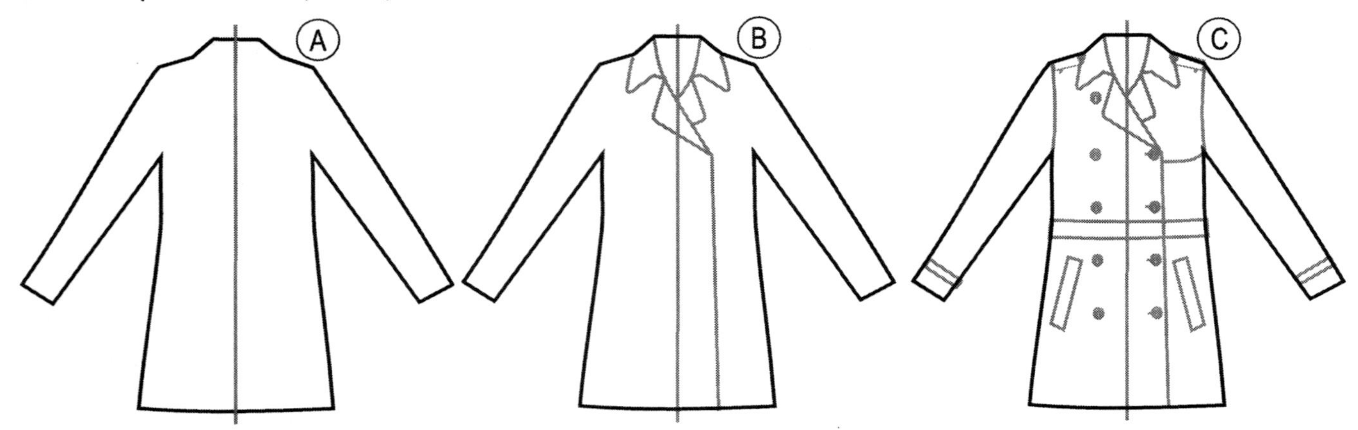

Creating style 1 front

Sample coat should be laid on a flat surface to draw the outline A, Drawing B shows the front edge, with the collar and lapel. Check at this stage you are happy with the results and add the other details to complete drawing C. Drawing C should be the final stage to check that you have translated the garment satisfactorily into a flat drawing and then complete the back and the front.

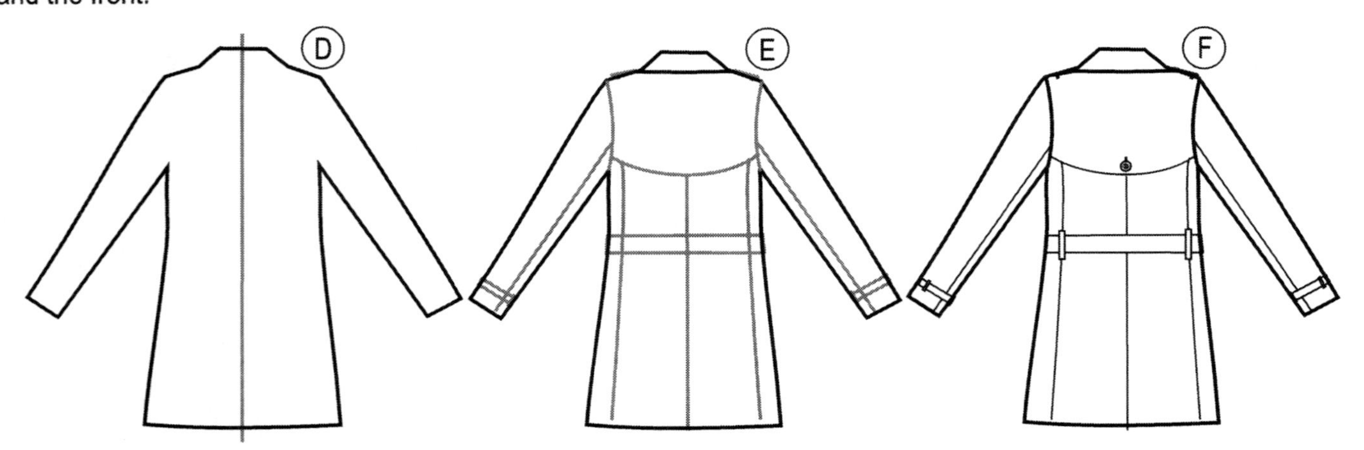

Style 1 back

Copy and paste the front outline and use for the back drawing D.

Drawing E shows the sketched in details.

Drawing F is the finished drawing of the back.

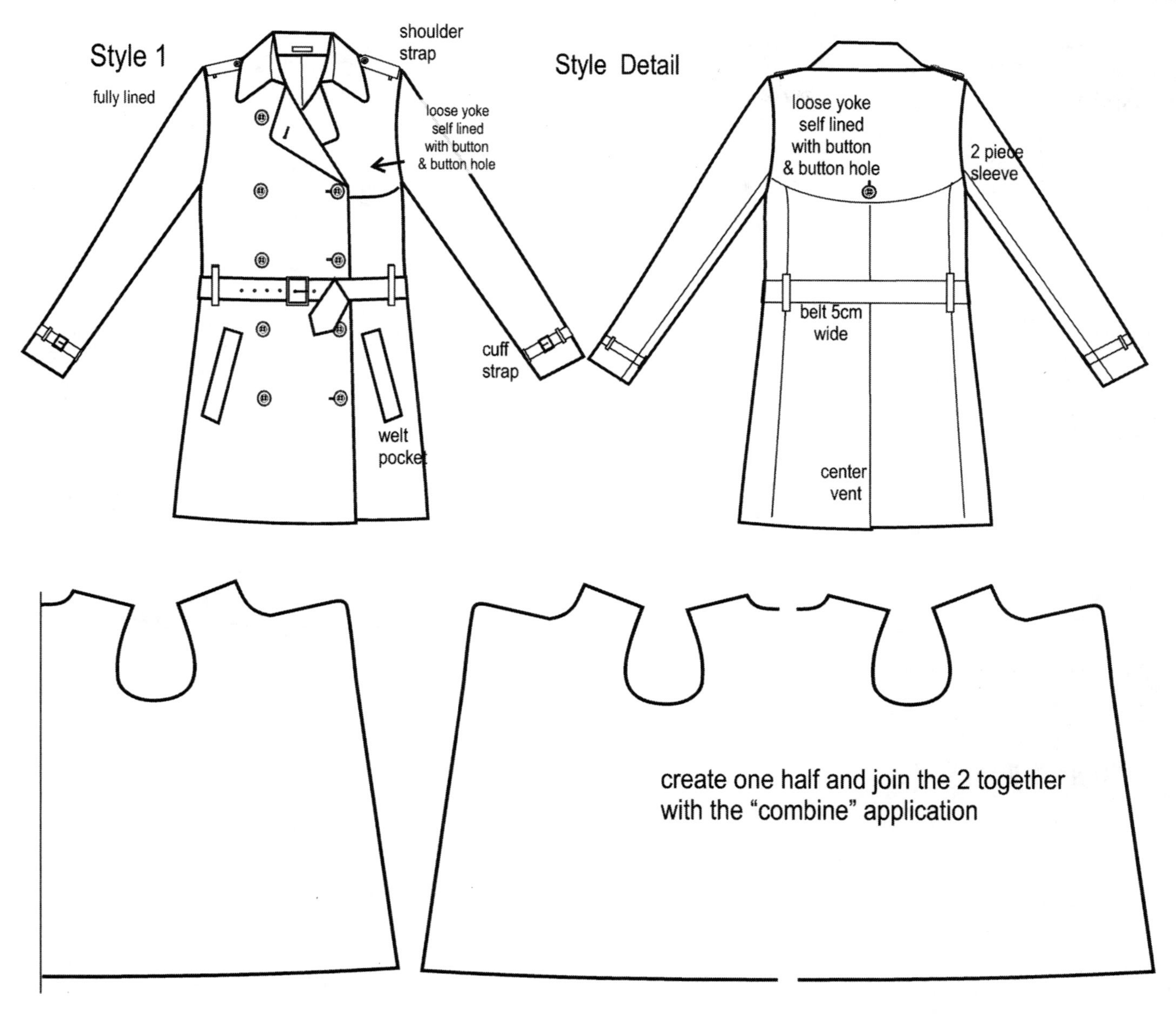

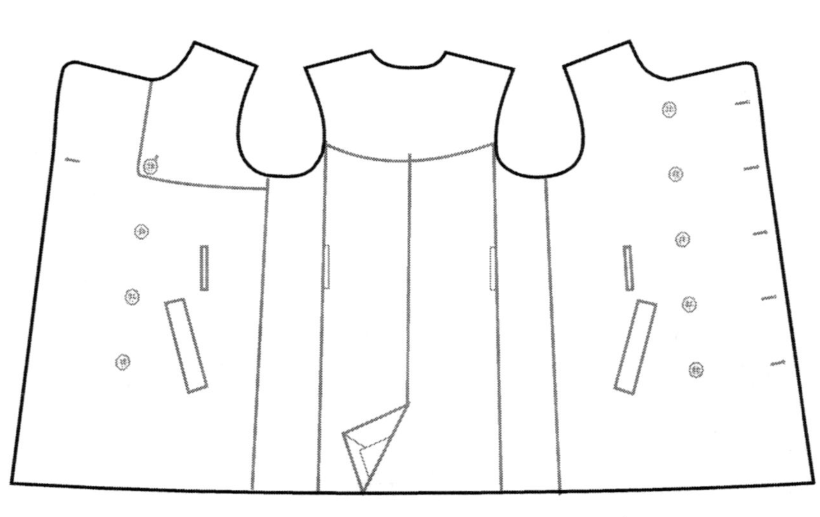

The following illustrations show the coat open as it would look without the shoulder seam sewn together. At a glance the pattern cutter can see what seams are in the coat, inside and out and how they are positioned in relation to each other (sometimes the lining seams don't mirror the outer seams). I have also added measurements for button spacing, vent lengths, yoke depths and pocket positions to this view.

If possible undoing the shoulder seams would be the best way to copy the outline, but this is not always practical. With practice you will be able to draw the outline satisfactorily for a coat or jacket, which can be reused for many styles as well as the linings.

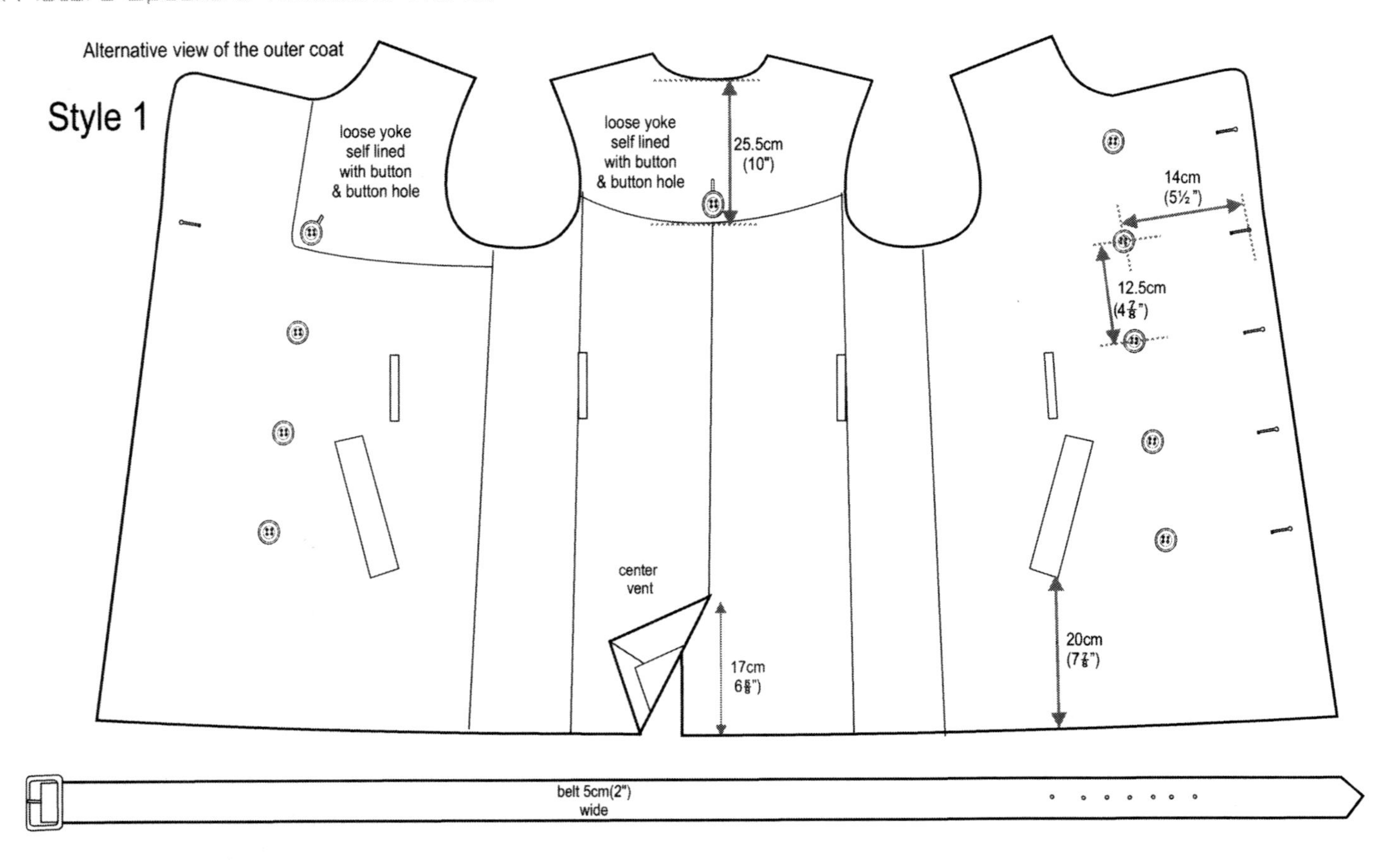
Alternative view of the outer coat
Style 1
loose yoke
self lined
with button
& button hole
loose yoke
self lined
with button
& button hole
25.5cm
(10")
14cm
(5½")
12.5cm
(4⅞")
center
vent
17cm
6⅝")
20cm
(7⅞")
belt 5cm(2")
wide

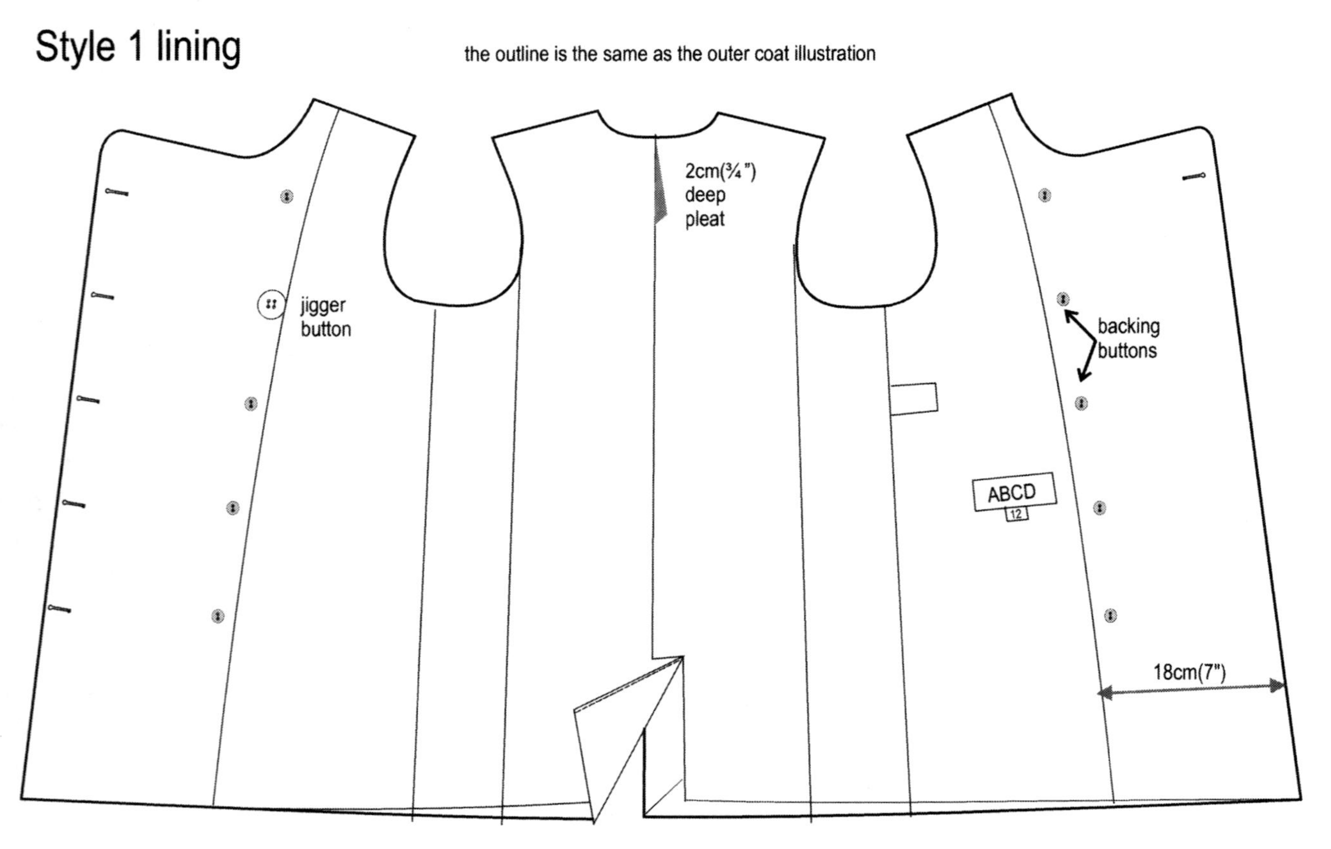
Style 1 lining
the outline is the same as the outer coat illustration
2cm(¾")
deep
pleat
jigger
button
backing
buttons
ABCD
12
18cm(7")

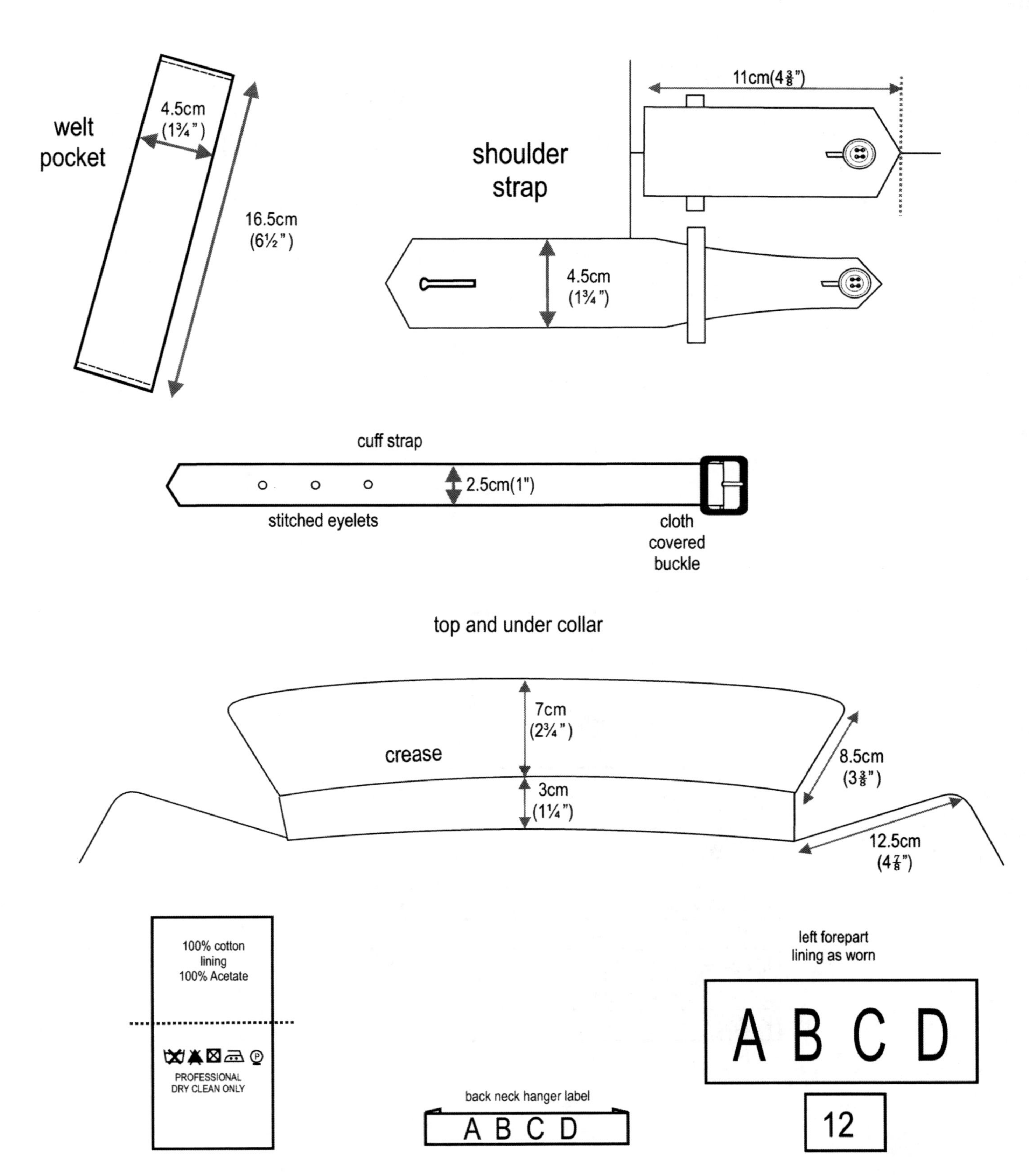
welt
pocket
4.5cm
(1¾")
16.5cm
(6½")
shoulder
strap
11cm(4⅜")
4.5cm
(1¾")
cuff strap
2.5cm(1")
stitched eyelets
cloth
covered
buckle
top and under collar
7cm
(2¾")
crease
8.5cm
(3⅜")
3cm
(1¼")
12.5cm
(4⅞")
100% cotton
lining
100% Acetate
PROFESSIONAL
DRY CLEAN ONLY
left forepart
lining as worn
A B C D
12
back neck hanger label
A B C D

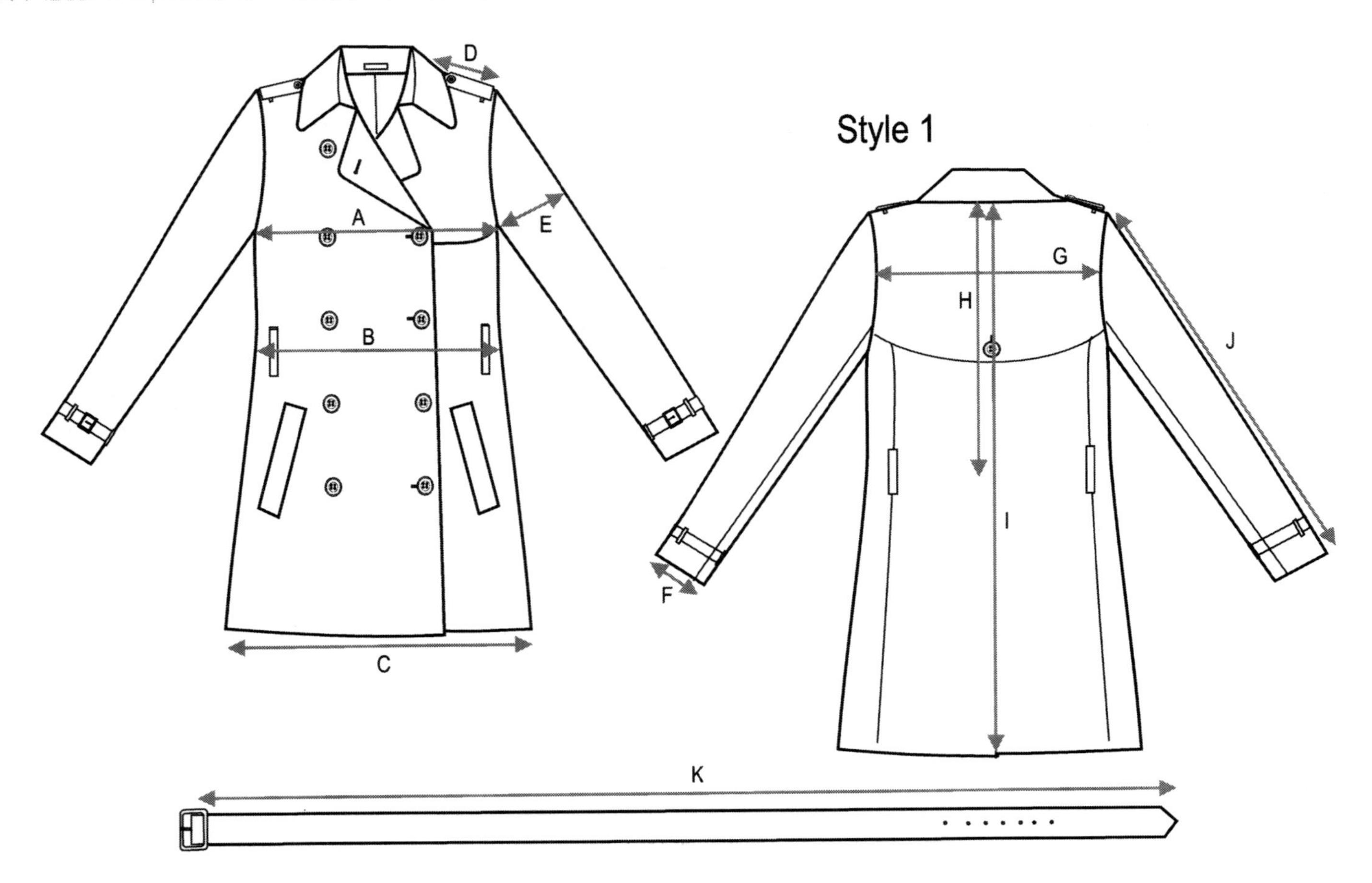

SIZE	UK 12	
	CMS	Inches
A. Bust at base of armhole	110	43⅜"
B. Waist	102	40¼"
C. Hem	128	50⅜"
D. Shoulder	12	4¾"
E. Biceps	40	15¾"
F. Cuff	29	11⅜"
G. Back width	38.5	15⅛
H. Neck seam to waist	41.5	16⅜"
I. Full length from neck seam	85	33½"
J. Sleeve crown to cuff	64	25¼"
K. Belt	129.5	51"

Drawing A is style 1 outline. In drawing B style 2 details have been sketched inside the outline. When satisfied that the collar, lapel, buttons and pockets are in the right position complete the style details as drawing C.

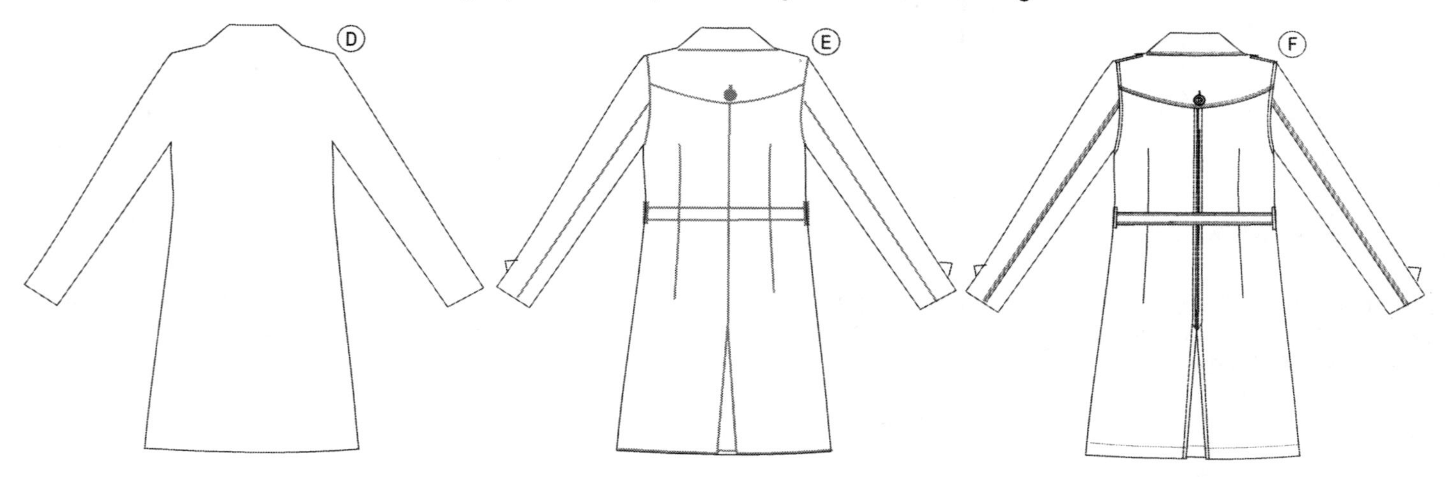

Drawing D is style 2 front outline. In drawing E the back details have been placed inside the outline. When satisfied the style details are correct complete drawing F.

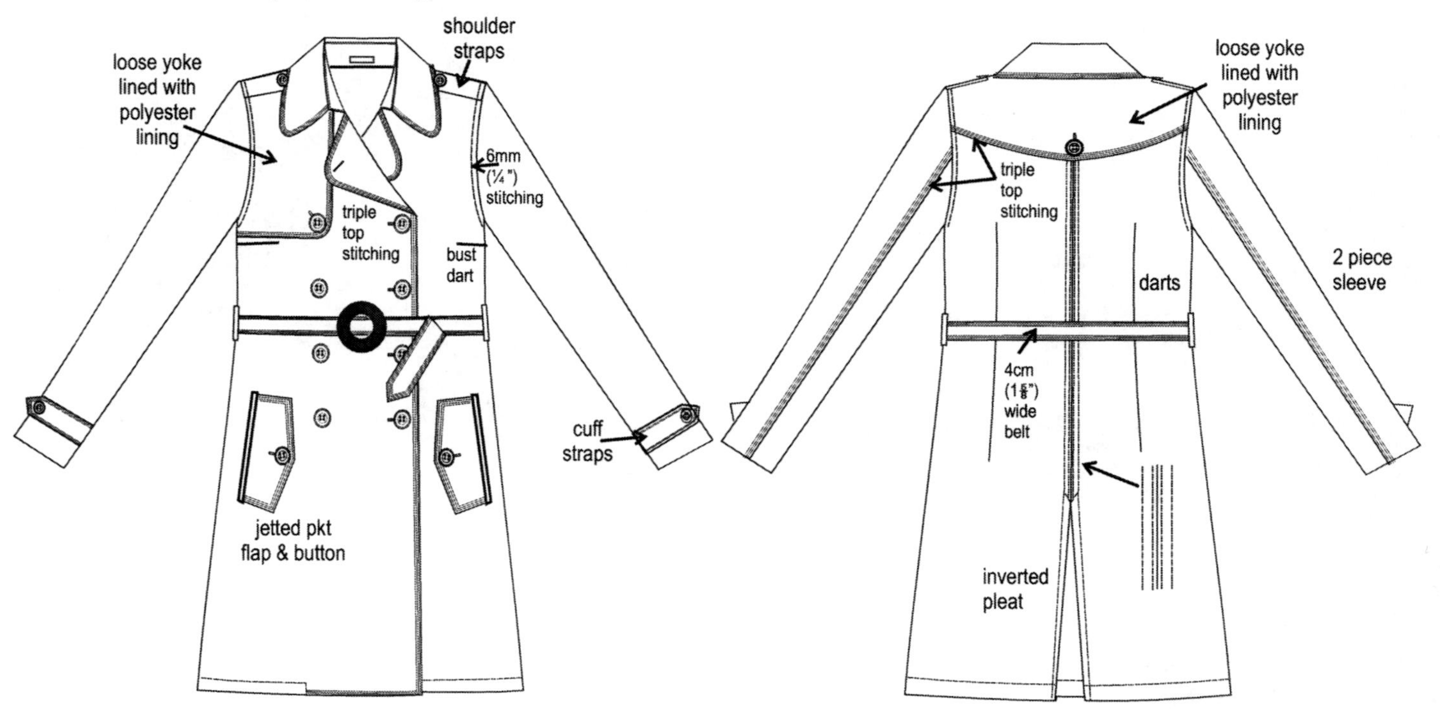

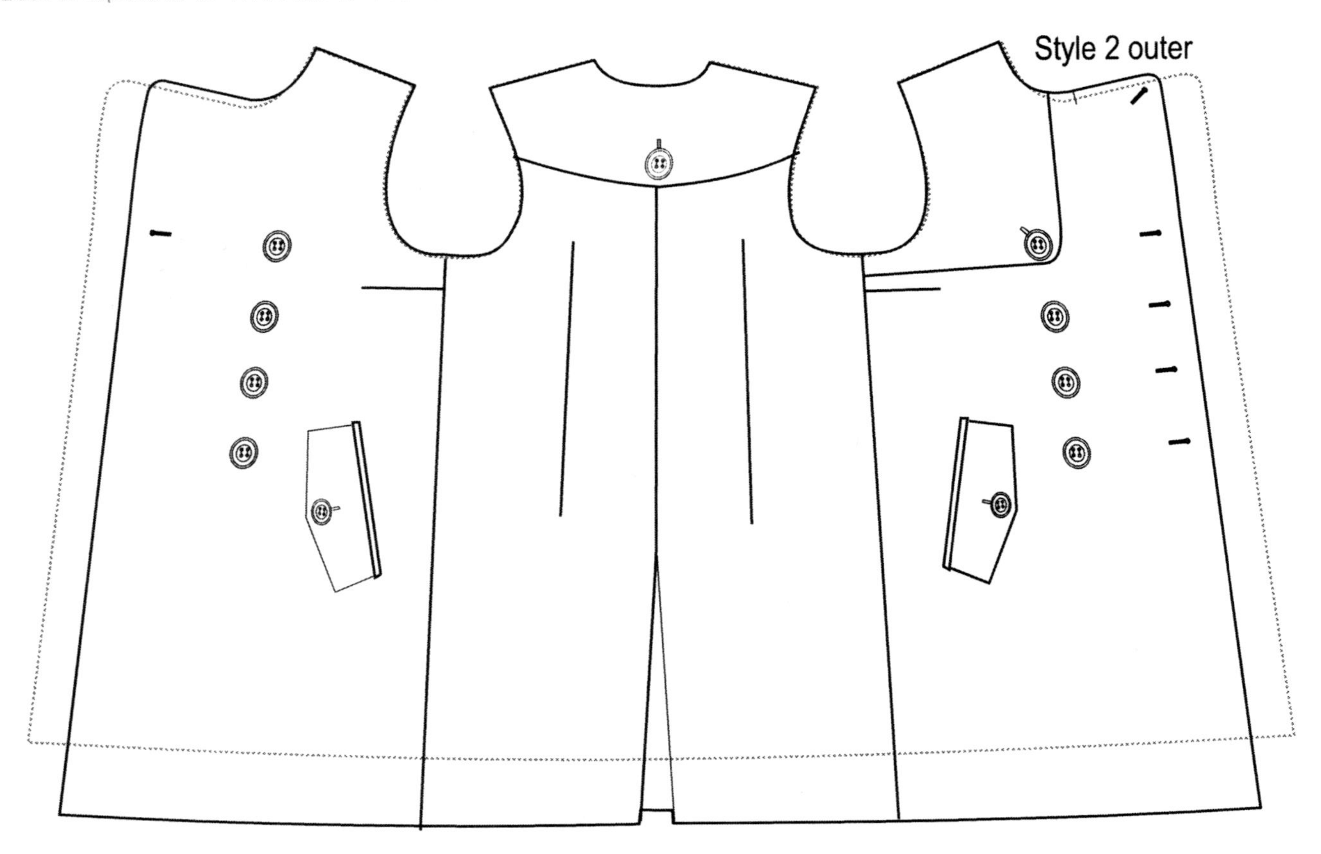

The dotted line is the outline of style 1.The detail for style 2 is added. I have reduced the width because there is less wrap over at the front button fastening, and the length is also slightly longer. The style details now look in proportion and correct in the amended outline.

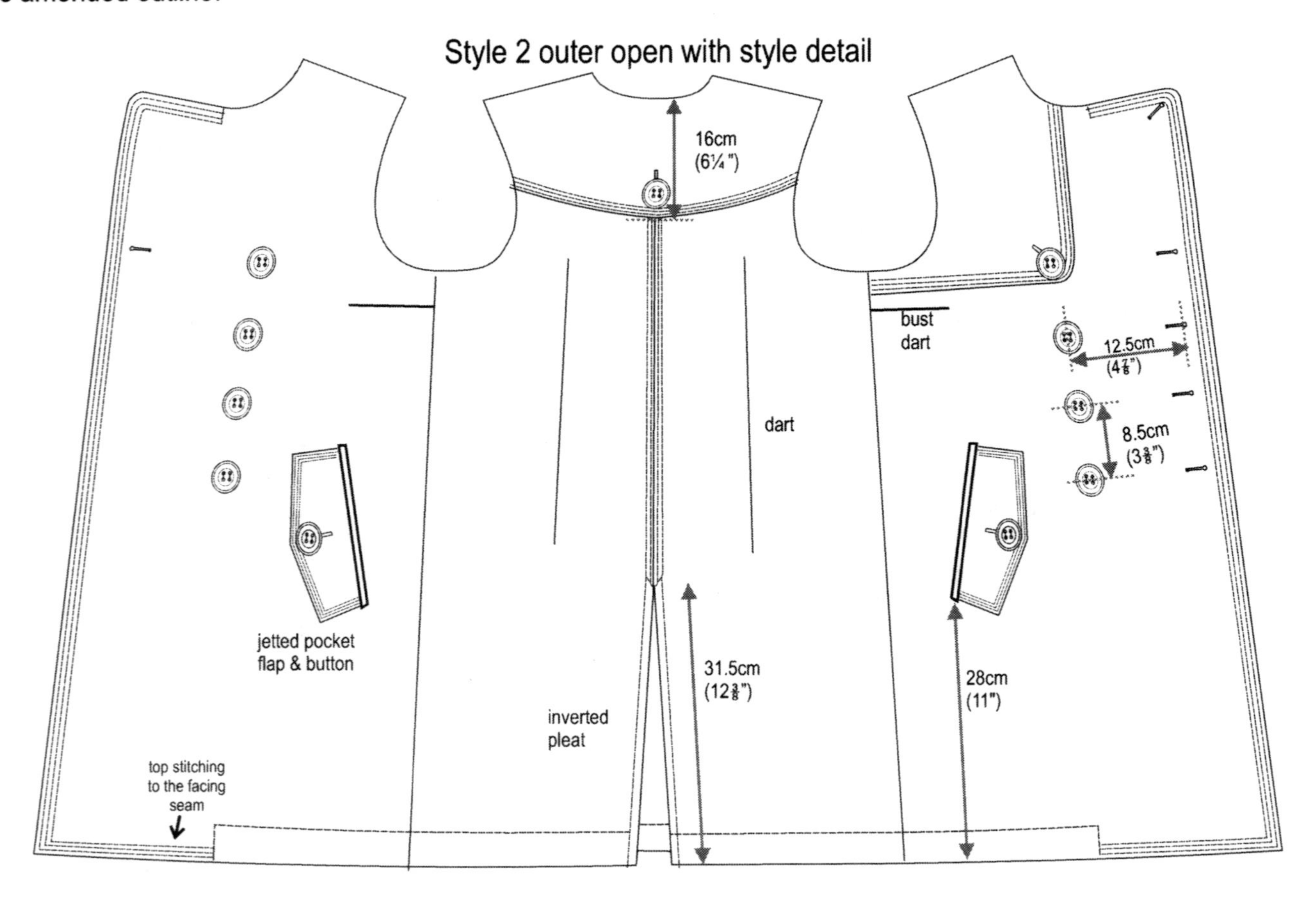

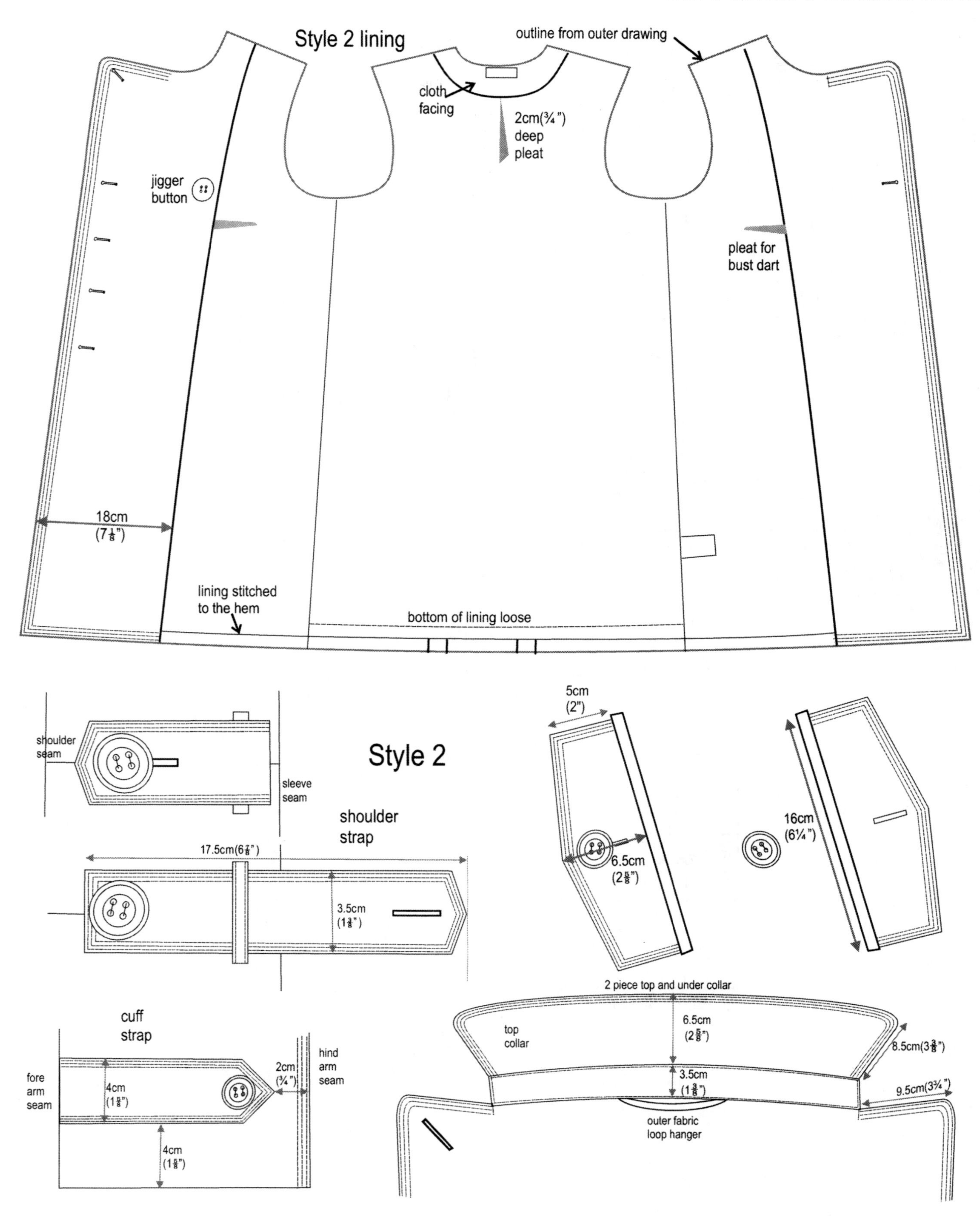

Style 2 lining
outline from outer drawing
cloth facing
2cm(¾") deep pleat
jigger button
pleat for bust dart
18cm (7⅛")
lining stitched to the hem
bottom of lining loose
shoulder seam
sleeve seam
Style 2
shoulder strap
17.5cm(6⅞")
3.5cm (1⅜")
5cm (2")
16cm (6¼")
6.5cm (2⅝")
cuff strap
fore arm seam
4cm (1⅝")
2cm (¾")
hind arm seam
4cm (1⅝")
2 piece top and under collar
top collar
6.5cm (2⅝")
8.5cm(3⅜")
3.5cm (1⅜")
9.5cm(3¾")
outer fabric loop hanger

Style 2

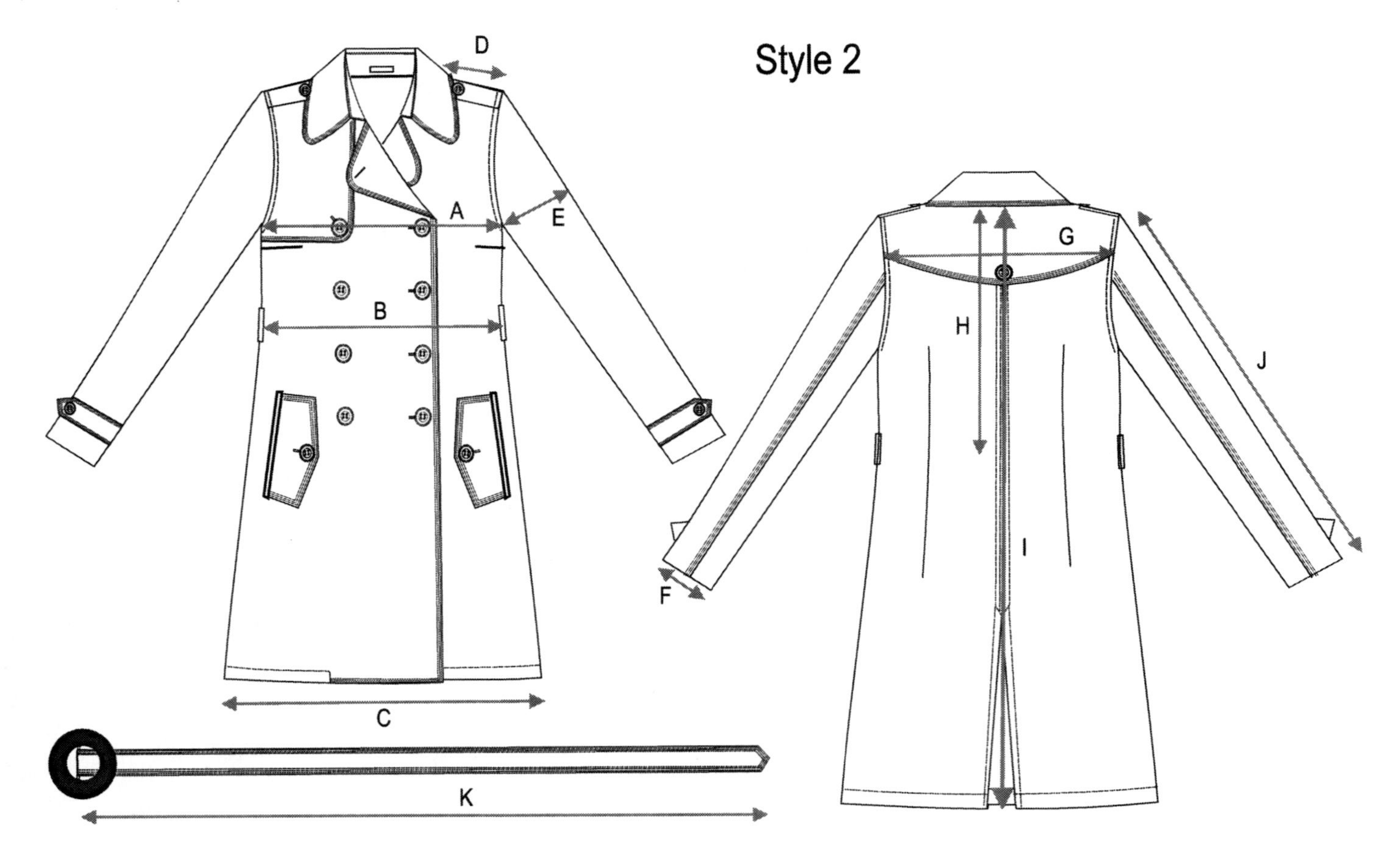

SIZE	UK 12	
	cms	Inches
A. Bust at base of armhole	110	43⅜"
B. Waist	102	40¼"
C. Hem	128	50⅜"
D. Shoulder	12	4¾"
E. Biceps	40	15¾"
F. Cuff	29	11⅜"
G. Back width	38.5	15⅛
H. Neck seam to waist	41.5	16⅜"
I. Full length from neck seam	88	34⅝"
J. Sleeve crown to cuff	64	25¼"
K. Belt	134.5	53"

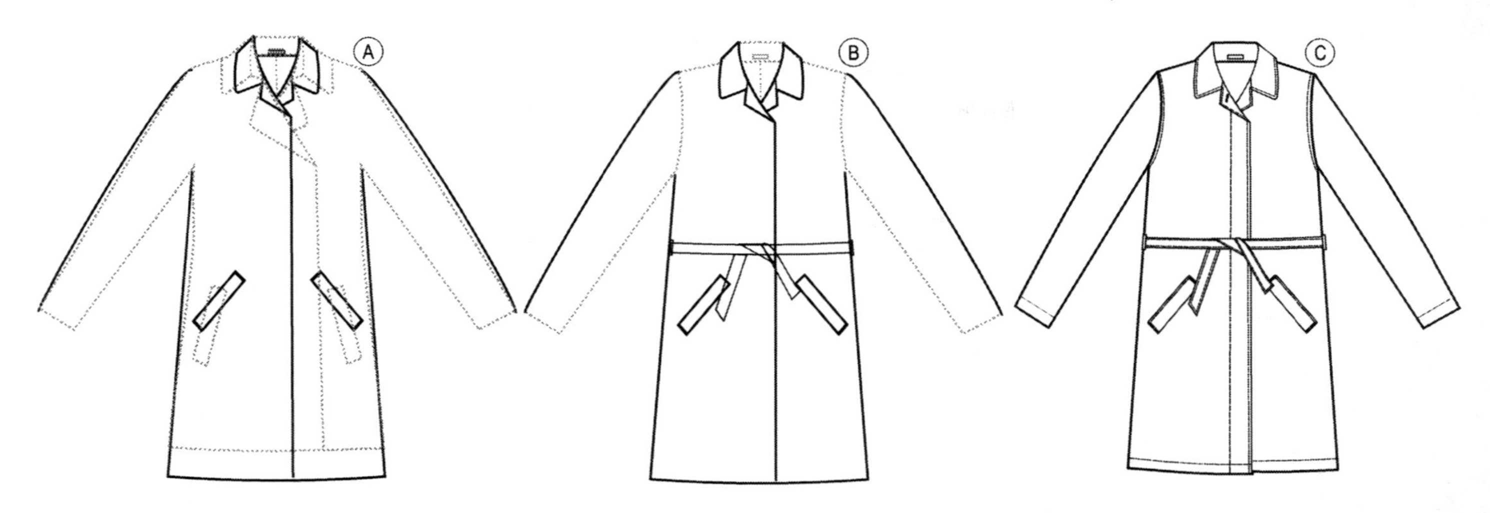

Drawing A shows the style changes for style 3 superimposed on to style 1. Drawing B the outline of the collar, lapel, front edge and pockets after style 1 details have been erased. If you are happy with the result at this stage then drawing C is completed adding all details.

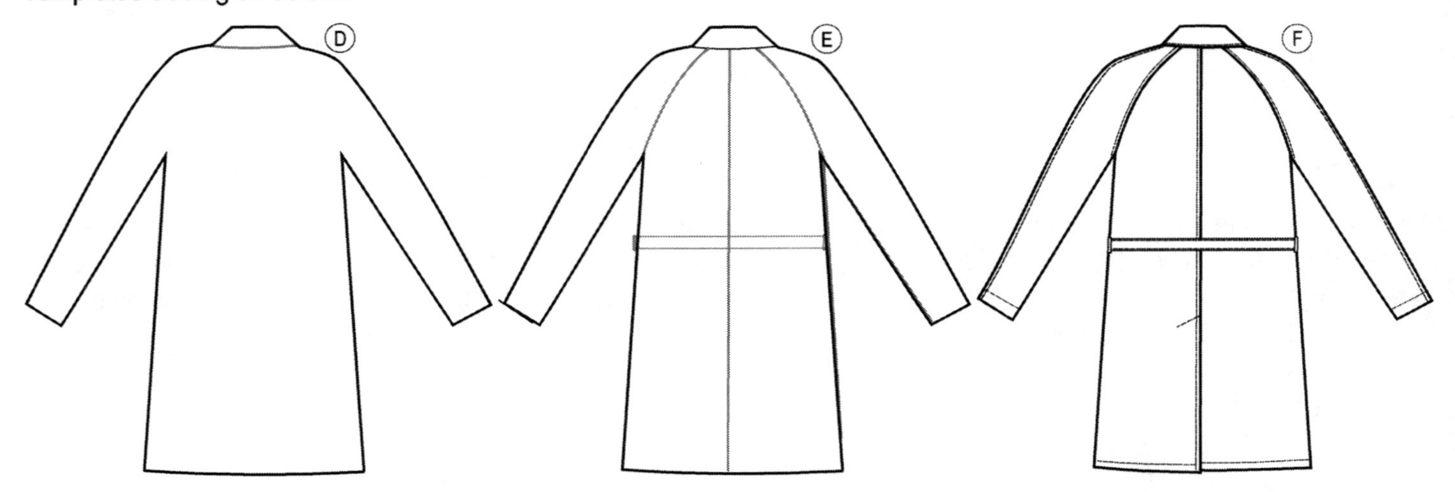

Drawing D starts with the front outline in black. Inside the outline I have changed the shape of the sleeve as the back is a raglan style. Drawing E is the back outline completed and the old outline erased. Drawing F is the back finished with stitch detail.

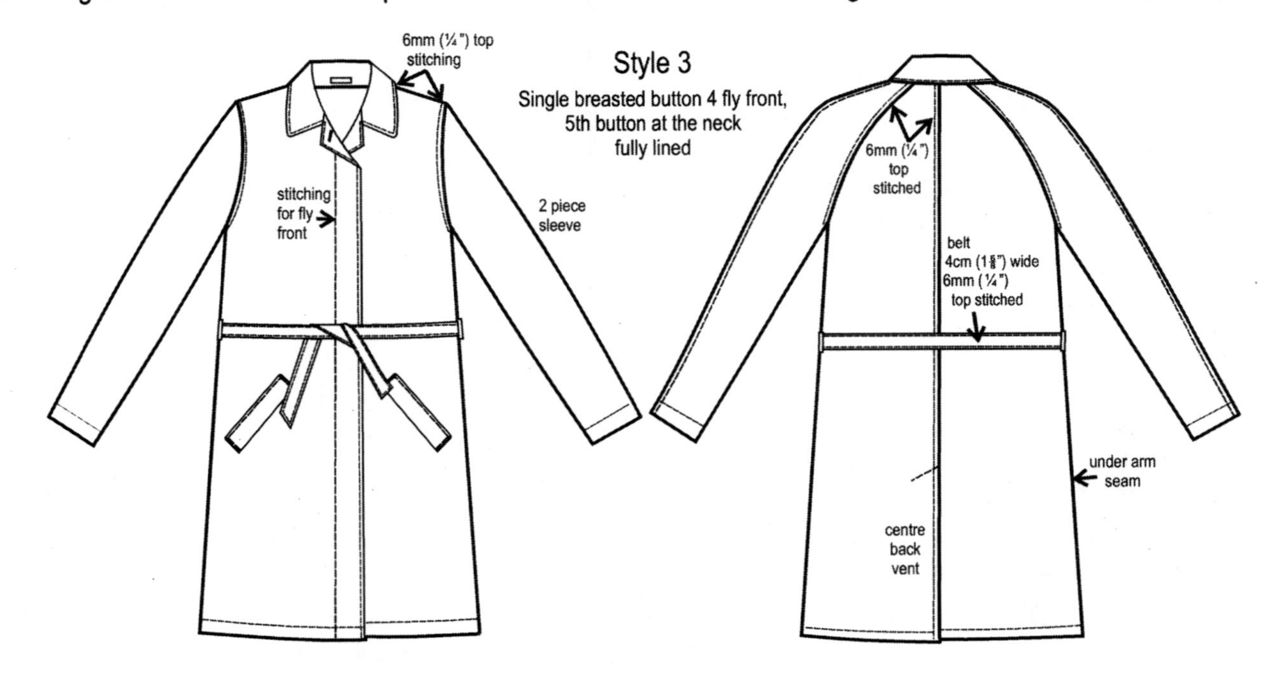

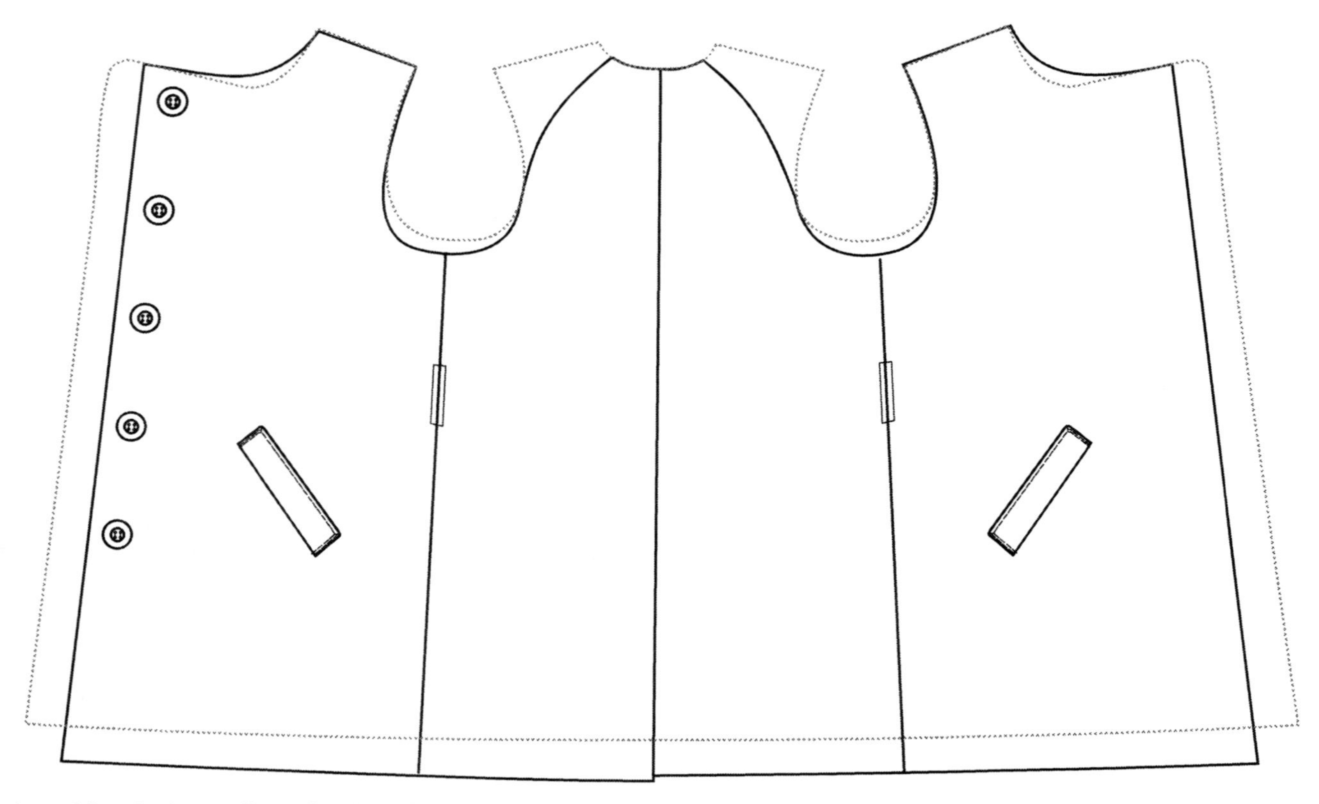

The dotted line is the outline of style 1.The detail for style 3 is added. Adjust the outline to what you consider necessary to suit the new style. Firstly I changed the back to a raglan sleeve and deepened the armhole slightly. Front edge to front edge is narrowed as this is now single breasted instead of double breasted. Finally the neck circle and length are adjusted to help represent style 3 as closely as possible to my sample coat.

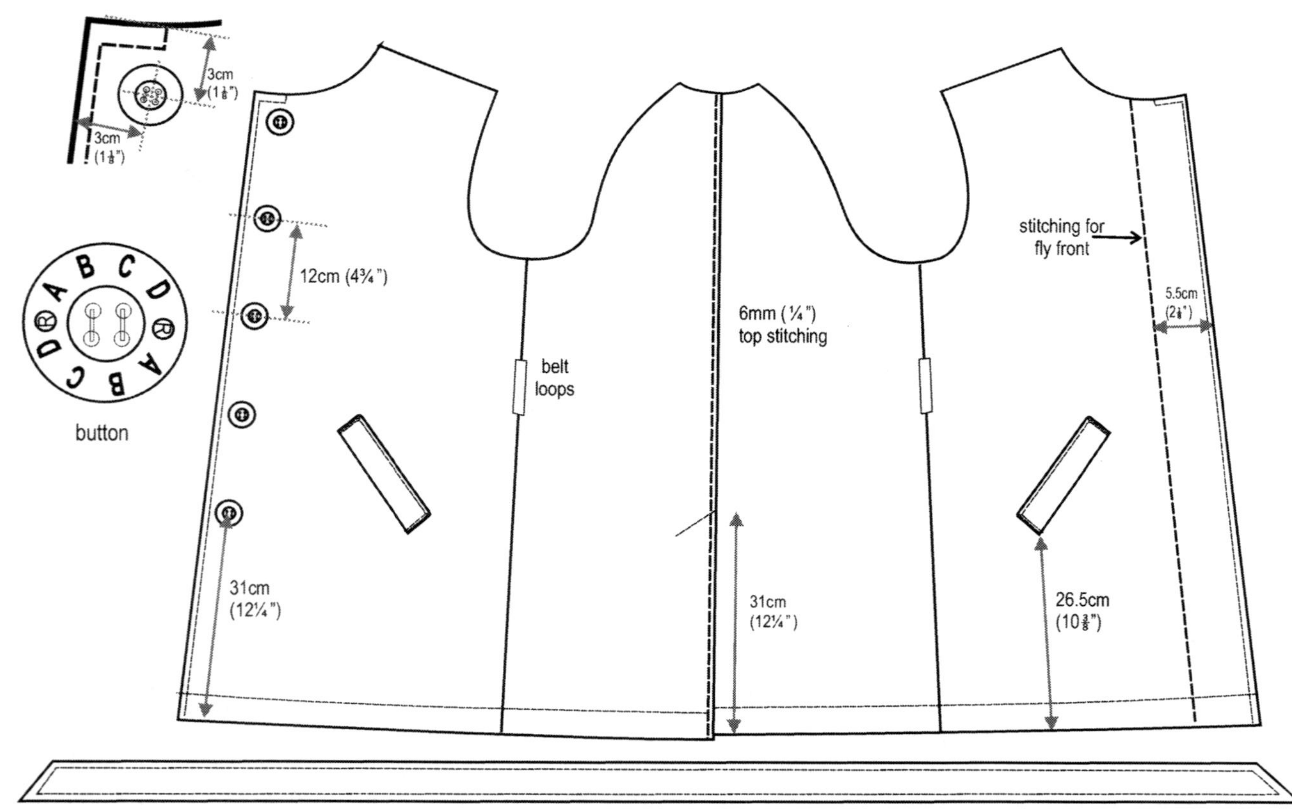

Add as much detail as possible. For example note the distance between details, such as the pocket and bottom button, are from the finished hem. Also note the distance between buttons and the distance from the center of the button to the finished front edge.

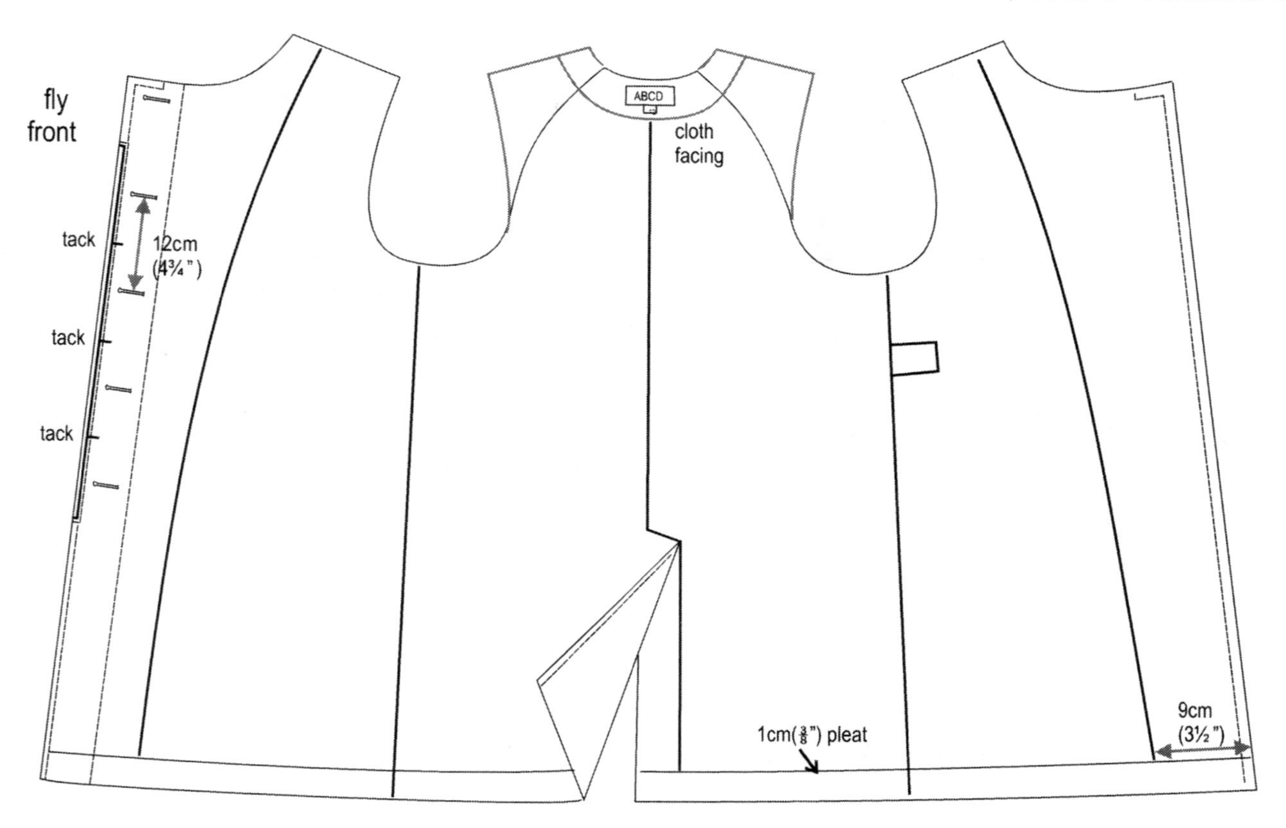

The black line is the outline of the outer illustration, but the lining is constructed with a set-in sleeve both at the back and the front.

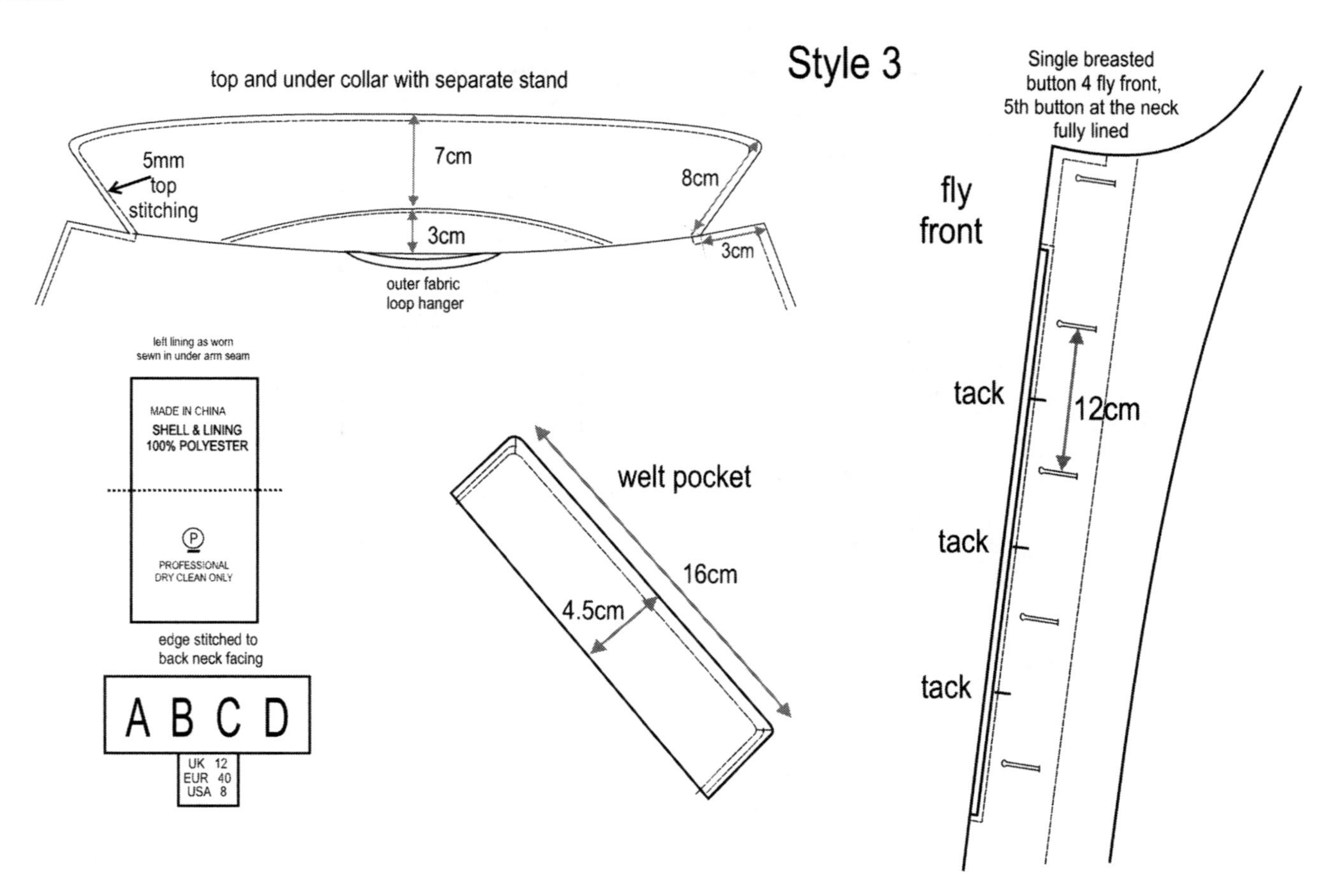

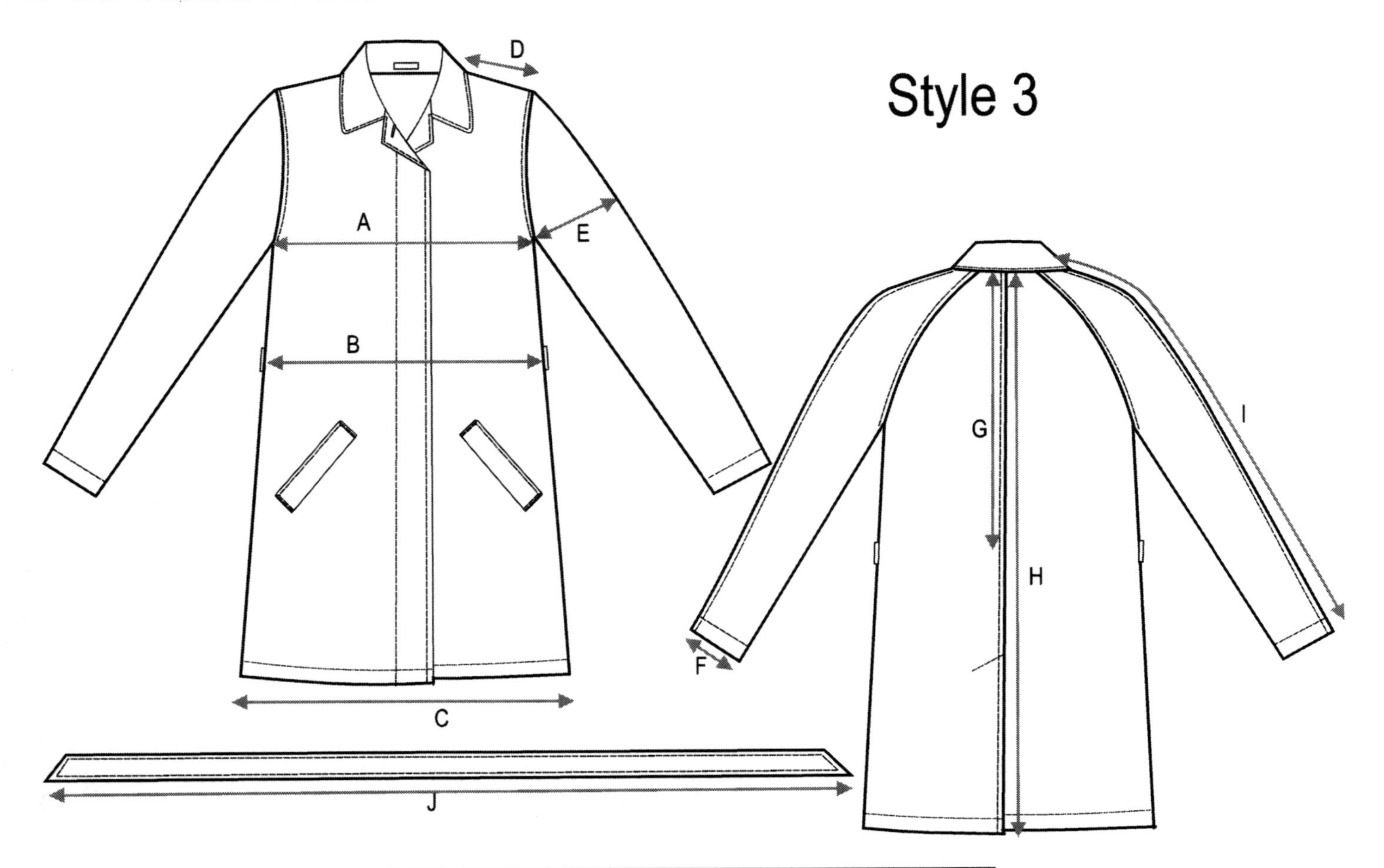

SIZE	12 UK	
	cms	Inches
A. Bust at base of armhole	114	44⅞"
B. Waist	118	46½"
C. Hem	120	47¼"
D. Shoulder	14.5	5¾"
E. Biceps	48	18⅞"
F. Cuff	30	11¾"
G. Neck seam to waist	46	18⅛"
H. Full length from neck seam	90	35⅜"
I. Neck seam to cuff	75.5	29¾"
J. Belt	140	55"

Using style 1 as the template the basic outline and details of style 4 are added, see illustration A and B. When satisfied with the result complete illustration C with all the style details.

Illustration D is the front outline for style 4. The style details have been sketched inside the outline on illustration E to show the basic outline of the back details. When satisfied with the results complete illustration F with all the remaining style details.

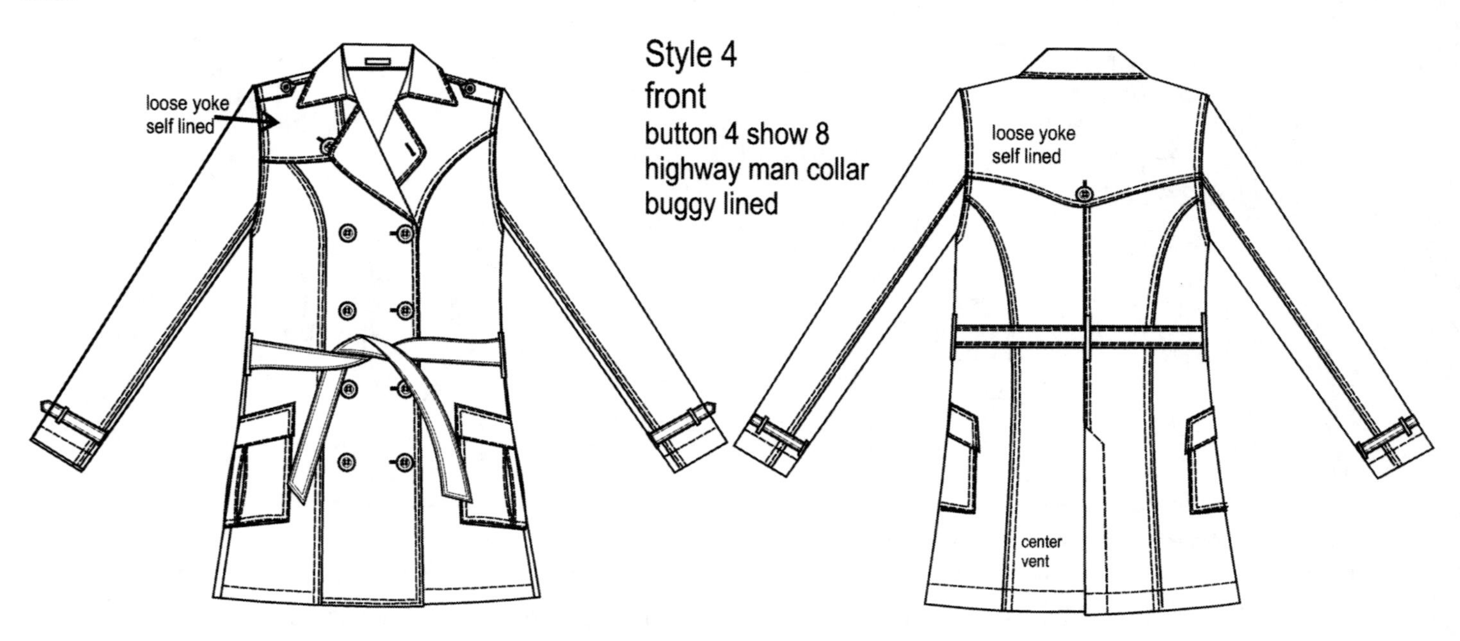

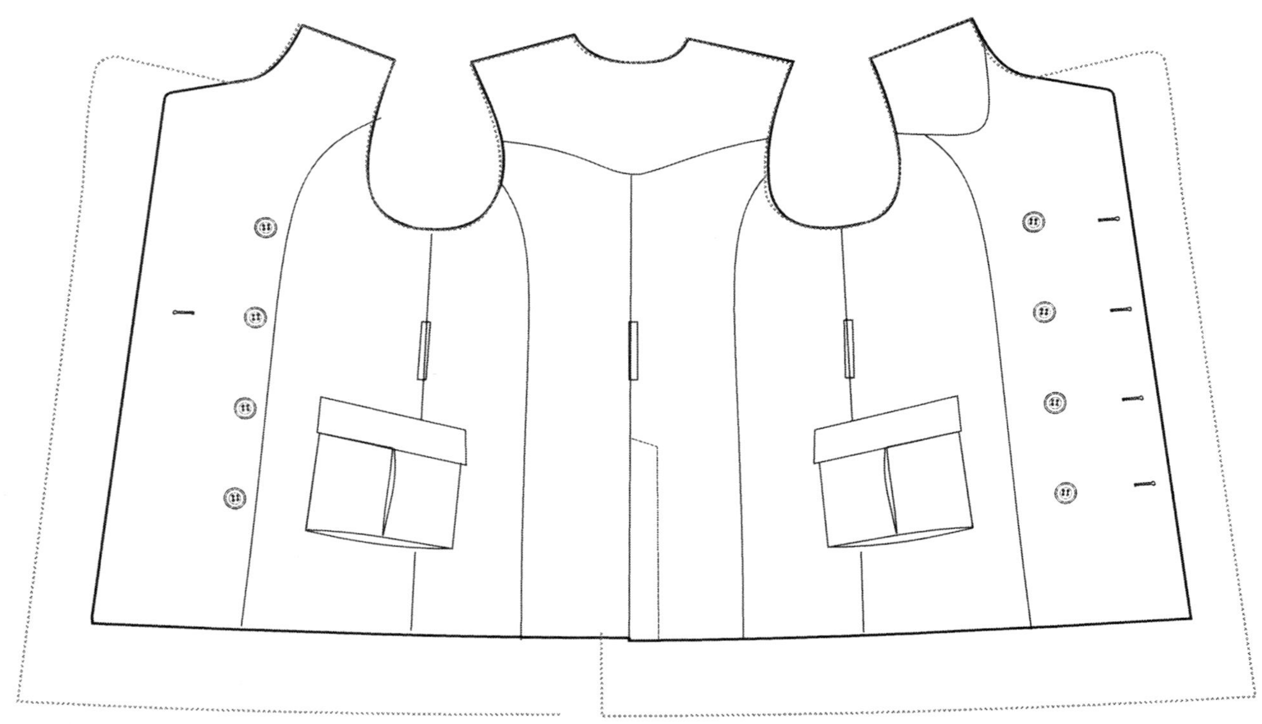

The dotted line is the outline of style 1.The detail for style 4 is added. The main differences in shape between the 2 coats is that style 4 is narrower across the width, the buttons are closer together with less wrap over at the center front and style 4 is slightly shorter. By taking this into account and moving the position of the front and bottom edges, I can accurately position the seams, panels, pockets and buttons. When satisfied that this represents the sample coat, add the rest of the detail and erase the outline of style 1.

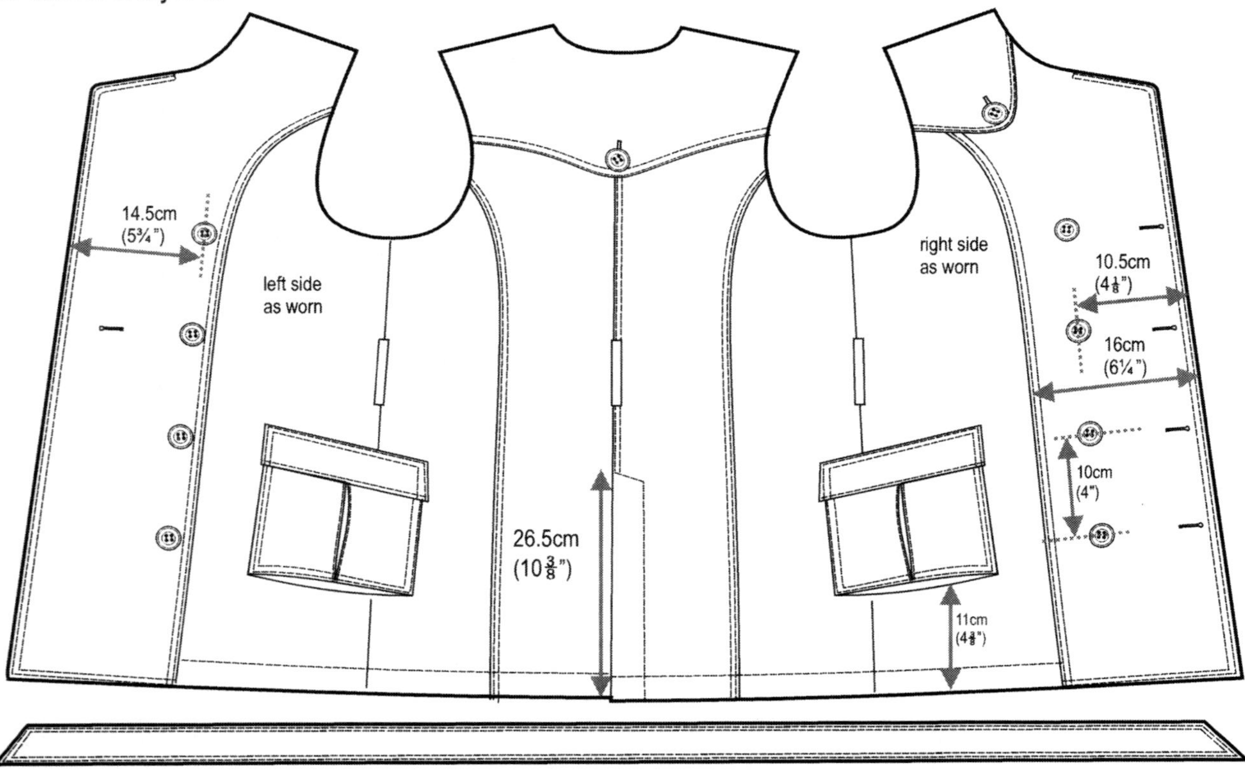

This style particularly benefits from being shown open,since the shape and positioning of the seams are the distinctive look of the coat. This illustration makes it very clear to the pattern cutter. Note that the buttons on the left side as worn are positioned closer to the front panel seam so that when the jacket is fastened, the right front edge will cover the front panel seam on the left side as worn to make the panels and seams more aesthetically pleasing.

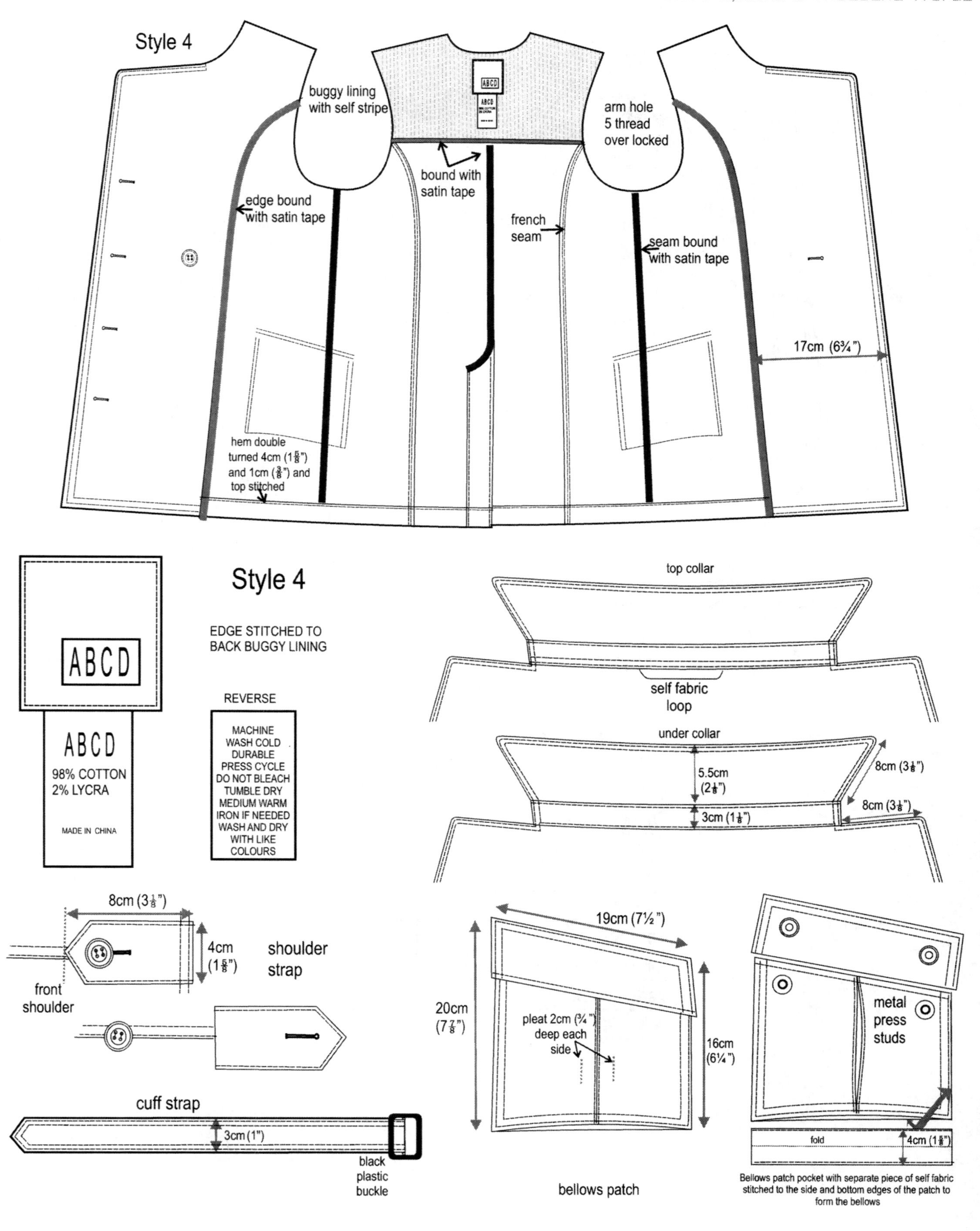
Style 4
buggy lining
with self stripe
arm hole
5 thread
over locked
bound with
satin tape
edge bound
with satin tape
french
seam
seam bound
with satin tape
17cm (6¾")
hem double
turned 4cm (1⅝")
and 1cm (⅜") and
top stitched
ABCD
Style 4
EDGE STITCHED TO
BACK BUGGY LINING
REVERSE
ABCD
98% COTTON
2% LYCRA
MADE IN CHINA
MACHINE
WASH COLD
DURABLE
PRESS CYCLE
DO NOT BLEACH
TUMBLE DRY
MEDIUM WARM
IRON IF NEEDED
WASH AND DRY
WITH LIKE
COLOURS
top collar
self fabric
loop
under collar
5.5cm
(2⅛")
3cm (1⅛")
8cm (3⅛")
8cm (3⅛")
8cm (3⅛")
4cm
(1⅝")
shoulder
strap
front
shoulder
cuff strap
3cm (1")
black
plastic
buckle
19cm (7½")
20cm
(7⅞")
pleat 2cm (¾")
deep each
side
16cm
(6¼")
bellows patch
metal
press
studs
fold
4cm (1⅝")
Bellows patch pocket with separate piece of self fabric stitched to the side and bottom edges of the patch to form the bellows

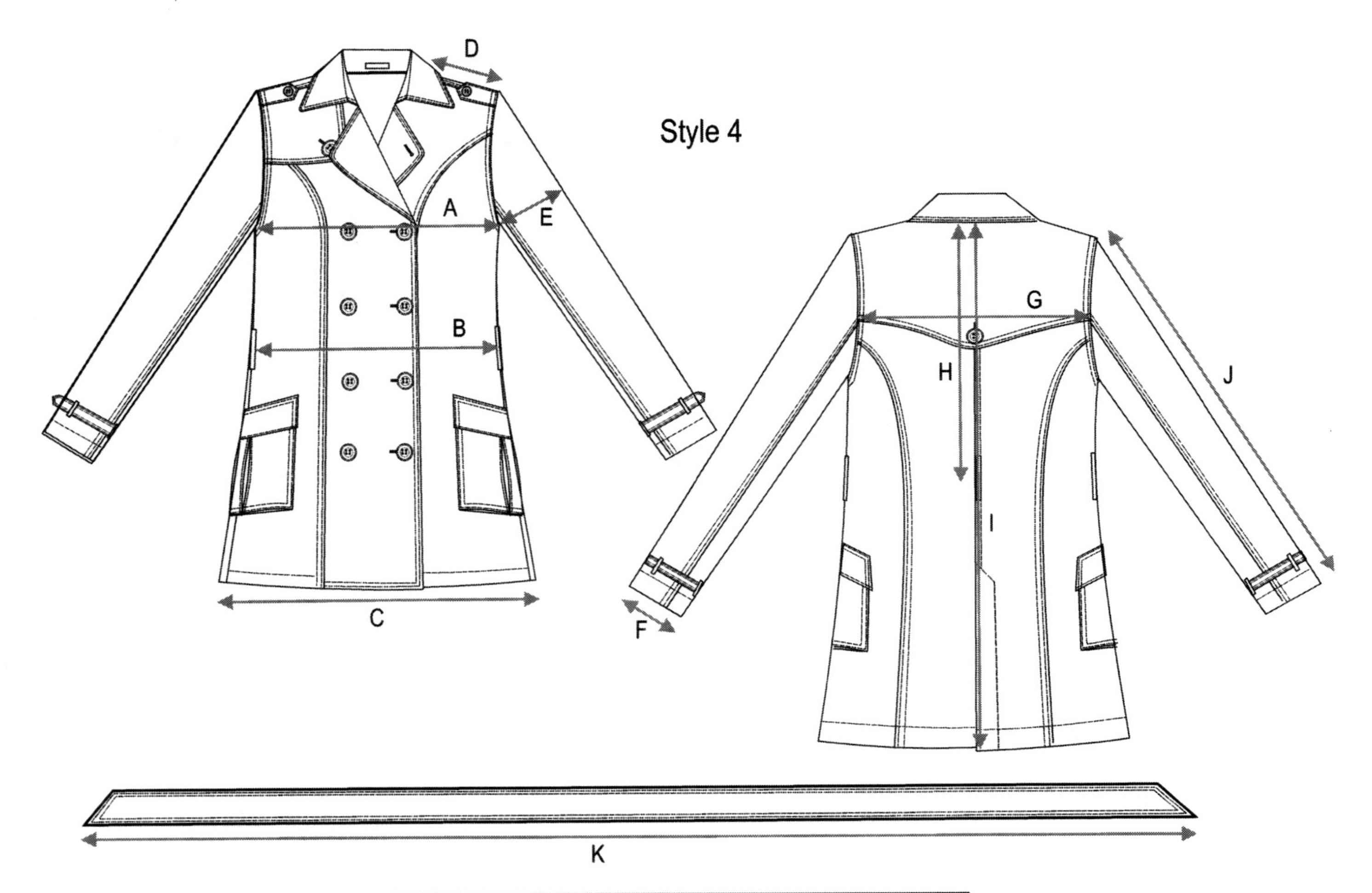

SIZE	UK 12	
	cms	Inches
A. Bust at base of armhole	105	41⅜"
B. Waist	92	36½"
C. Hem	120	47¼"
D. Shoulder	11.5	4½"
E. Biceps	36	14⅛"
F. Cuff	34	13⅜"
G. Back width	37.5	14¾"
H. Neck seam to waist	41.5	16⅜"
I. Full length from neck seam	83	32⅝"
J. Sleeve crown to cuff	64	25¼"
K. Belt	130	51¼"

Drawing A dotted line is style 4 outline, the solid line is style 5 outline. Drawing B is the style detail of style 5 sketched in. Drawing C is the completed style.

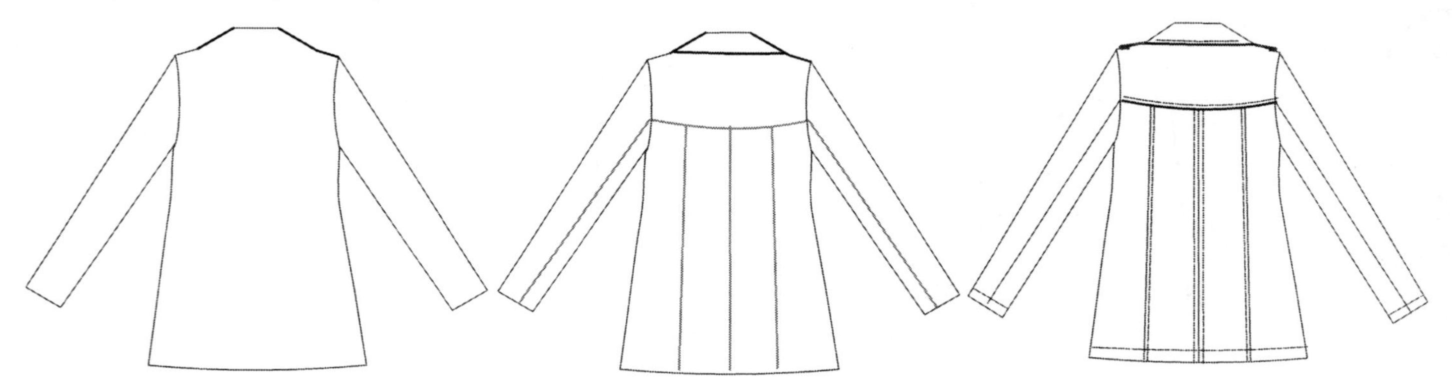

Use the front outline and add the back details

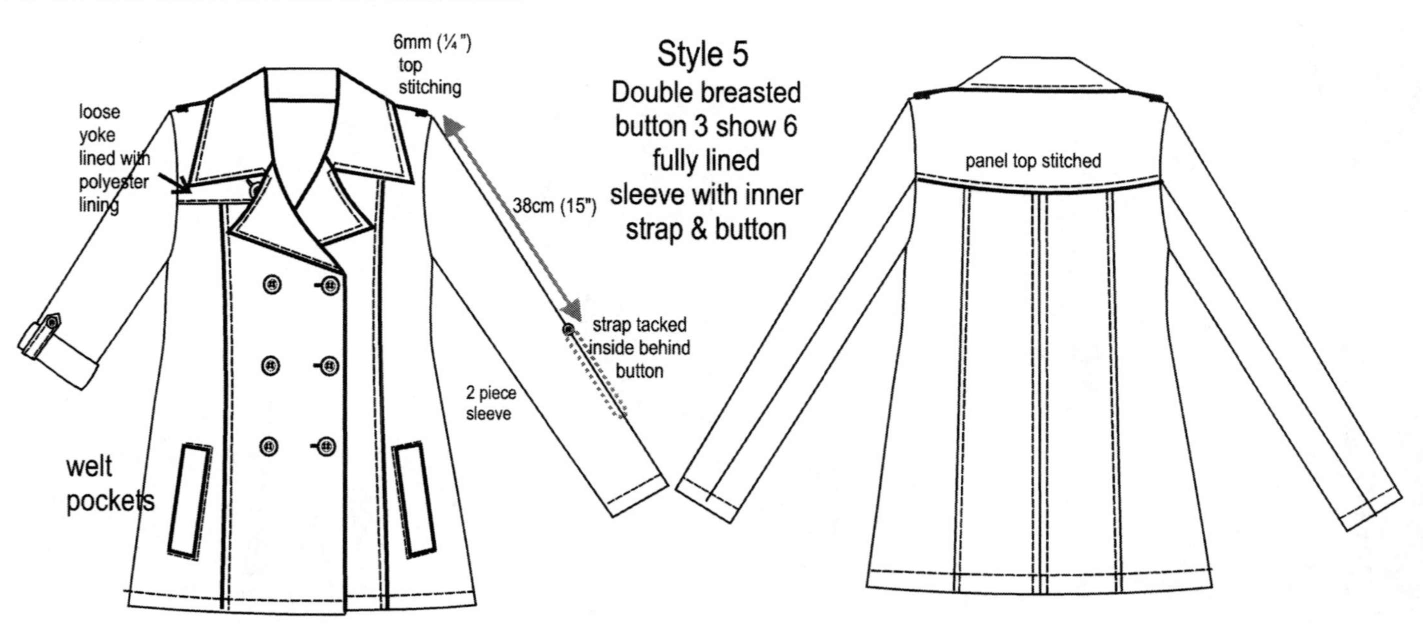

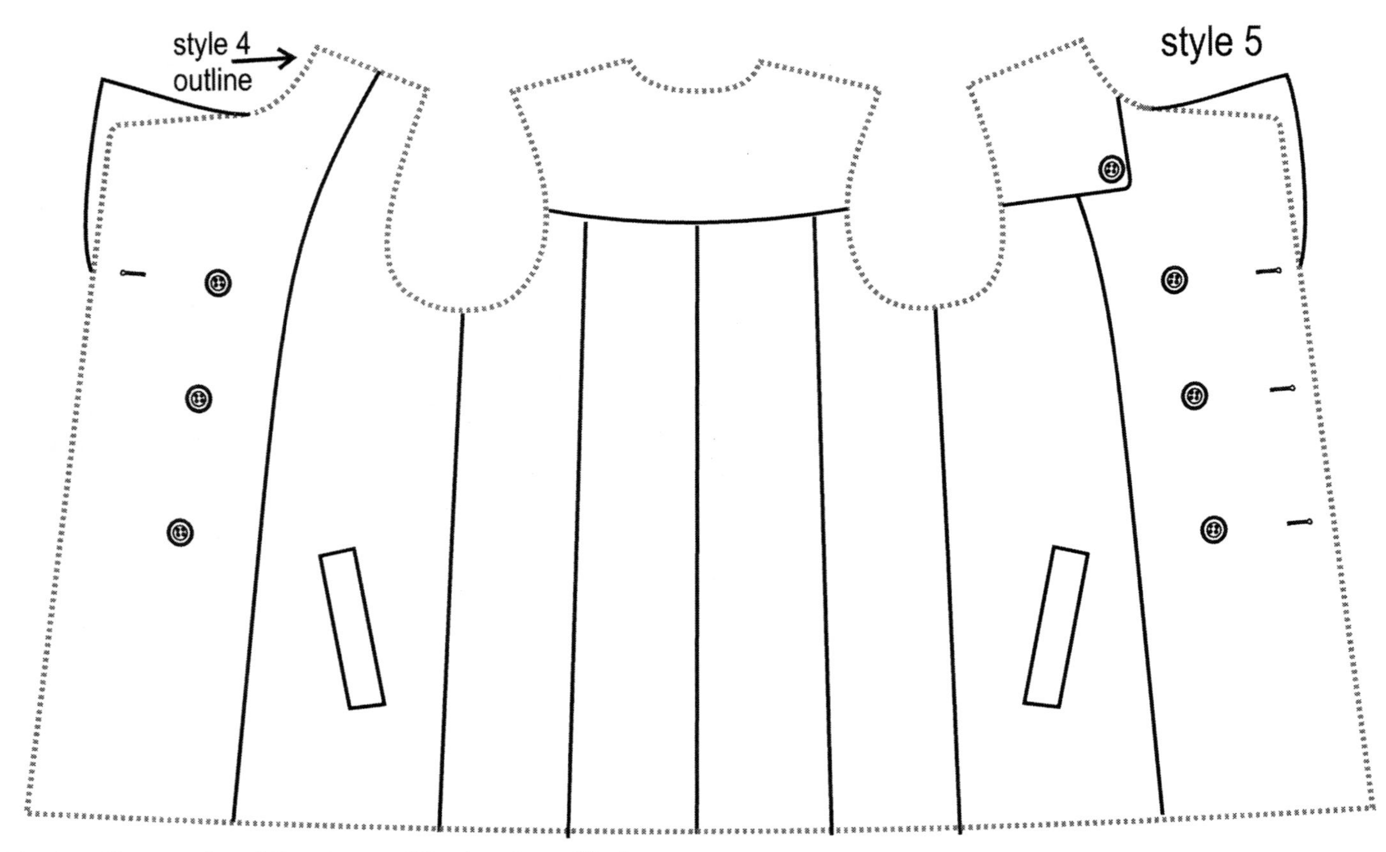

Style 4 outline used and the shape of the lapel modified.

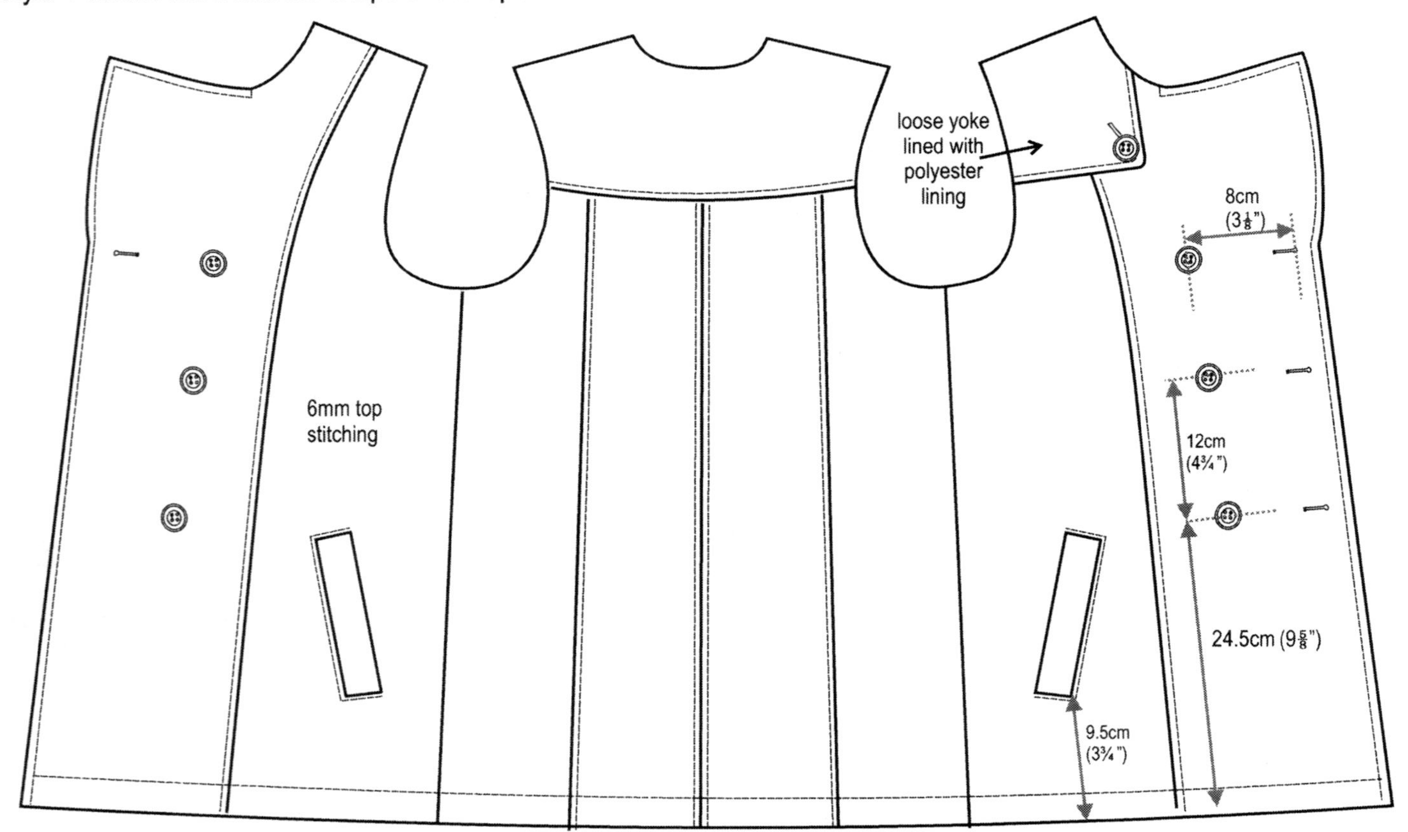

Style 5 opened out completed.

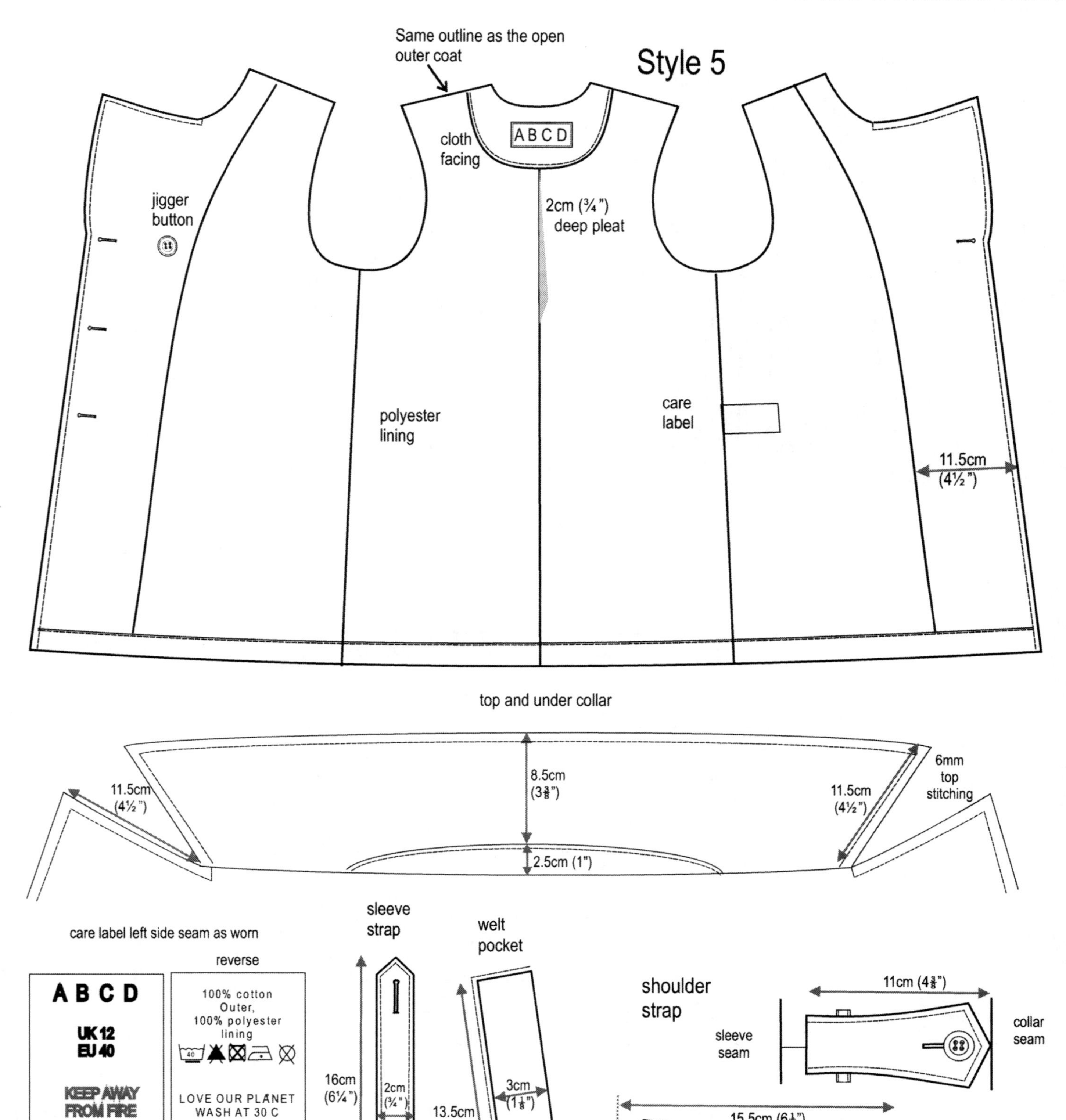

Same outline as the open outer coat
Style 5
ABCD
cloth facing
jigger button
2cm (¾") deep pleat
polyester lining
care label
11.5cm (4½")
top and under collar
8.5cm (3⅜")
11.5cm (4½")
11.5cm (4½")
6mm top stitching
2.5cm (1")
sleeve strap
welt pocket
care label left side seam as worn
reverse
A B C D
UK 12
EU 40
KEEP AWAY FROM FIRE
MADE IN CHINA
100% cotton Outer, 100% polyester lining
LOVE OUR PLANET WASH AT 30 C
16cm (6¼")
2cm (¾")
13.5cm (5⅜")
3cm (1⅛")
shoulder strap
11cm (4⅜")
sleeve seam
collar seam
15.5cm (6⅛")
5cm (2")
3cm (1⅛")
shoulder seam

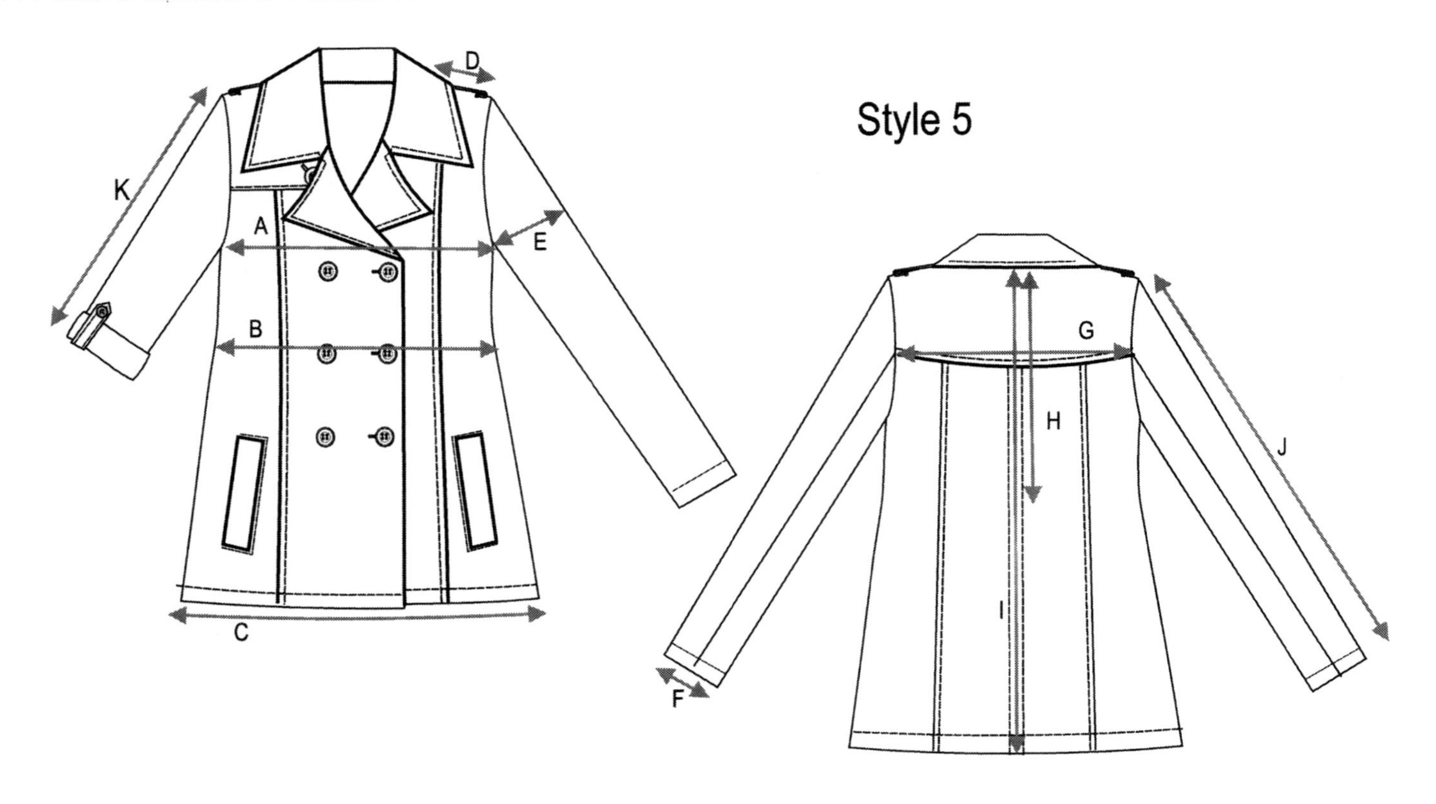

SIZE	UK 12	
	cms	Inches
A. Bust at base of armhole	105	41⅜"
B. Waist	92	36¼"
C. Hem	126	49⅝"
D. Shoulder	11.5	4½"
E. Biceps	36	14¼
F. Cuff	30	11¾"
G. Back width	37.5	14¾"
H. Neck seam to waist	40	15¾"
I. Full length from neck seam	72	28⅜"
J. Sleeve crown to cuff	64	25¼"
K. Sleeve when fastened with strap	44	17⅜"

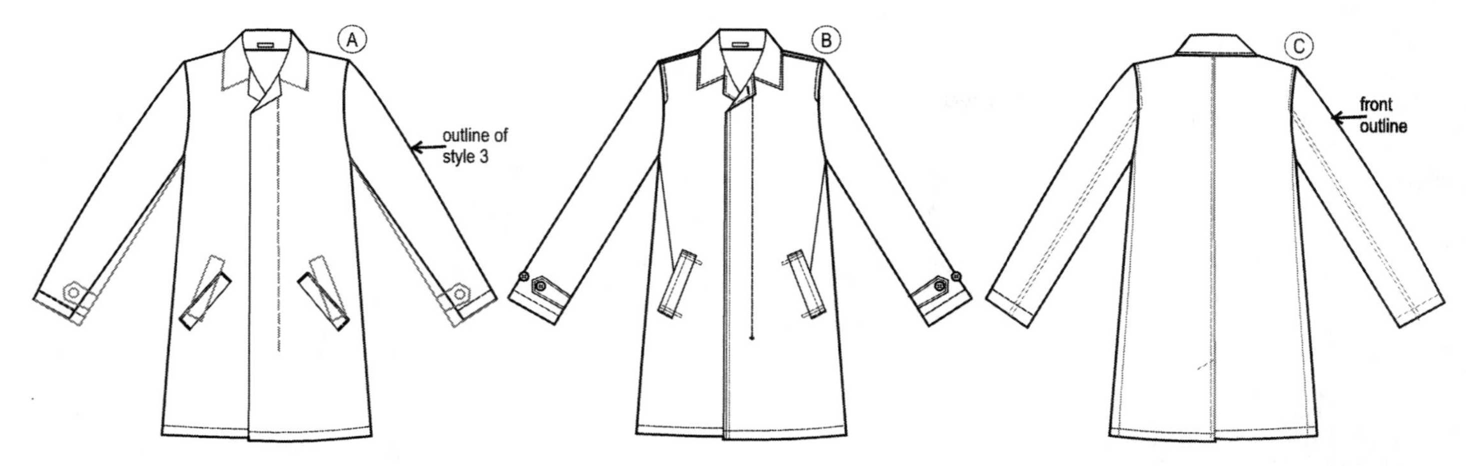

Style 6 is a men's fly front fastening, the male version of the ladies style 3. To illustrate style 6 I used the mirror image of style 3 to create the men's fastening. Drawing A is the mirror image, and sketched inside the outline are the shapes for style 6. Drawing B is the completed front. The front outline is copied for the back in drawing C and the detail added.

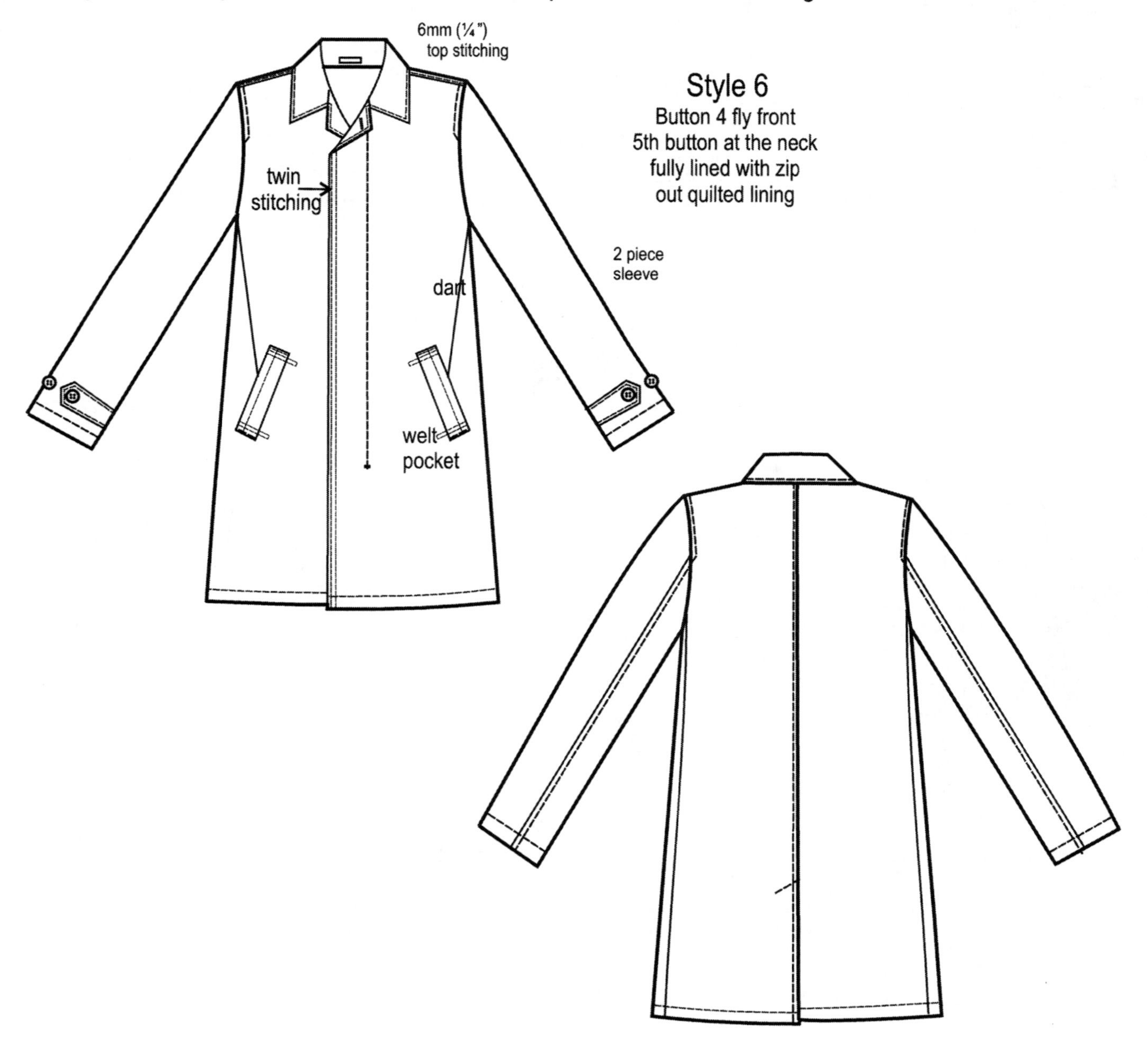

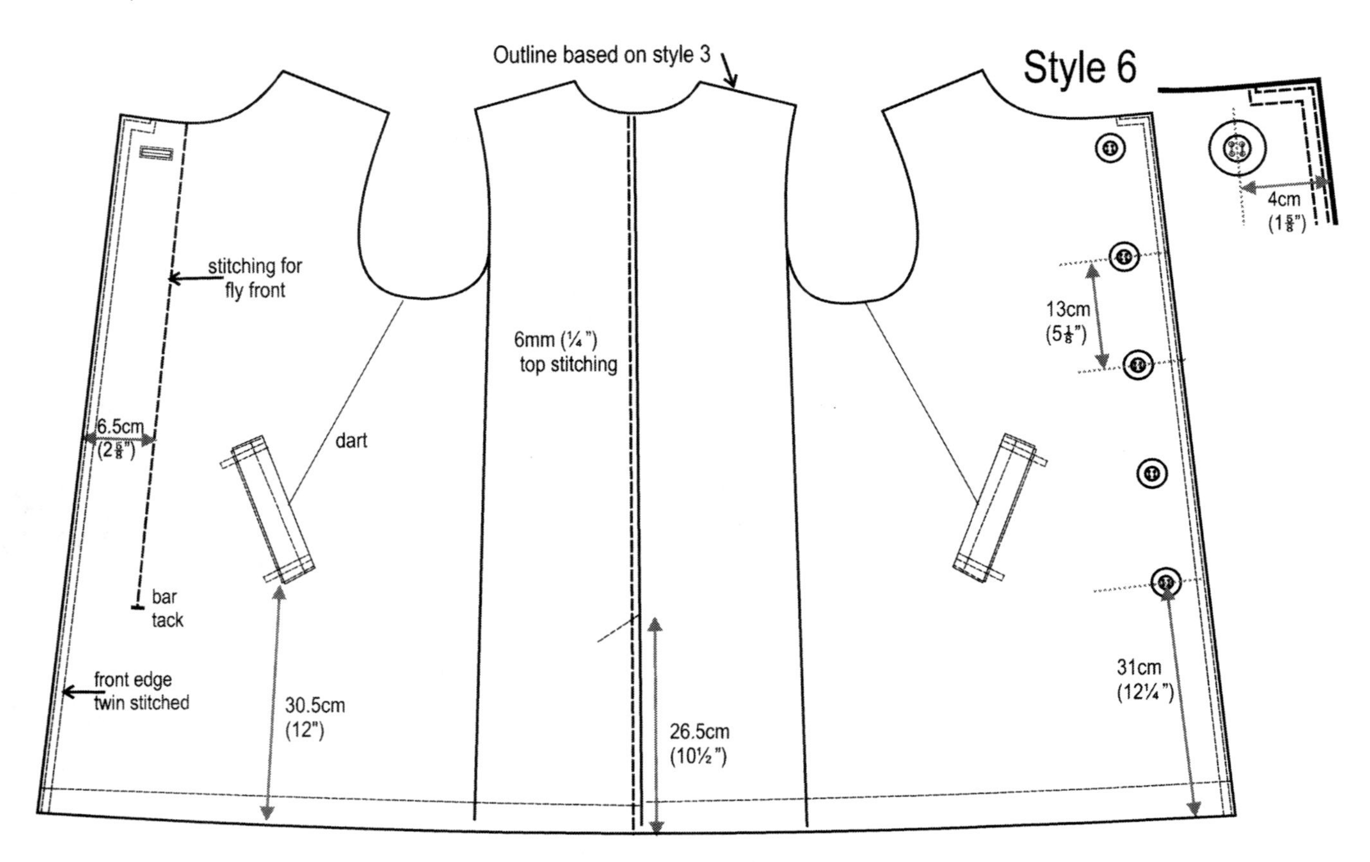
Outline based on style 3
Style 6
4cm
(1⅝")
stitching for
fly front
13cm
(5⅛")
6mm (¼")
top stitching
6.5cm
(2⅝")
dart
bar
tack
front edge
twin stitched
30.5cm
(12")
26.5cm
(10½")
31cm
(12¼")

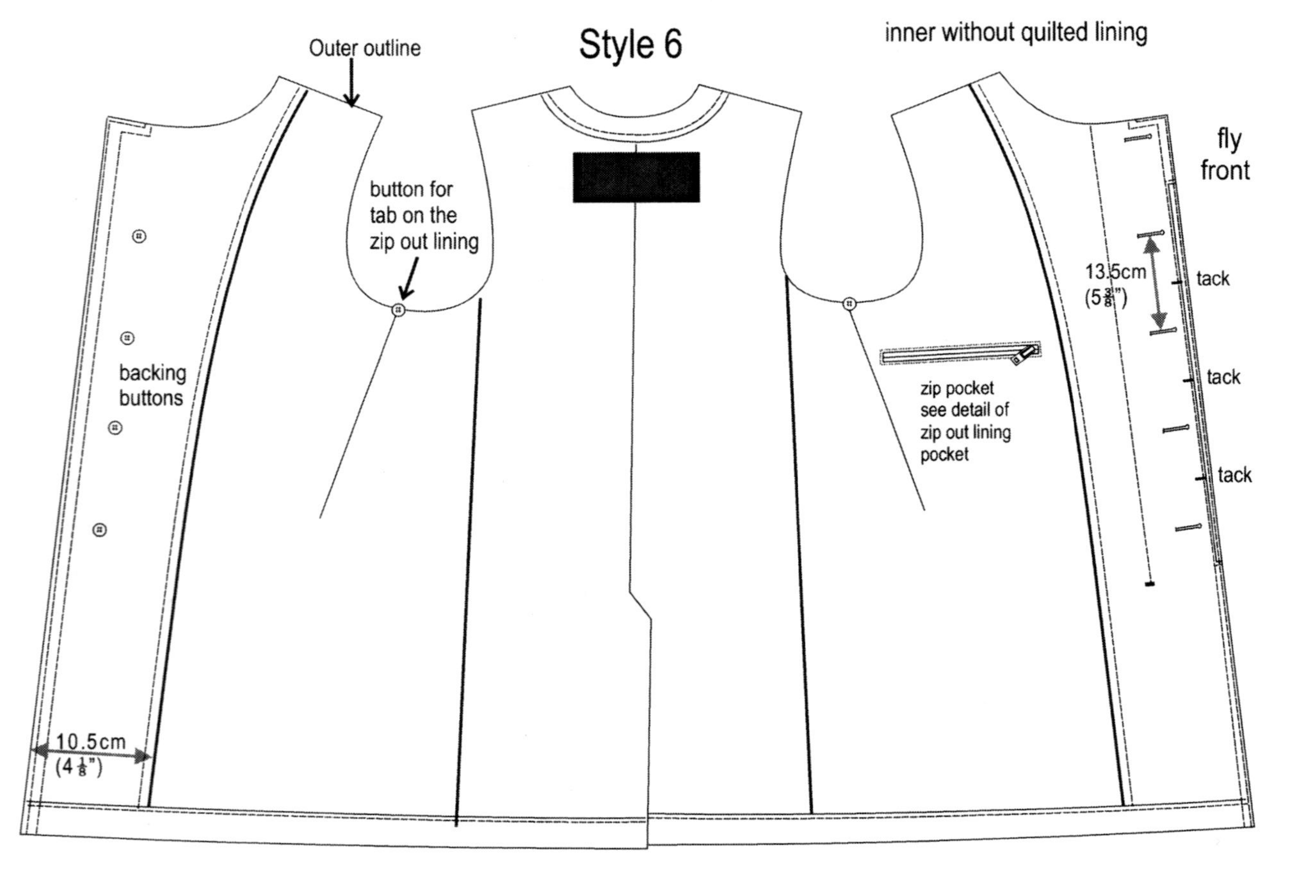
Outer outline
Style 6
inner without quilted lining
button for
tab on the
zip out lining
fly
front
13.5cm
(5⅜")
tack
backing
buttons
tack
zip pocket
see detail of
zip out lining
pocket
tack
10.5cm
(4⅛")

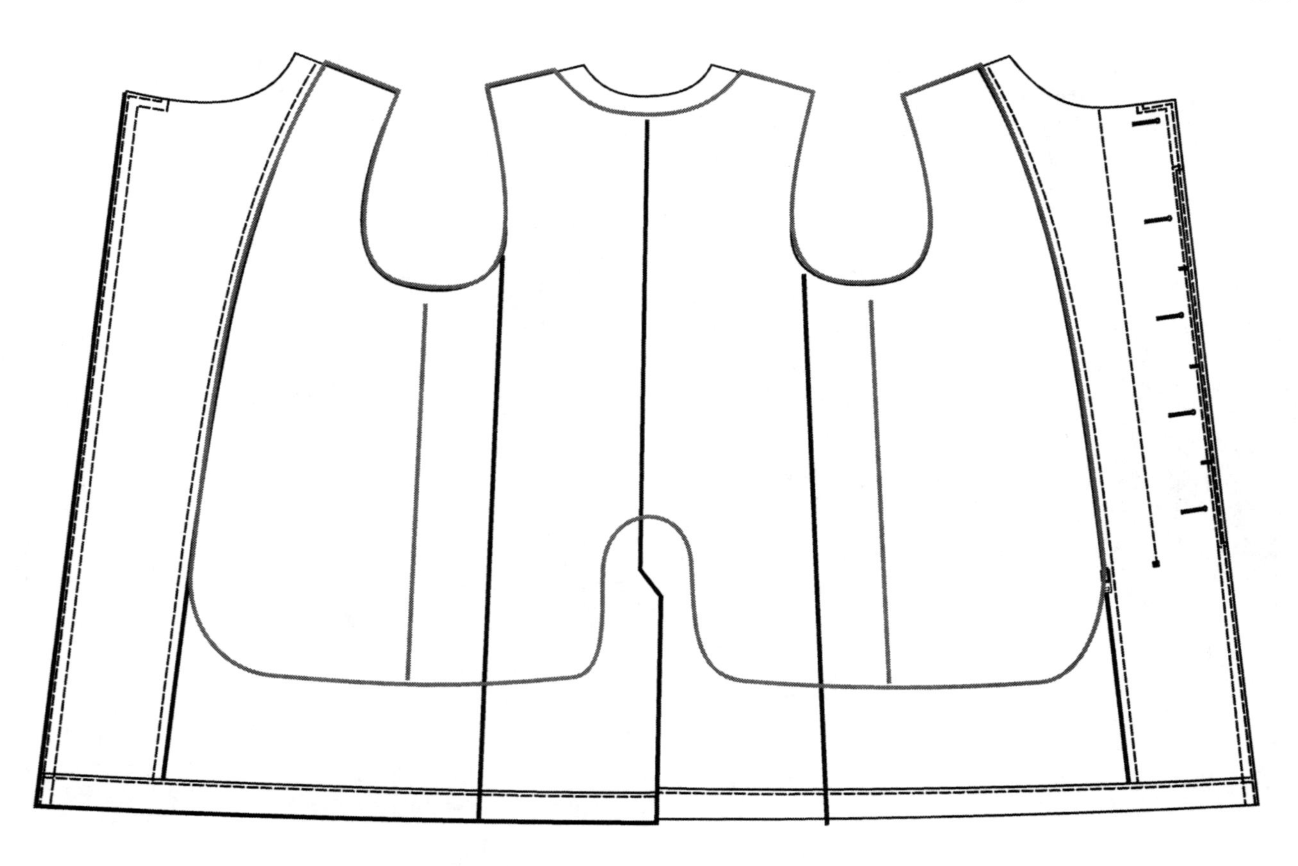

The outline of the zip outlining is in grey. This must be a whole object (no breaks in the lines) so that color can be added.

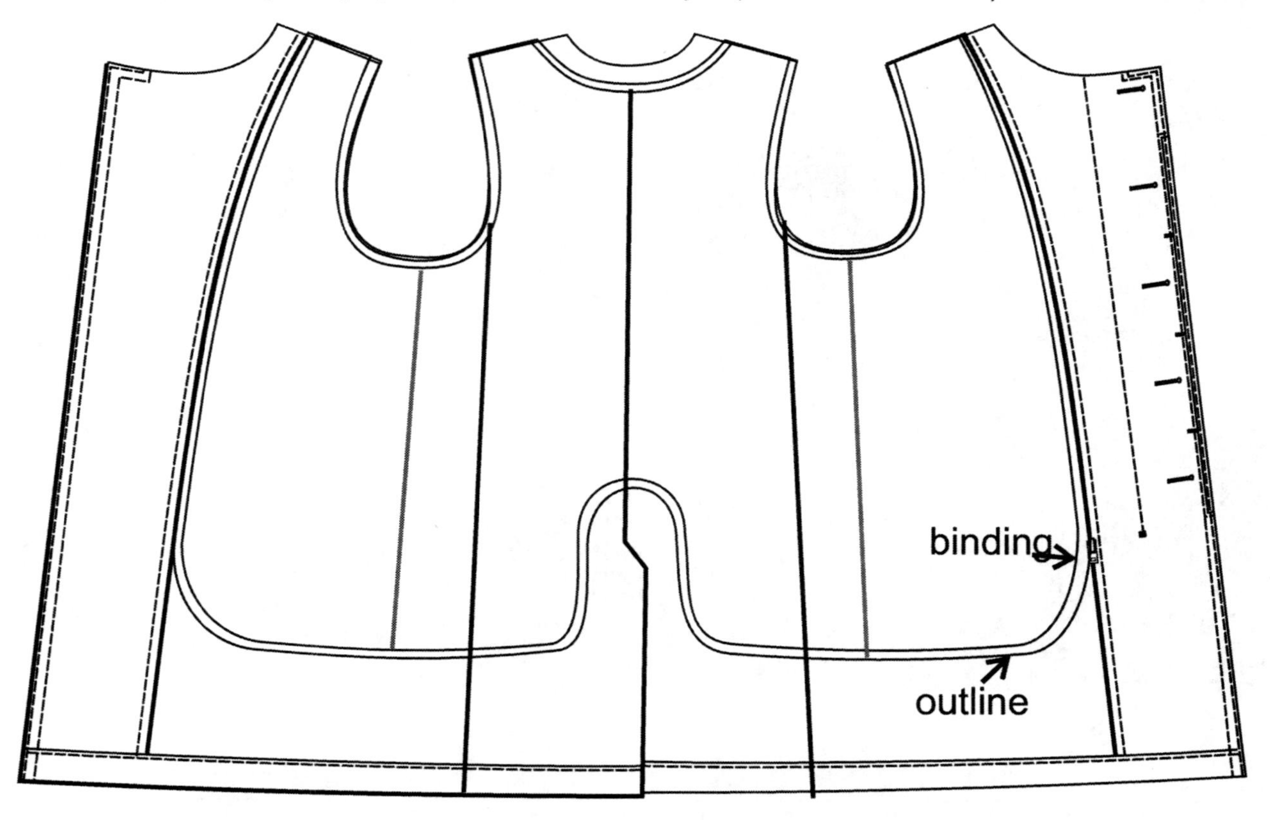

The outline is copied and pasted and scaled down to create the binding. There are now 2 whole objects

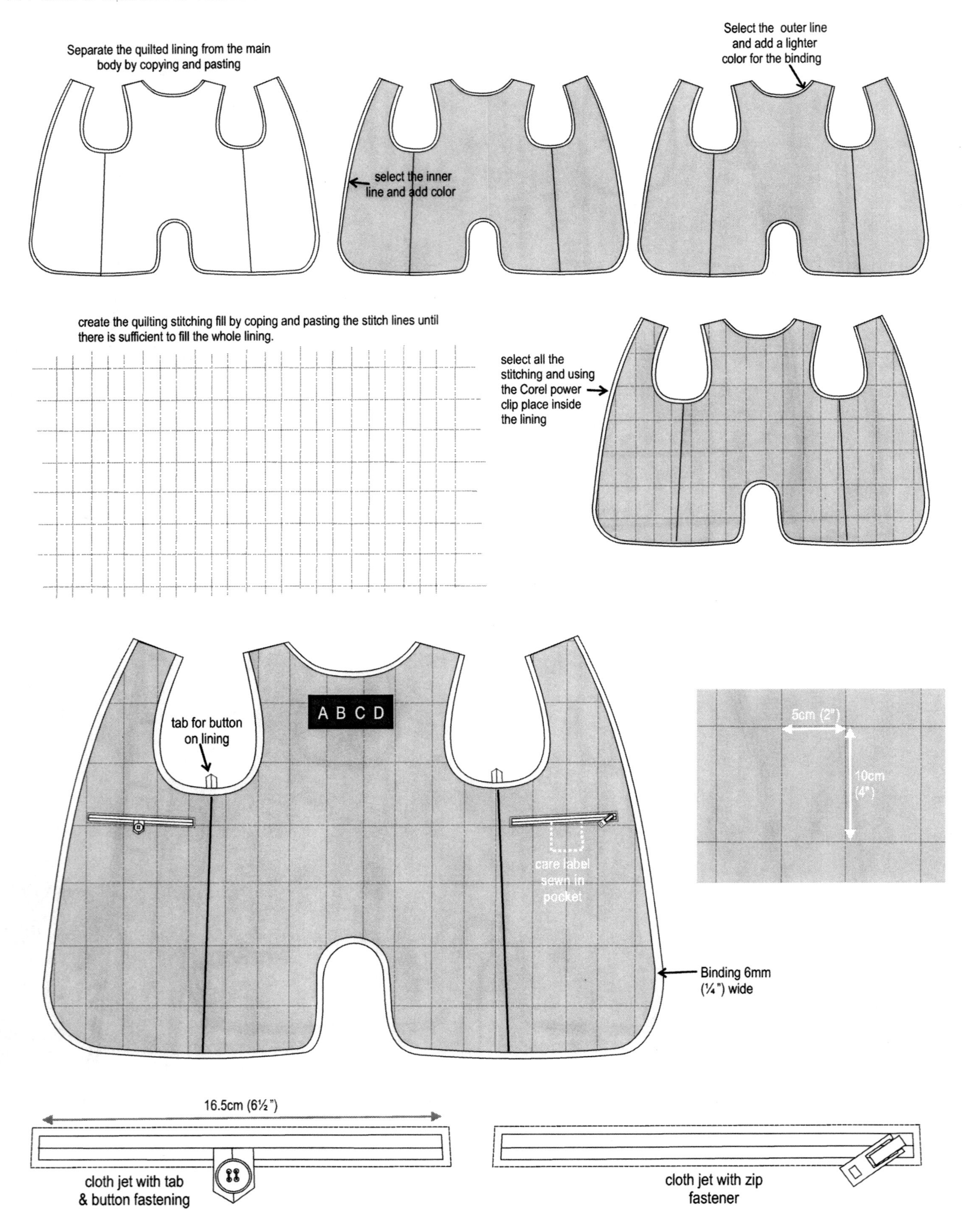
Separate the quilted lining from the main body by copying and pasting
select the inner line and add color
Select the outer line and add a lighter color for the binding
create the quilting stitching fill by coping and pasting the stitch lines until there is sufficient to fill the whole lining.
select all the stitching and using the Corel power clip place inside the lining
A B C D
tab for button on lining
care label sewn in pocket
Binding 6mm (¼") wide
5cm (2")
10cm (4")
16.5cm (6½")
cloth jet with tab & button fastening
cloth jet with zip fastener

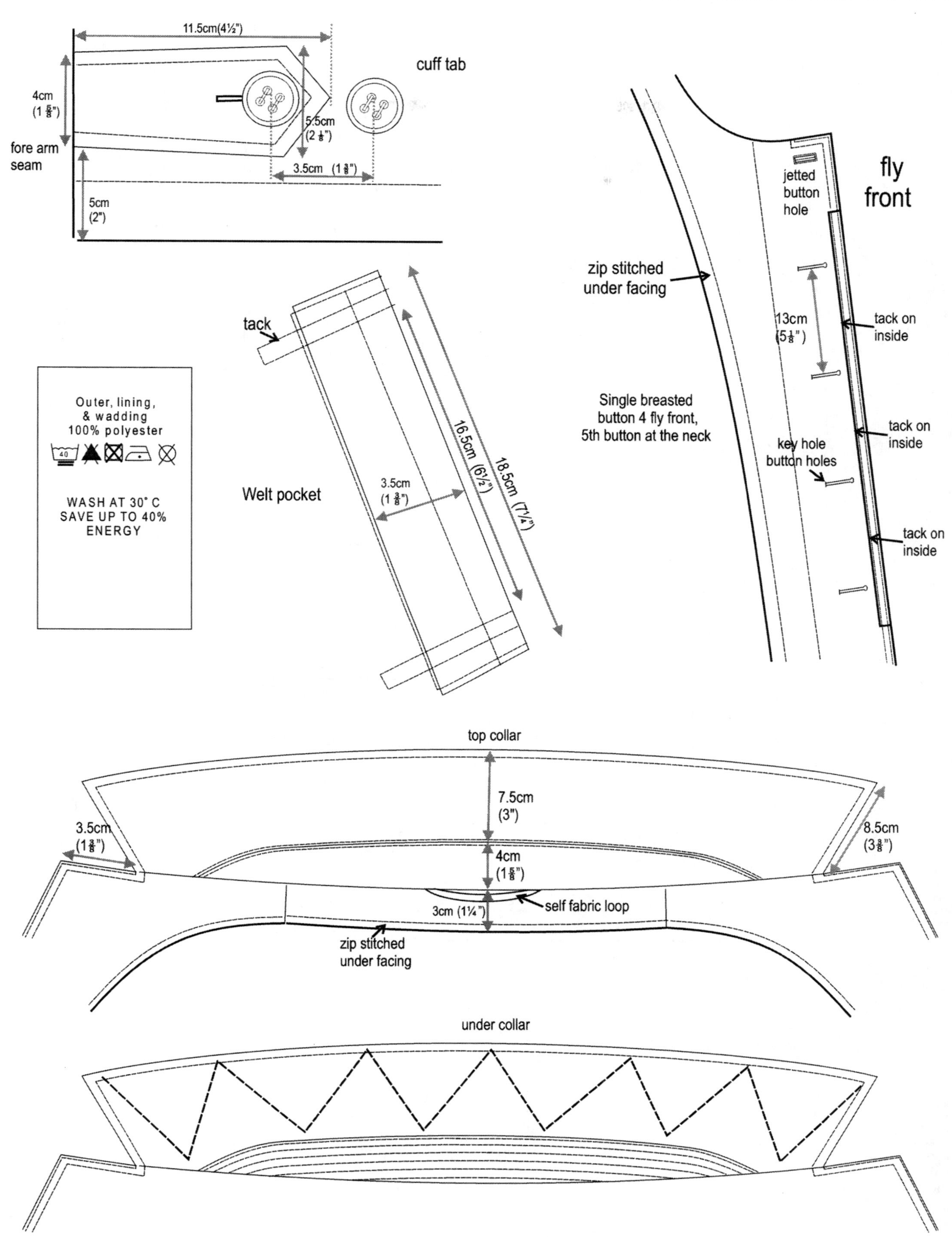

11.5cm(4½")
cuff tab
4cm
(1 5/8")
5.5cm
(2 1/8")
fore arm
seam
3.5cm (1 3/8")
5cm
(2")
fly
front
jetted
button
hole
zip stitched
under facing
tack
13cm
(5 1/8")
tack on
inside
Outer, lining,
& wadding
100% polyester
40
WASH AT 30° C
SAVE UP TO 40%
ENERGY
Single breasted
button 4 fly front,
5th button at the neck
16.5cm (6½")
18.5cm (7¼")
key hole
button holes
tack on
inside
3.5cm
(1 3/8")
Welt pocket
tack on
inside
top collar
7.5cm
(3")
3.5cm
(1 3/8")
8.5cm
(3 3/8")
4cm
(1 5/8")
3cm (1¼")
self fabric loop
zip stitched
under facing
under collar

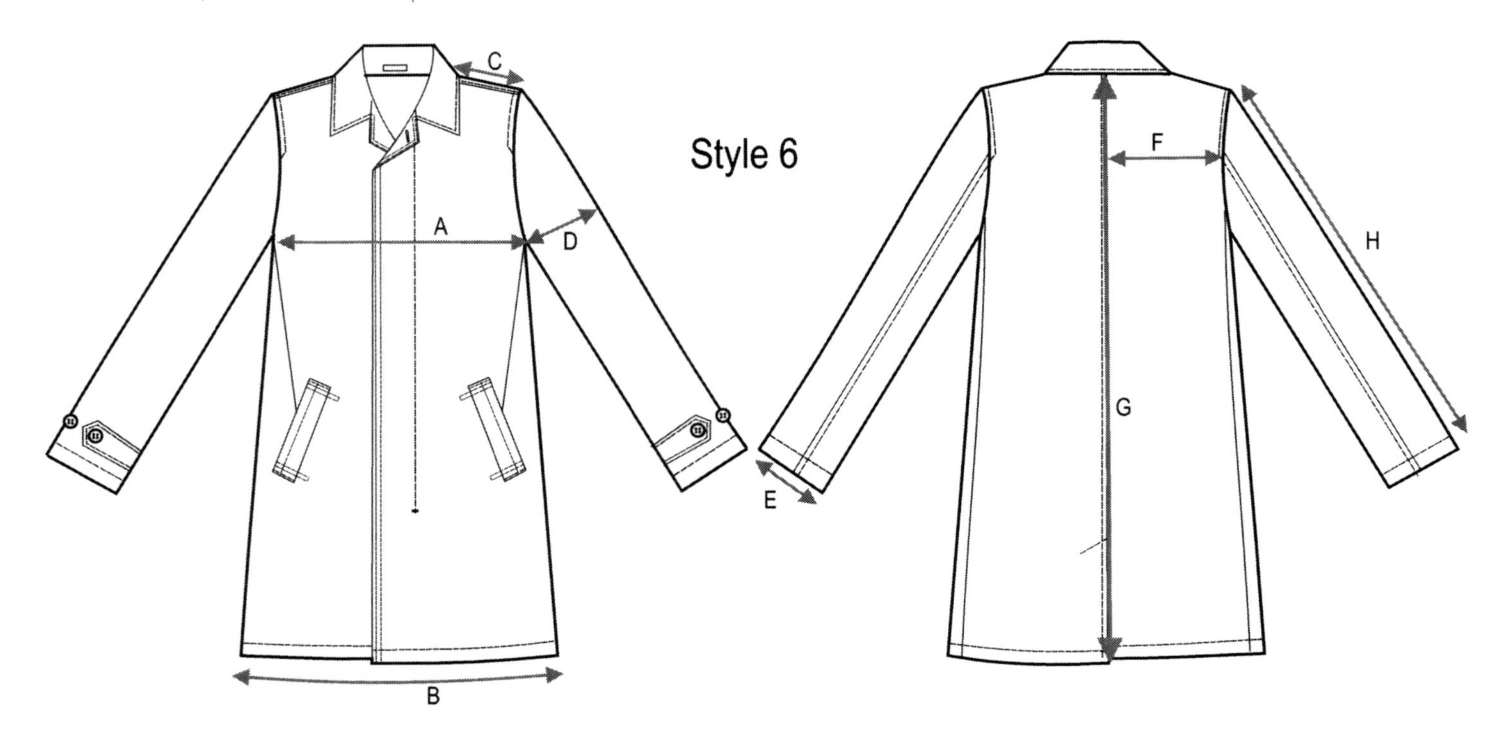

SIZE	L	
	cms	Inches
A. Chest at base of armhole	130	51¼"
B. Hem	136	53½"
C. Shoulder	18	7⅛"
D. Biceps	47	18½"
E. Cuff	37	14½"
F. Half back	26	10¼"
G. Full length from neck seam	100	39⅜"
H. Sleeve crown to cuff	68	26¾"

CHAPTER 8

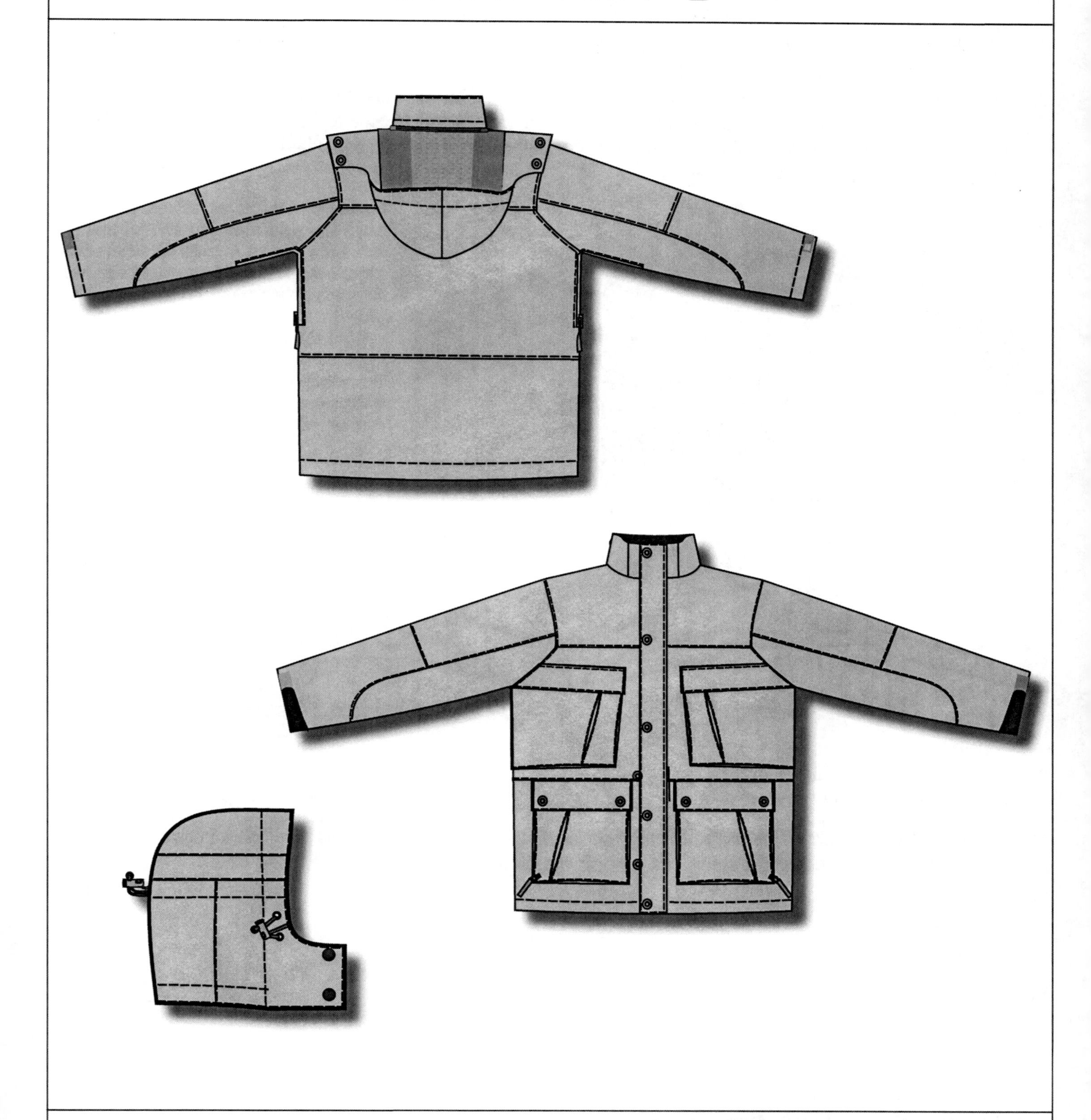

WATERPROOF ANORAK

This type of garment is very complex with many layers of detail and is usually referred to as a performance garment. It is ergonomically designed for maximum comfort, efficiency, safety, and ease of use.

The specification I have devised here is very detailed, and it can be viewed as a complete specification or a series of mini specifications. The complete specification will take time to complete. The advantages of doing the full spec are:

1. This will be a blue print for all other anoraks in your range. I doubt any will be more complex than this one, and most anoraks/parkas will have similar style features that can be quickly adapted from this style.
2. This is an expensive garment and it is essential that all parts fit and are assembled correctly.
3. It is not always possible to send a complete finalized sample for a factory to copy and even if you could, it is infinitely better to have a detailed record of the whole and each component of the garment to be instantly sent to any factory worldwide if you have a problem with supply.

Sometimes it might be difficult to get the proportions right when you start to draw the outline of a garment. Although this jacket seems a simple shape, I found the angle of the sleeves, the shape of the armhole, the positioning of the pockets and panel seams difficult to reproduce satisfactorily.

To overcome this I laid the jacket on the floor and photographed it, copied the photo into Corel and drew around the key shapes as figure 1.

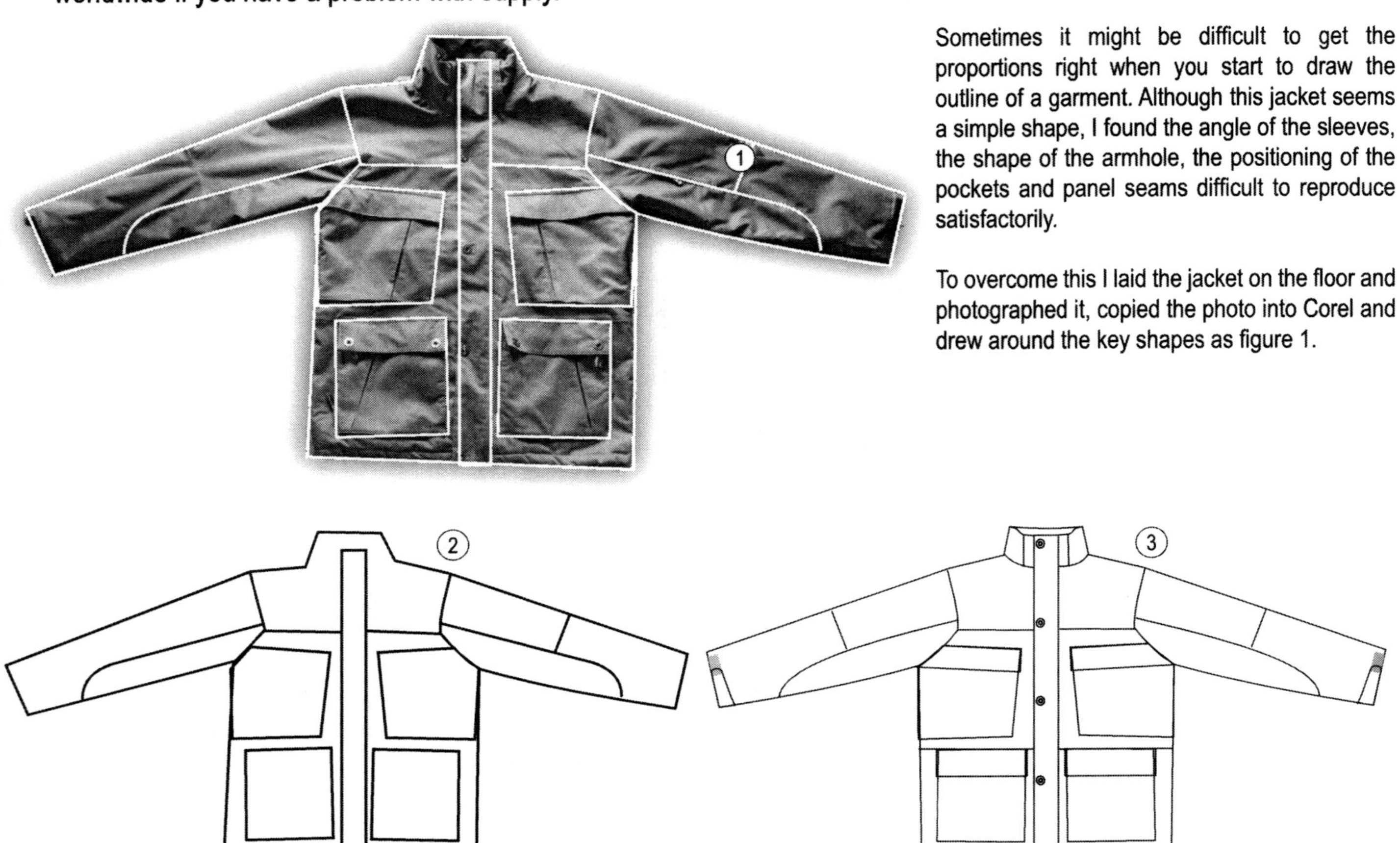

Figure 2 is the tracing copied off the photo. Although the lines are slightly at an angle this is sufficient to give me the right proportions. Figure 3 is the drawing tidied up and ready to use for the specification.

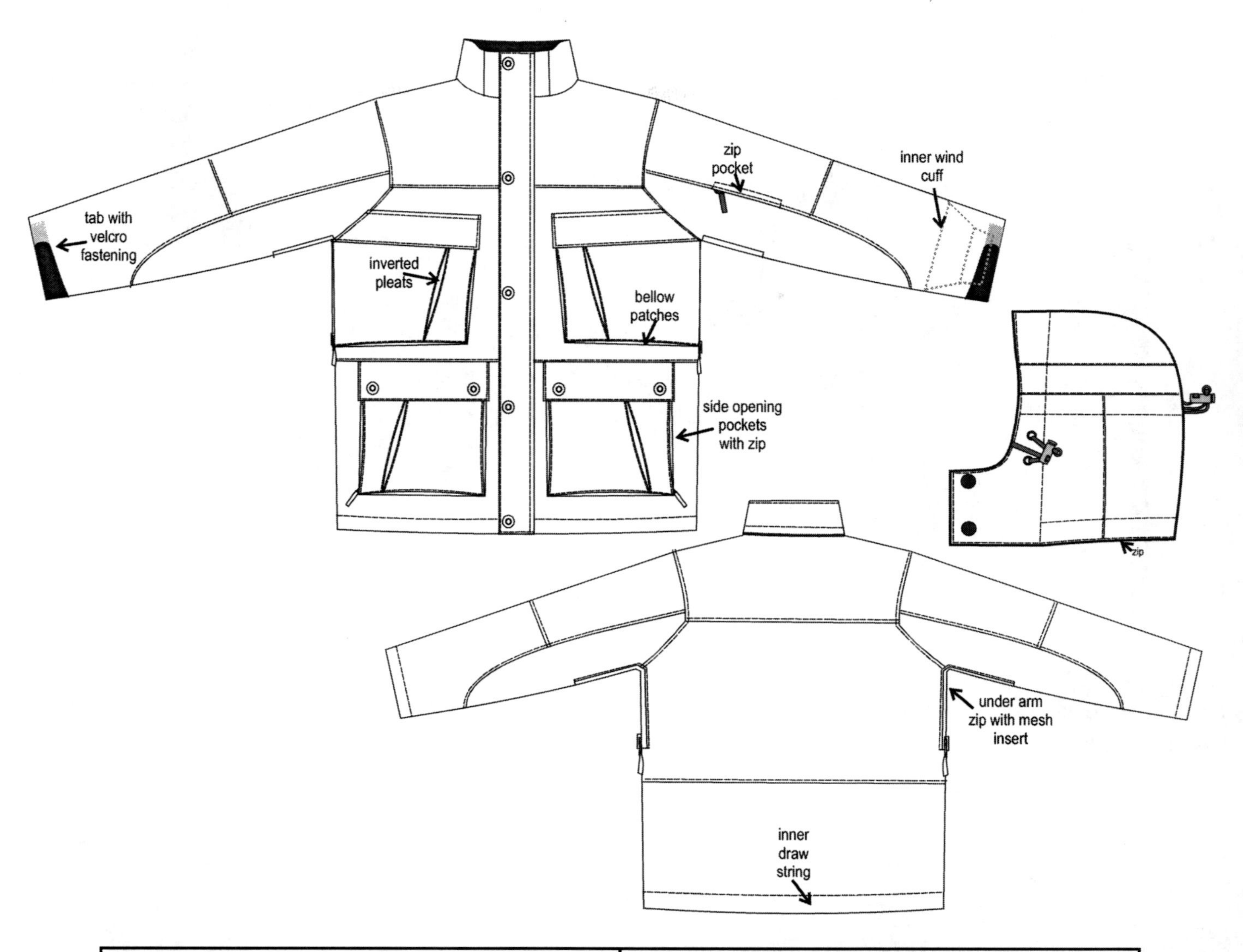

Waterproof anorak	
• 3 panel front. • 3 panel back. • 4 panel sleeve. • 6 panel hood. • Taped seams edge stitched. • Hood attached with zip. • Outer collar with zip for hood. • Inner collar brushed black fabric. • Storm flap with zip and press stud fastening. • Four outer bellows patches with zip openings, inverted pleats, and flaps with press stud fastenings. • Bottom pockets with side entry zip pockets.	• Cuff with tab and Velcro fastening. • Sleeve with zip pocket left side as worn. • Inner wind cuff. • Under arm zip opening gusset with breathable mesh insert. • Draw cords at hem and on hood. • Lining with wadding. • Inner zip welt pocket left side as worn. • Inner mesh pocket right side as worn. • Plastic pocket with velcro fastening skirt lining left side as worn. • Zip pocket left facing as worn. • Loops and holder for phone or Mp3 player lead. • Zip guard right side as worn.

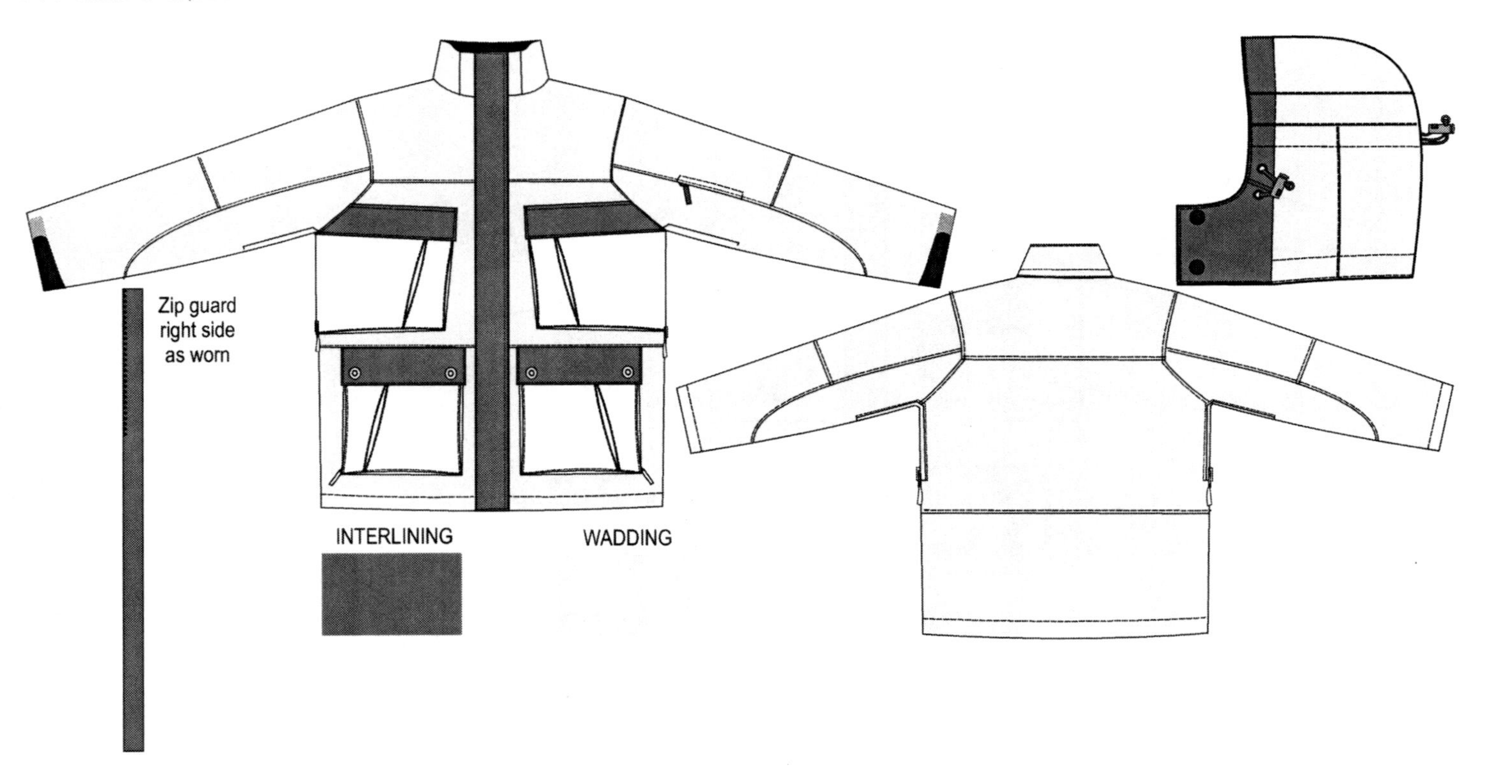

Wadding and Interlining
I am always looking for better ways to illustrate specifications and this seemed an easy way to show which parts need wadding and interlining.

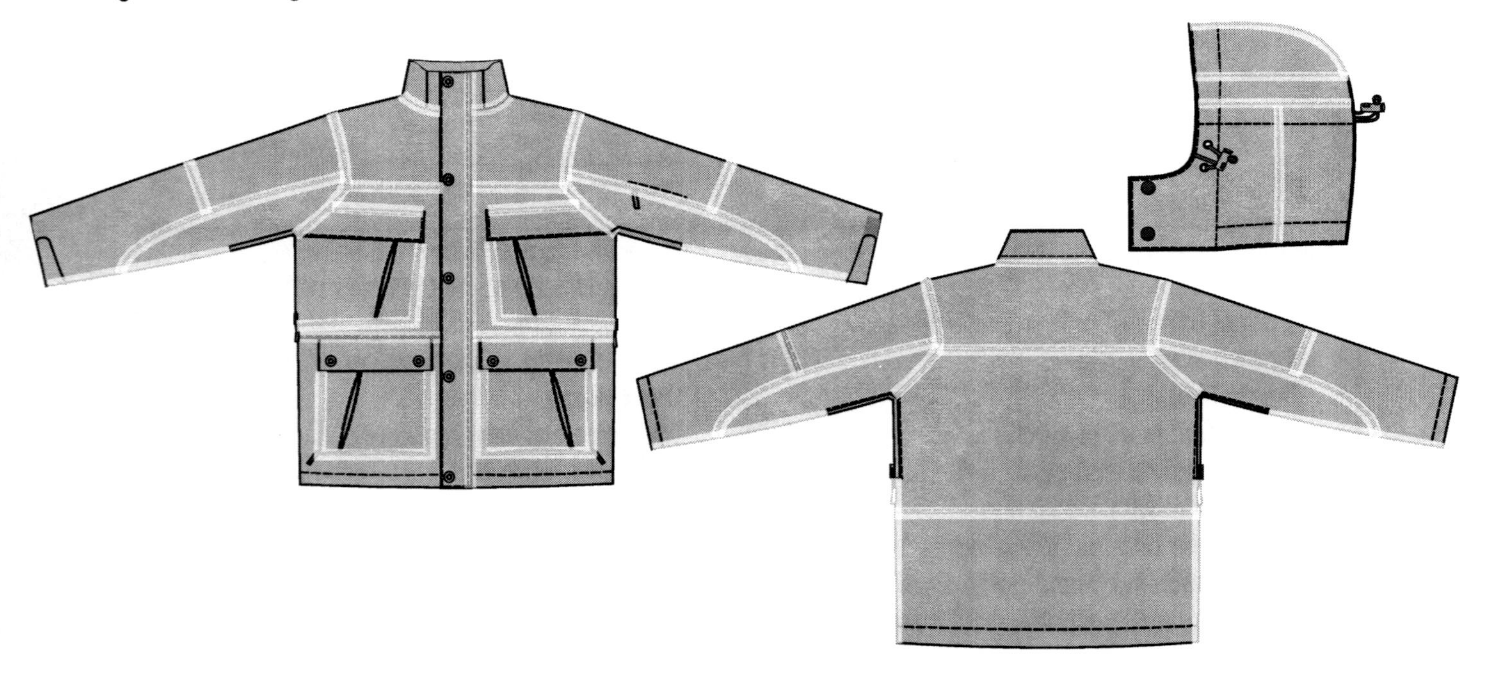

Taped Seams
To make a garment completely waterproof all seams that are exposed to the elements are taped inside after sewing to seal the needle holes, preventing water getting into the garment. Most factories making waterproof garments know which seams to seal, but to avoid any misunderstanding these illustrations will confirm the seams to be taped.

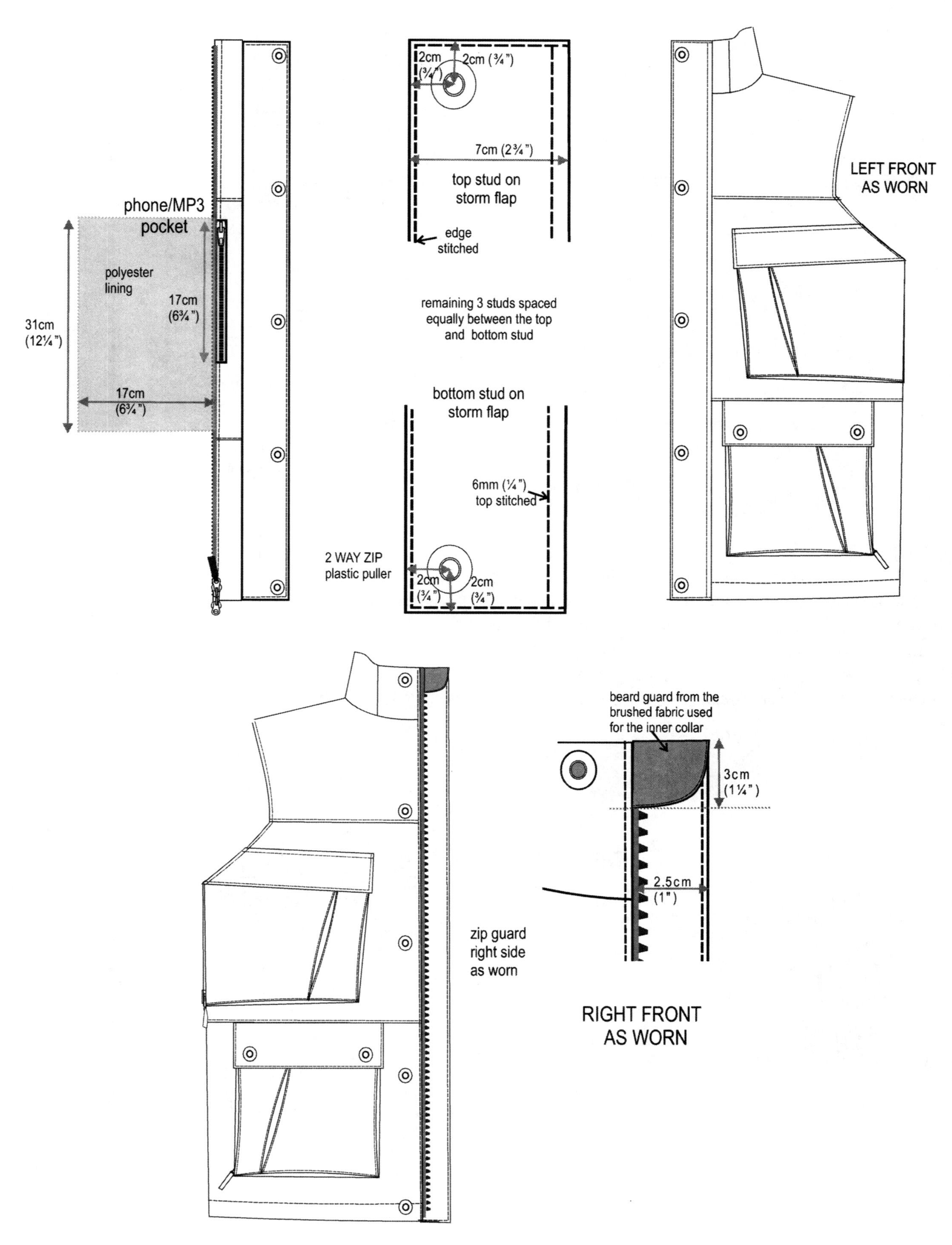

phone/MP3 pocket
polyester lining
17cm (6¾")
31cm (12¼")
17cm (6¾")
2cm (¾")
2cm (¾")
7cm (2¾")
top stud on storm flap
edge stitched
remaining 3 studs spaced equally between the top and bottom stud
bottom stud on storm flap
6mm (¼") top stitched
2 WAY ZIP plastic puller
2cm (¾")
2cm (¾")
LEFT FRONT AS WORN
beard guard from the brushed fabric used for the inner collar
3cm (1¼")
2.5cm (1")
zip guard right side as worn
RIGHT FRONT AS WORN

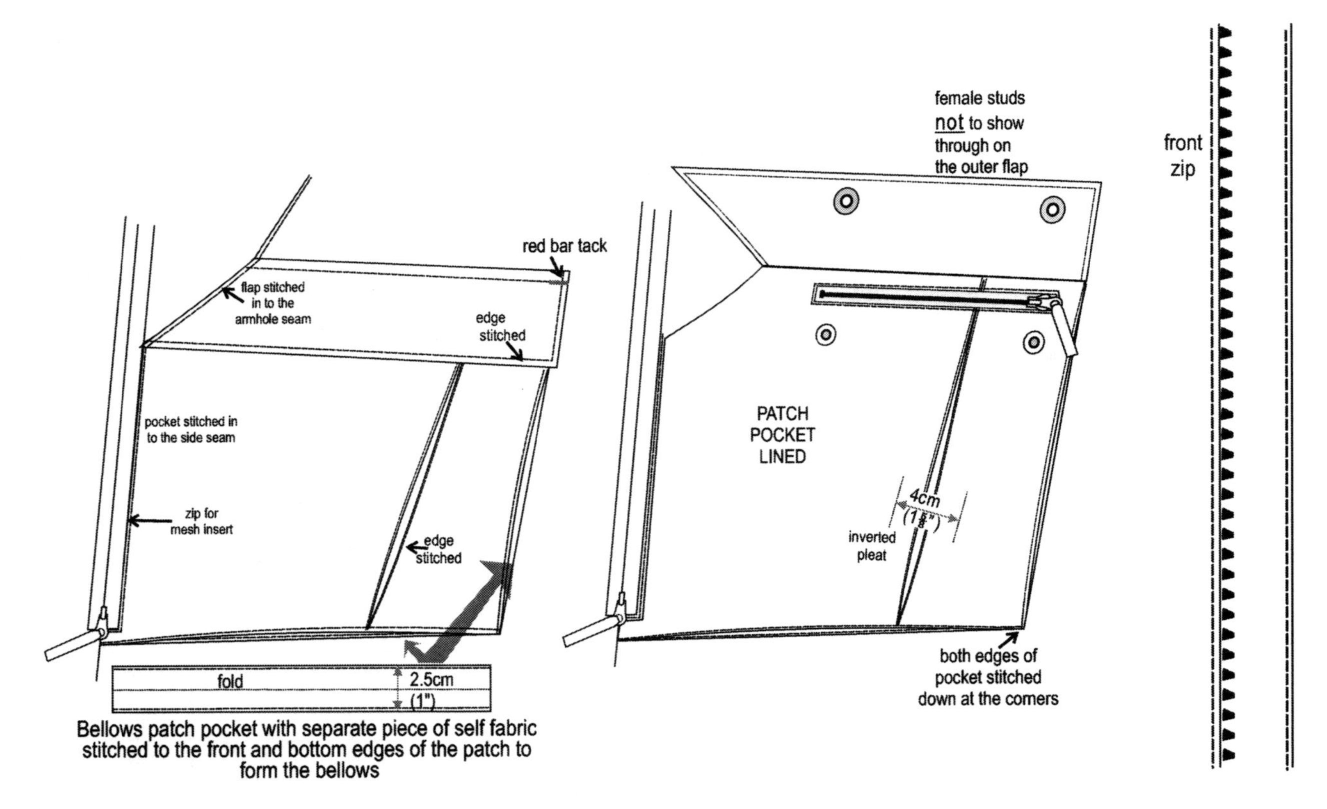

Bellows patch pocket with separate piece of self fabric stitched to the front and bottom edges of the patch to form the bellows

TOP POCKET

- Bellows patch with inverted pleat edge stitched to front panel.
- Self lined flap with press stud fastening, (stud not to show on the outer flap).
- Pocket opening with zip inserted into the patch under the flap.
- Top of flap and patch stitched in to the armhole seam.
- Side of the patch stitched in to the side seam zip seam.
- Outer patch lined with black polyester body lining after pleat is sewn in the patch.

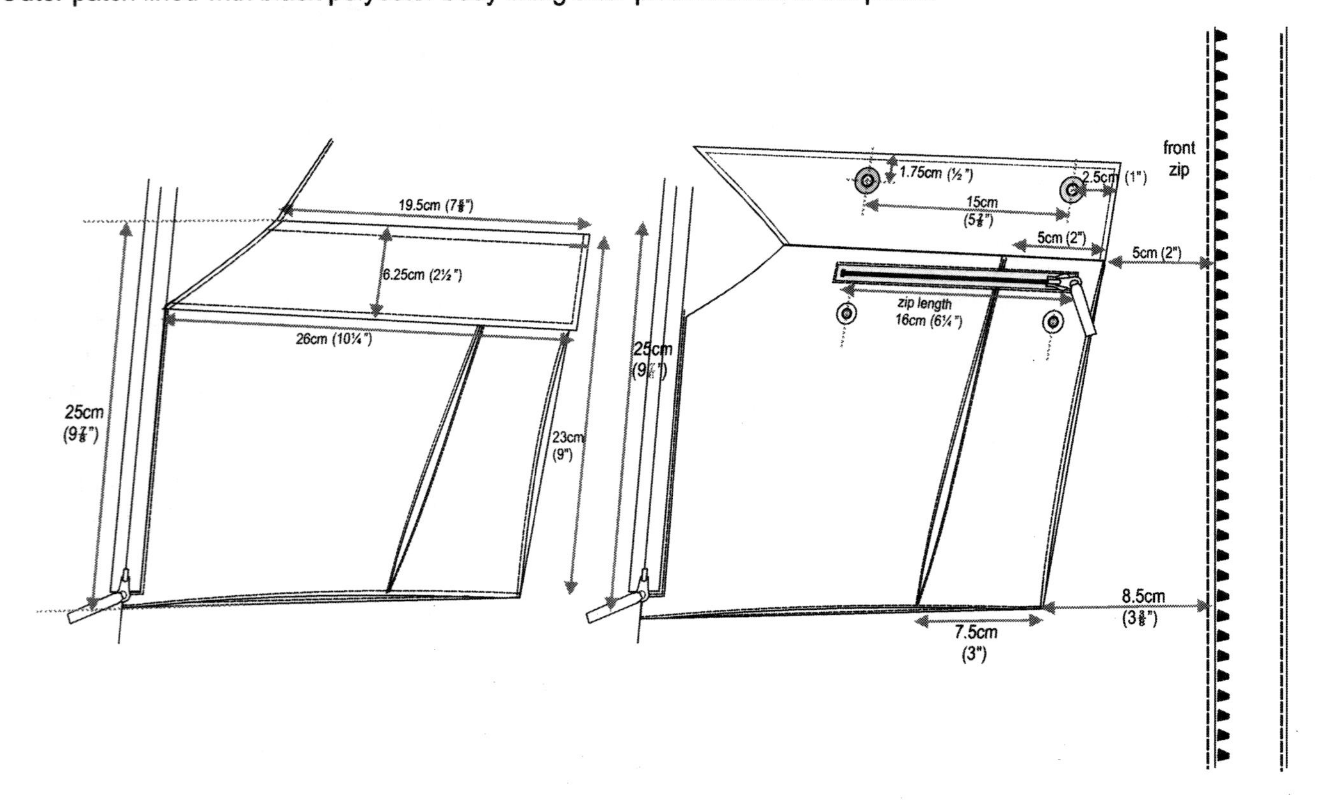

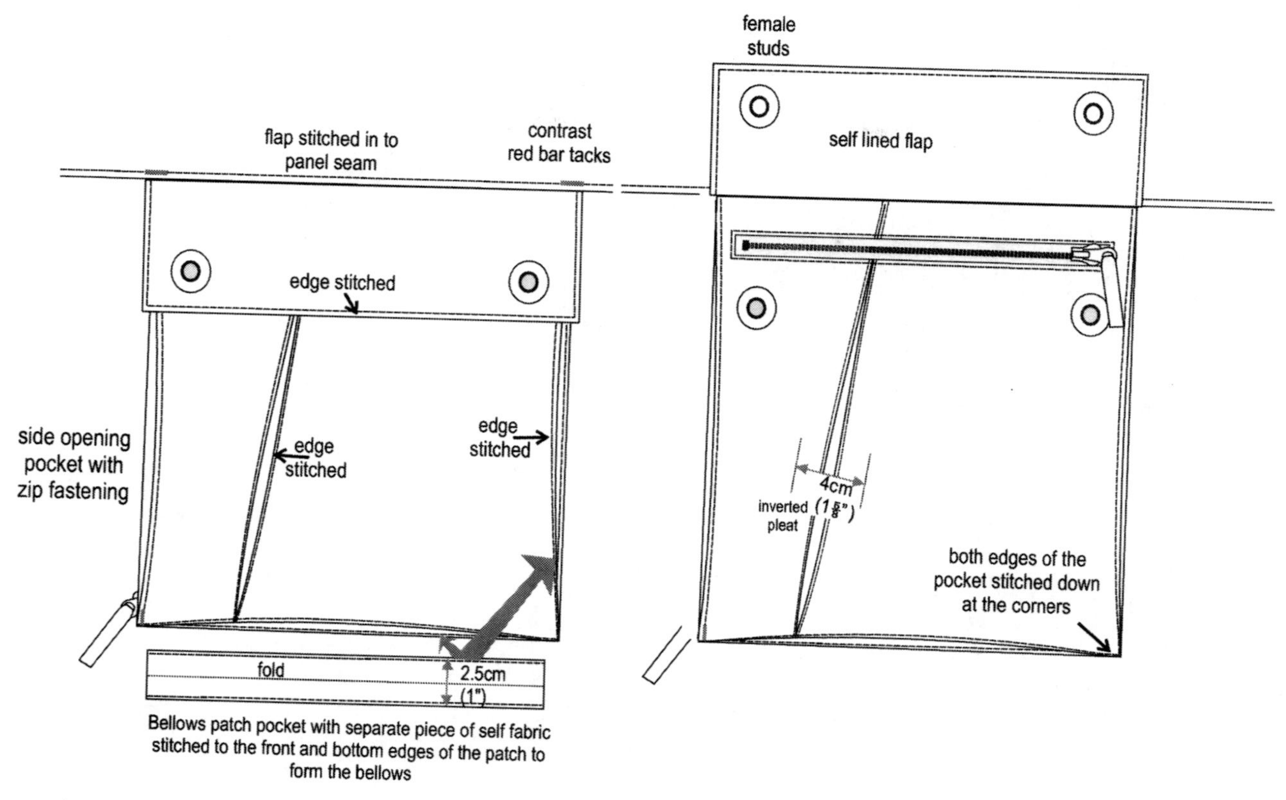

Bellows patch pocket with separate piece of self fabric stitched to the front and bottom edges of the patch to form the bellows

Bottom pockets

- Bellows patch with inverted pleat, edge stitched to front panel.
- Self lined flap with press stud fastening stitched in to the panel seam.
- Separate side pocket with zip fastening.
- Outer patch lined with black polyester body lining after pleat is sewn in the patch.

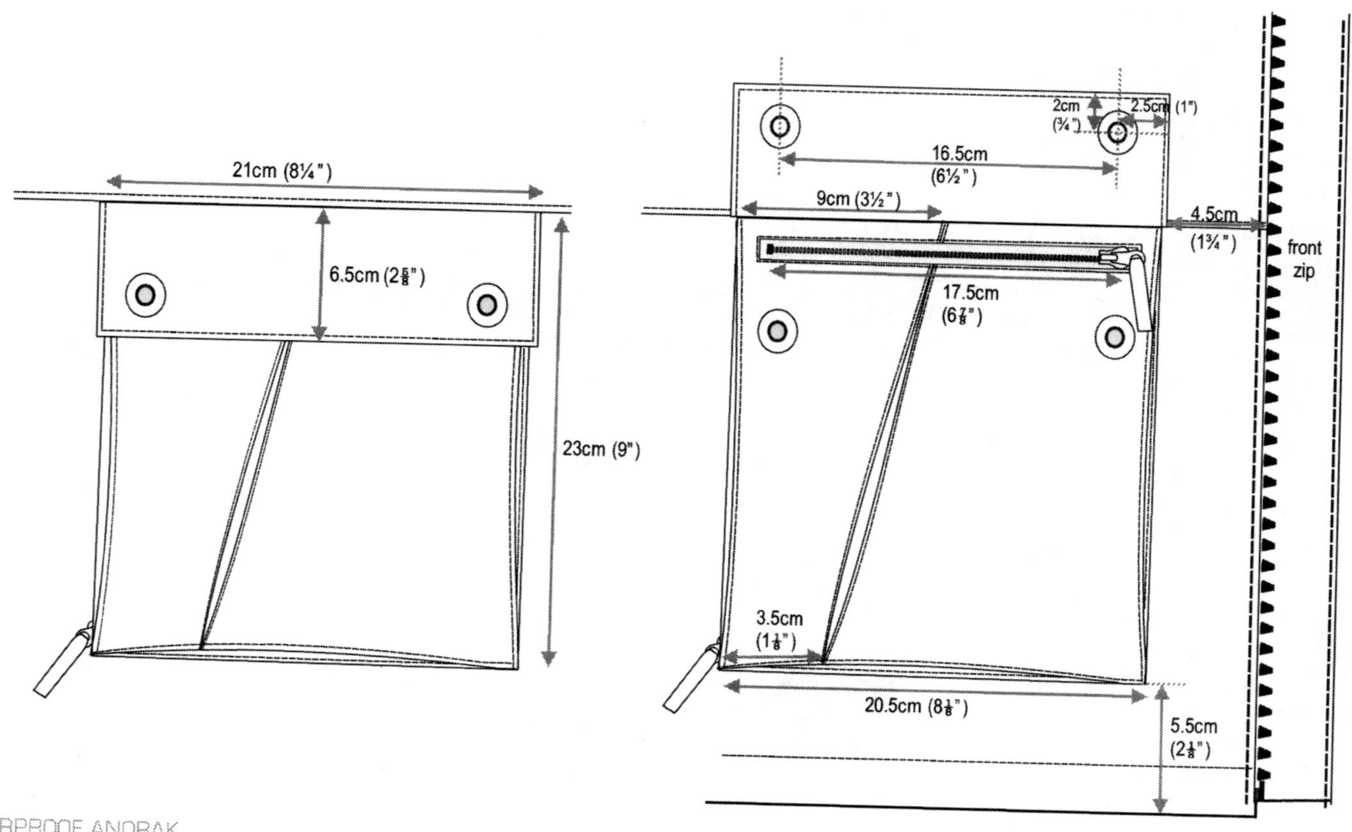

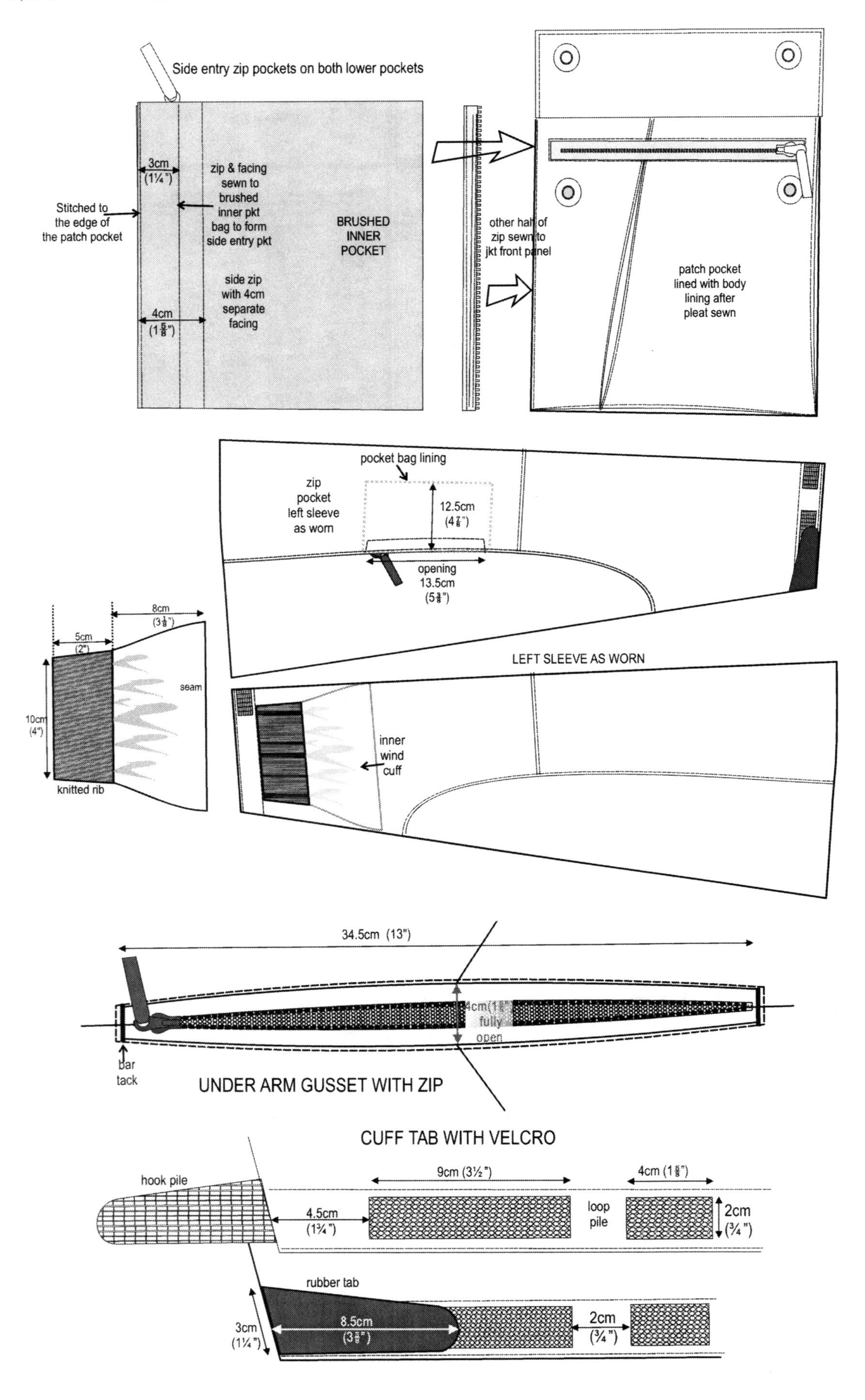
Side entry zip pockets on both lower pockets
3cm
(1¼")
Stitched to the edge of the patch pocket
zip & facing sewn to brushed inner pkt bag to form side entry pkt
BRUSHED INNER POCKET
side zip with 4cm separate facing
4cm
(1⅝")
other half of zip sewn to jkt front panel
patch pocket lined with body lining after pleat sewn
pocket bag lining
zip pocket left sleeve as worn
12.5cm
(4⅞")
opening
13.5cm
(5⅜")
8cm
(3⅛")
5cm
(2")
10cm
(4")
seam
knitted rib
LEFT SLEEVE AS WORN
inner wind cuff
34.5cm (13")
4cm(1⅝") fully open
bar tack
UNDER ARM GUSSET WITH ZIP
CUFF TAB WITH VELCRO
hook pile
9cm (3½")
4cm (1⅝")
4.5cm
(1¾")
loop pile
2cm
(¾")
rubber tab
3cm
(1¼")
8.5cm
(3⅜")
2cm
(¾")

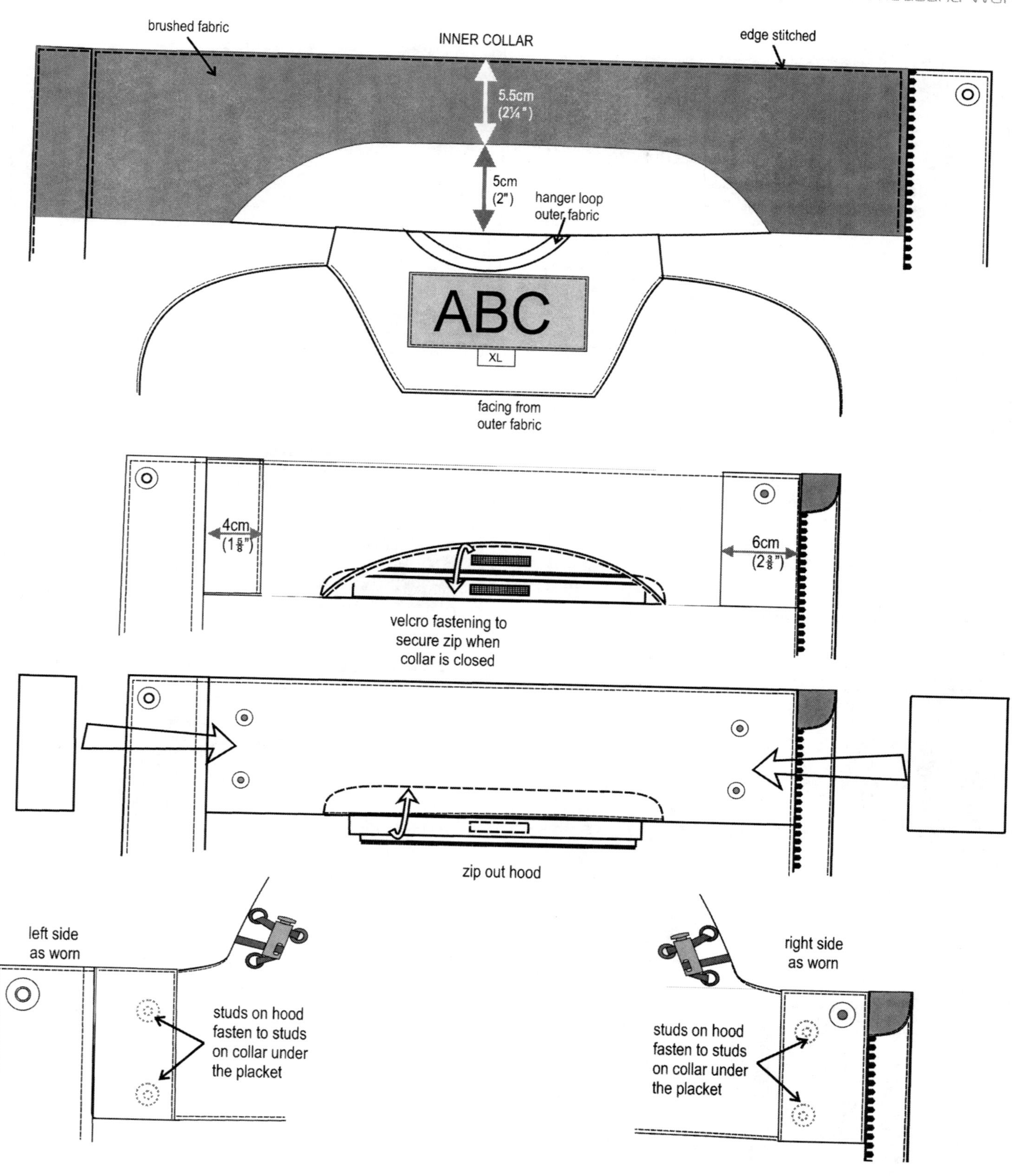
brushed fabric
INNER COLLAR
edge stitched
5.5cm
(2¼")
5cm
(2")
hanger loop
outer fabric
ABC
XL
facing from
outer fabric
4cm
(1⅝")
6cm
(2⅜")
velcro fastening to
secure zip when
collar is closed
zip out hood
left side
as worn
studs on hood
fasten to studs
on collar under
the placket
right side
as worn
studs on hood
fasten to studs
on collar under
the placket

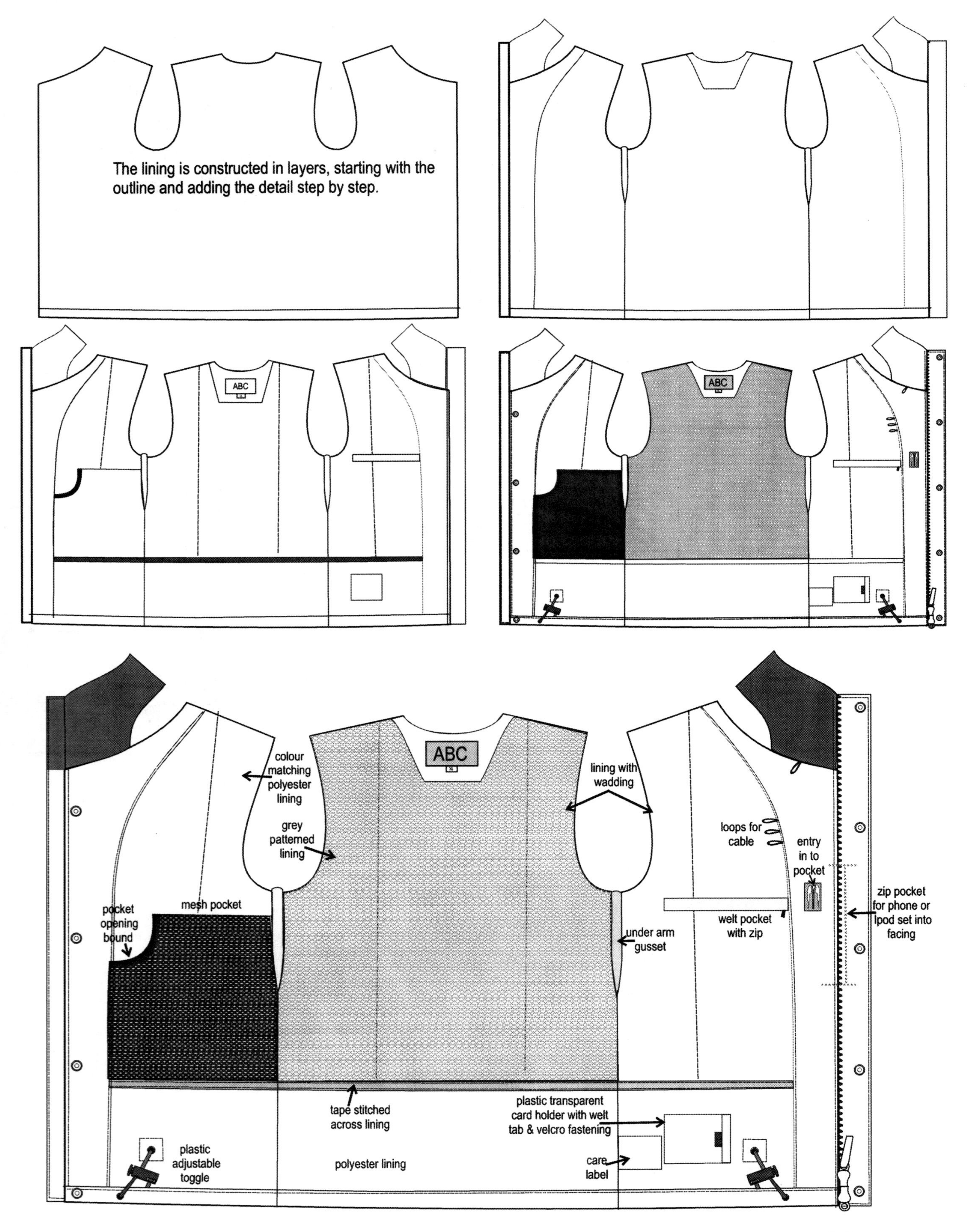
The lining is constructed in layers, starting with the outline and adding the detail step by step.
ABC
colour matching polyester lining
grey patterned lining
lining with wadding
loops for cable
entry in to pocket
zip pocket for phone or Ipod set into facing
pocket opening bound
mesh pocket
under arm gusset
welt pocket with zip
tape stitched across lining
plastic transparent card holder with welt tab & velcro fastening
plastic adjustable toggle
polyester lining
care label

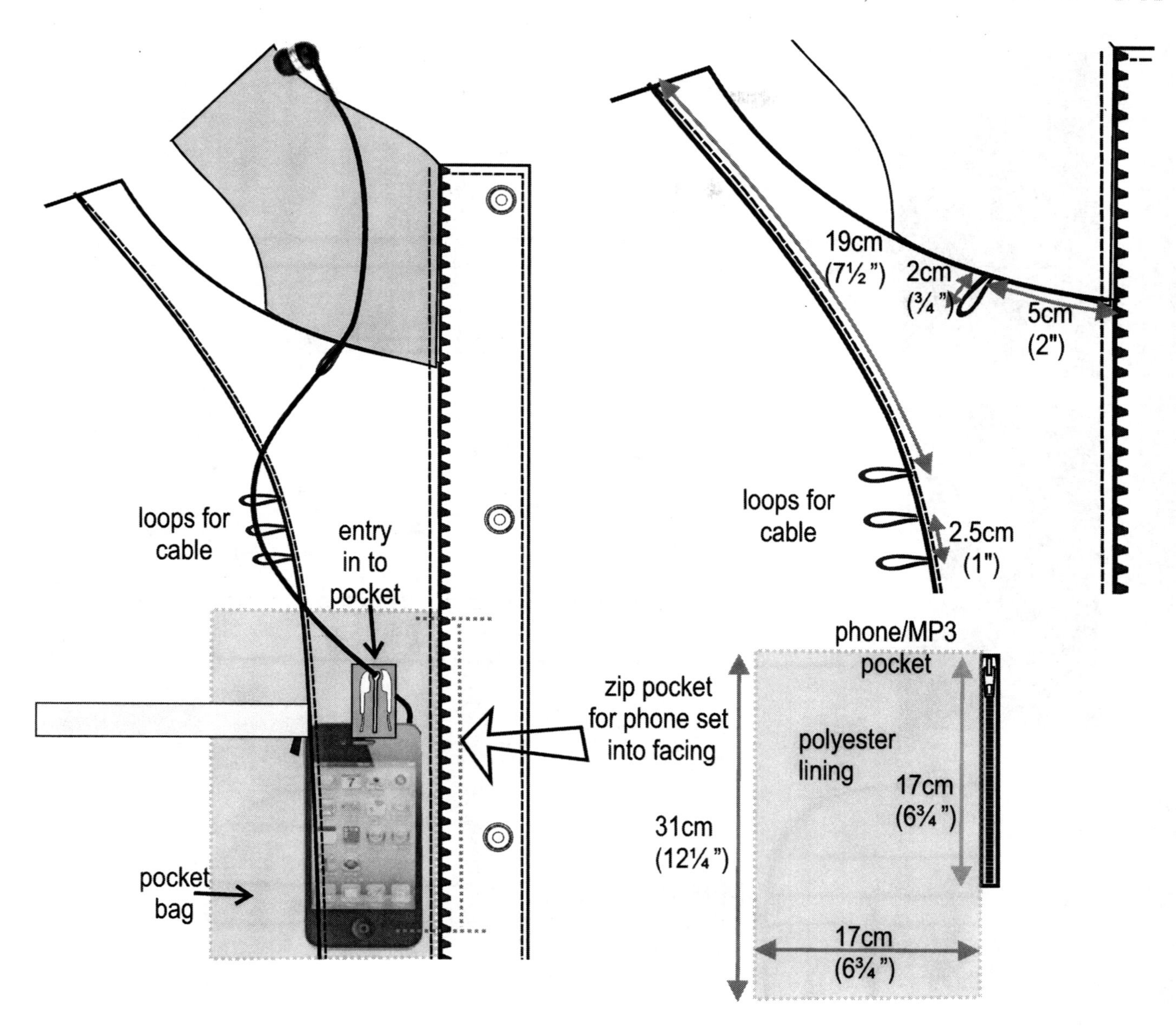

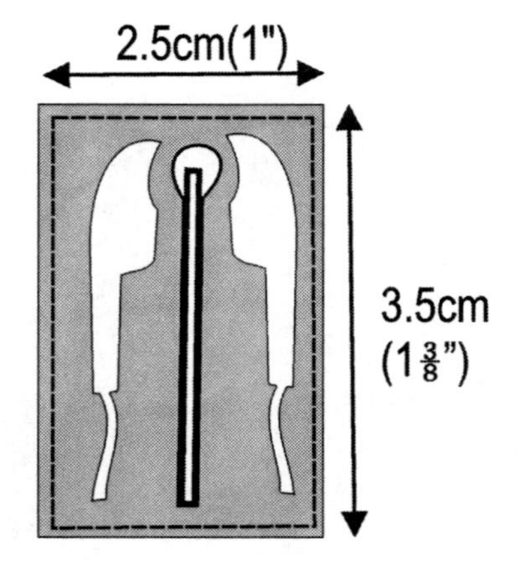

- Zip pocket for iPod or phone stitched behind inner facing left side as worn.
- Nylon cord looped and stitched into the collar and facing seam.
- Plastic earphone logo stitched centrally to the facing over the inner pocket.
- Opening formed for earphone cable with a 2.5cm (1") lock stitched cut opening.

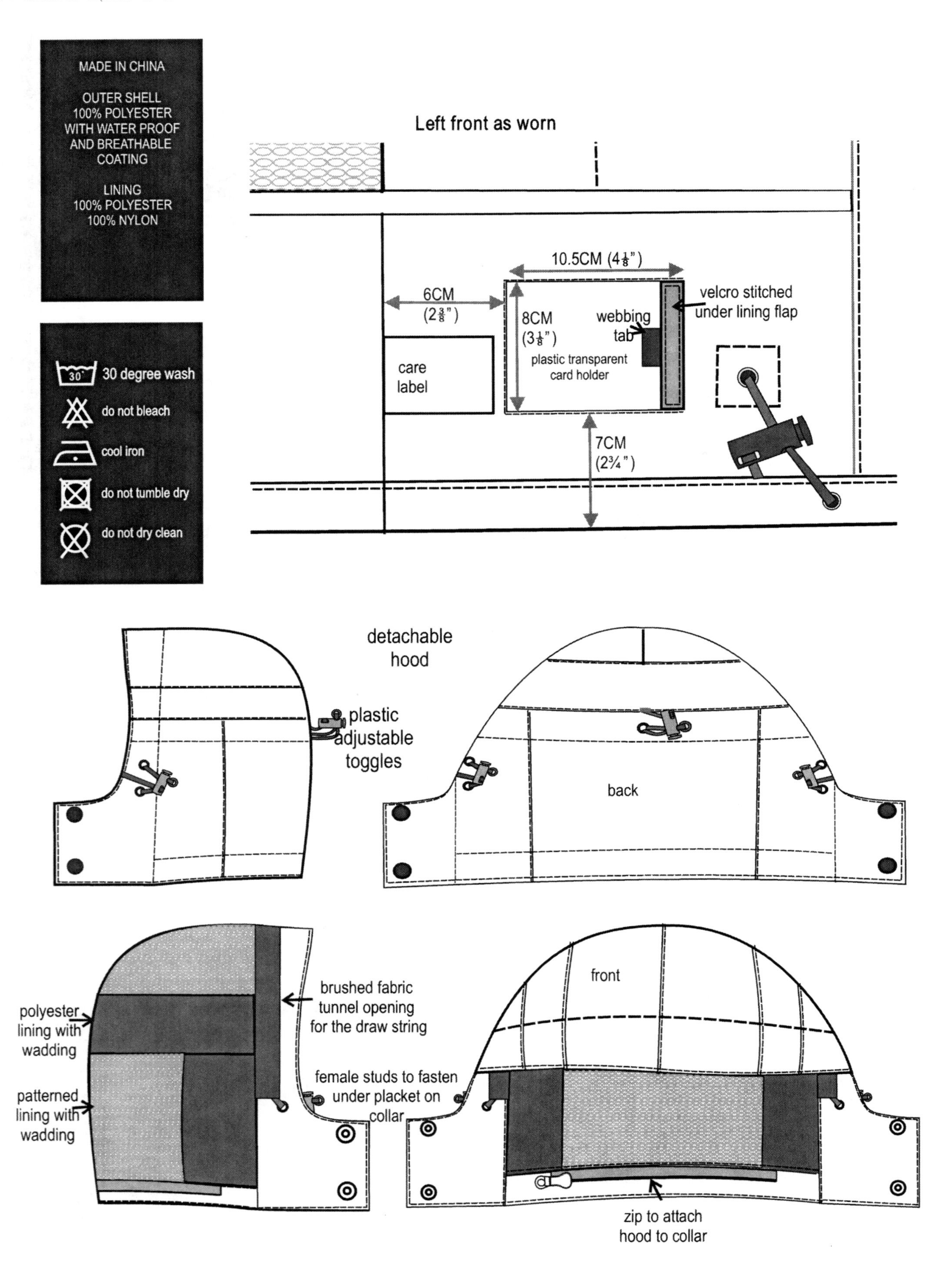
MADE IN CHINA
OUTER SHELL
100% POLYESTER
WITH WATER PROOF
AND BREATHABLE
COATING
LINING
100% POLYESTER
100% NYLON
30 degree wash
do not bleach
cool iron
do not tumble dry
do not dry clean
Left front as worn
10.5CM (4⅛")
6CM
(2⅜")
8CM
(3⅛")
webbing
tab
plastic transparent
card holder
velcro stitched
under lining flap
care
label
7CM
(2¾")
detachable
hood
plastic
adjustable
toggles
back
polyester
lining with
wadding
patterned
lining with
wadding
brushed fabric
tunnel opening
for the draw string
female studs to fasten
under placket on
collar
front
zip to attach
hood to collar

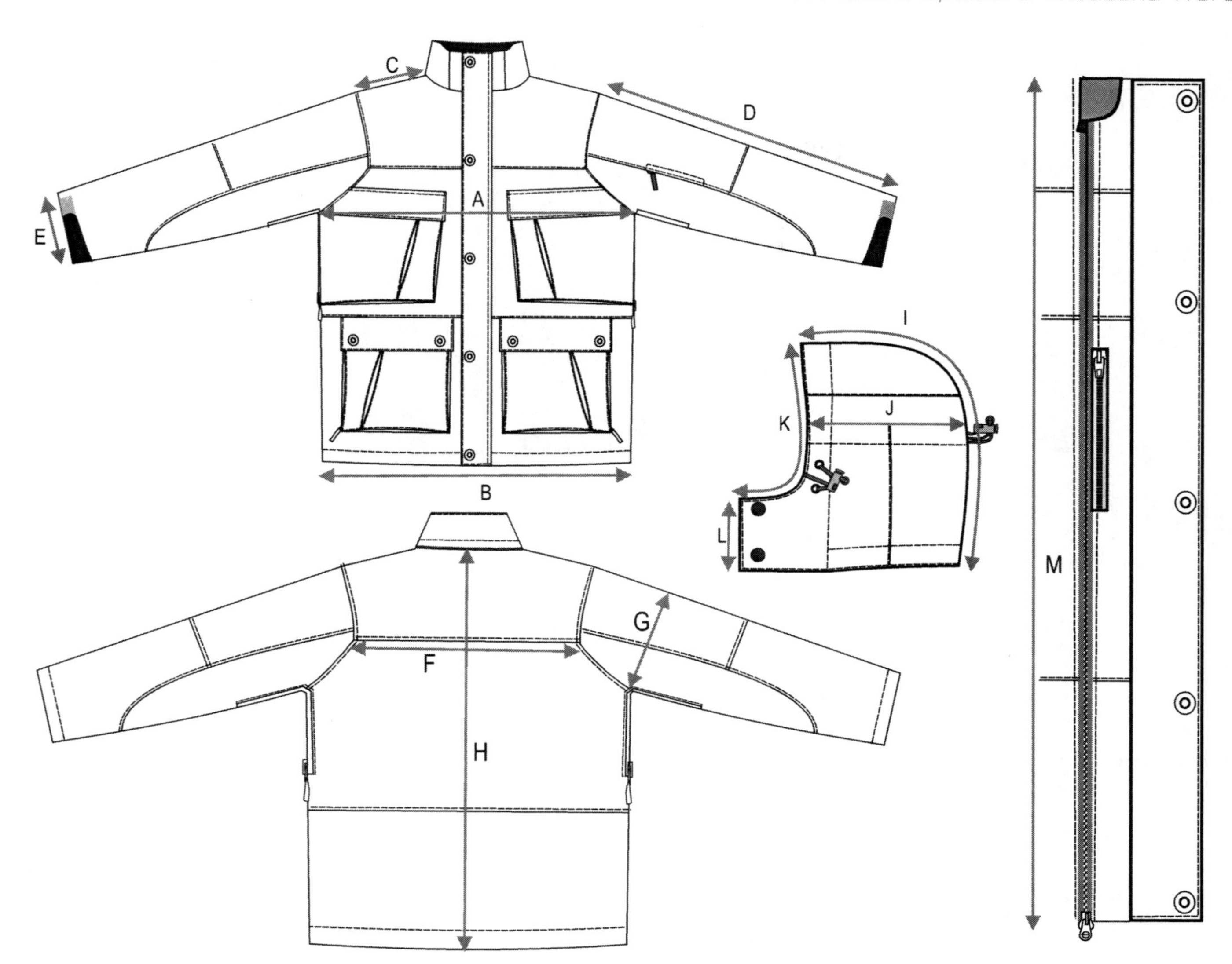

SIZE	L	
	cms	Inches
A. Chest at base of armhole coat fastened half measurement	67	26⅜"
B. Hem coat fastened half measurement	60	23⅝"
C. Natural shoulder line sleeve seam to neck seam	17	6¾"
D. Sleeve crown to cuff	70	27½"
E. Cuff half measurement	17	6¾"
F. Cross back width	47	18½"
G. Biceps half measurement	30.5	12"
H. Full length from neck seam	85	33½"
I. Hood front edge to neck seam	55	21⅝"
J. Hood width, front edge to centre back	26	10¼"
K. Hood opening	34	13⅜"
L. Depth of front fastening	10	4"
M. Front zip length	85	33½"

CHAPTER 9

LADIES FASHION TROUSER

As this is a fashion trouser let's assume that this product is still under development and the process may be done in one of several ways. The style is either copied from a similar style or is a fusion of several different styles. The first scenario could be that the head office design department and technologists will develop the product through initial patterns, mock ups and first samples. When the right result is achieved an initial specification will be sent to the factories. The second scenario could be that a specification is written and sent to the factory for them to develop the pattern and make the first sample. At this stage it is not necessary to send a full graded size chart, only the measurements of the sample size. When the fit of the first sample from the factory is approved, the graded chart can be finalized. Whichever path is taken the specification is an essential tool in the development of the product. The more detail that can be included the less chance there is of mistakes happening. If there is an agreed departure from the specification, then it can be quickly amended and reissued to the factory.

A & B consist of creating the outline. C: add detail outline and check proportions are correct. D: use front outline to create the back and outline the detail.

E, F, G & H: adding layers of details to finish the drawings.

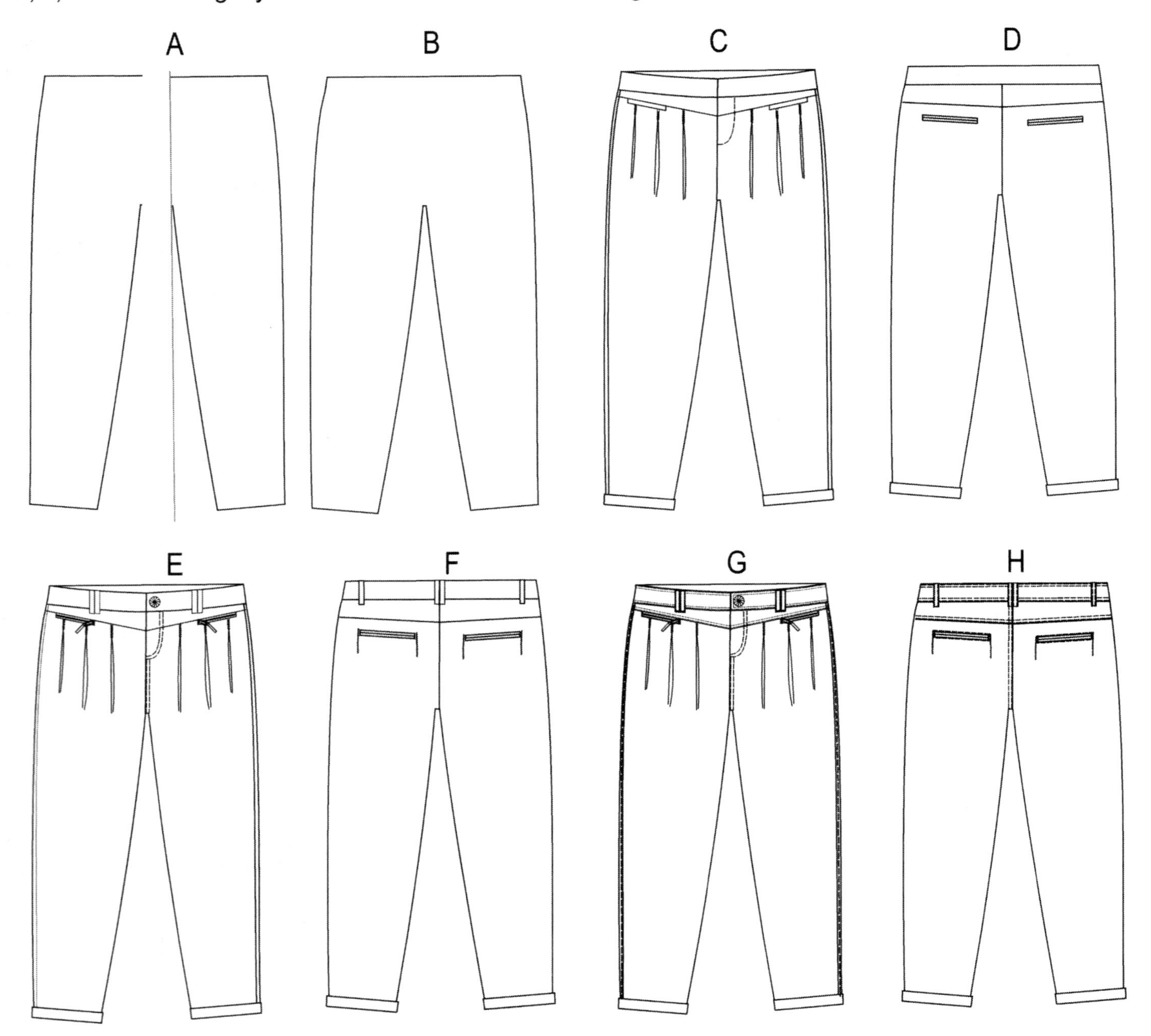

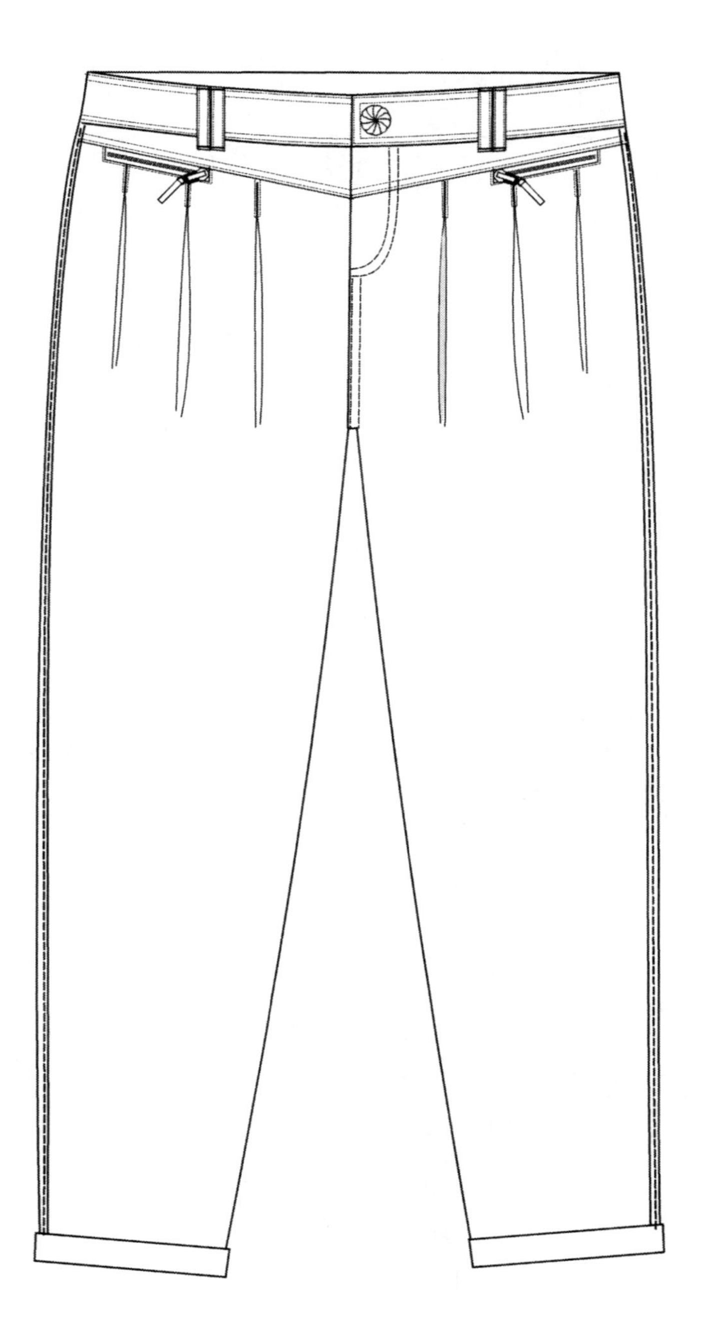

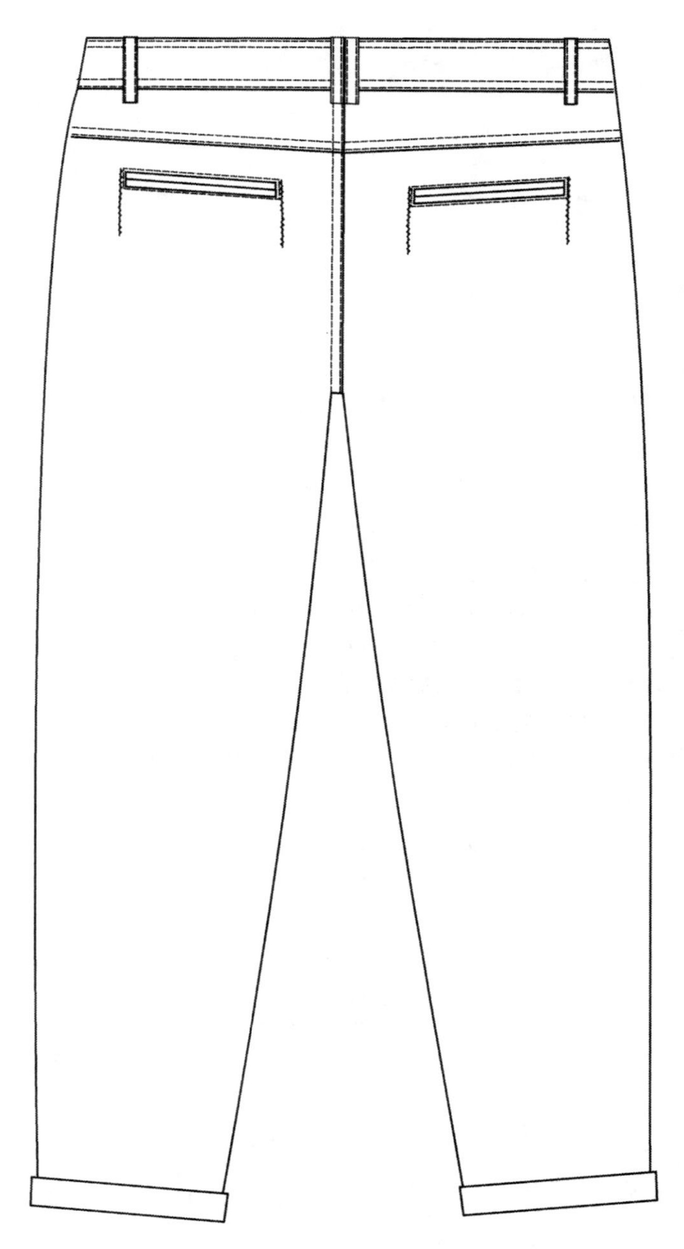

- Cotton trouser.
- Front zip twin stitched.
- Back & front yoke twin stitched.
- Zip pockets with metal puller set in the front yokes.
- Two jetted pockets with mock tear & cross stitching.
- 3 inverted pleats in each front.
- Double belt loops at the front & center back.
- Single loops on the back panels near the side seam.
- Metal button front fastening.
- All seams 5–thread over–locked.
- Side seam, center back & center front seams twin stitched.
- Waist band twin stitched.
- Pocketing & waist band floral design.
- Bottoms with turn ups.

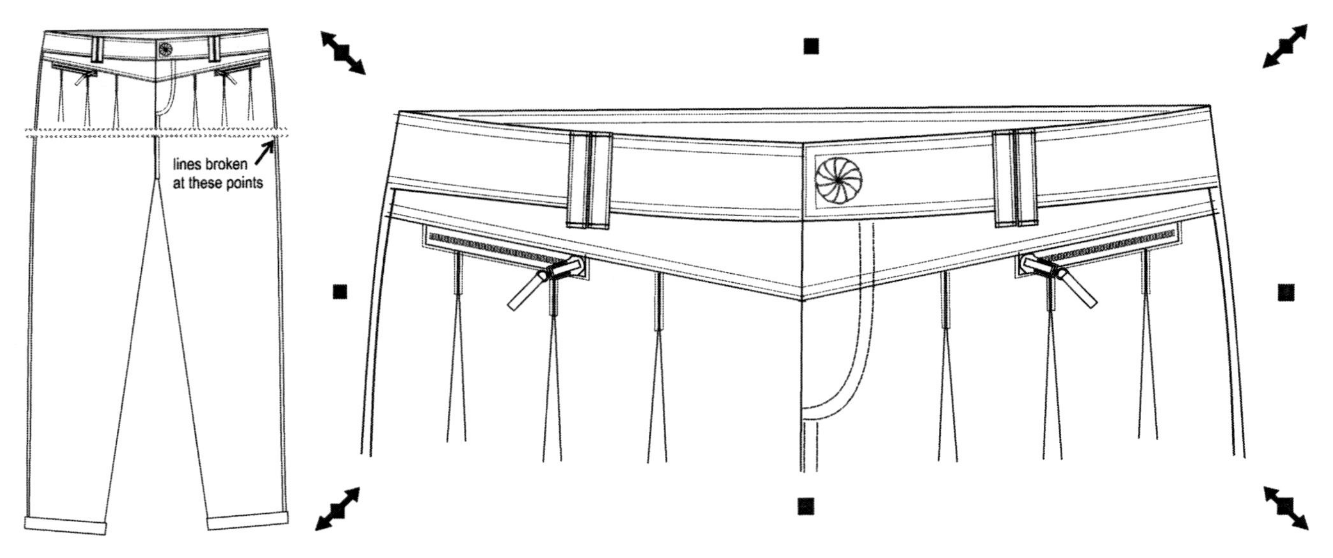

I can add the detail on the full length drawing of the trouser by using the zoom tool, but on the finished drawing it will not be clear to the factory. In this instance I have broken the lines apart to separate the top section from the legs and then deleted the lines not required. It can be done with the cropping tool, but cropping does not always keep the original properties of the drawing. Experiment, see which way suits you best. Expand the drawing to the width of the page to show the detail much more clearly and add text. Make sure when you increase the size of the drawing that you drag the outer corners to ensure that you are keeping the same proportion. As the drawing gets larger the lines will get thinner, so you may have to increase their width.

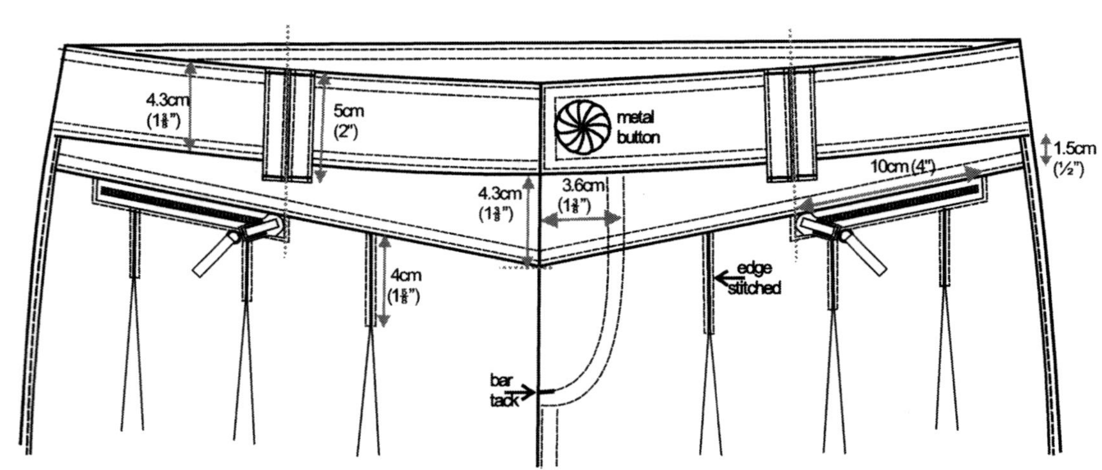

Fronts
- Three inverted pleats on each front 2cm (¾") deep.
- Seams 5–thread over–locked.
- Outside leg & yokes twin stitched.

Pockets
- Zip with metal puller positioned centrally over the back 2 pleats.
- Zip pocket, effective depth 12cm (4¾").
- Poly/cotton floral print pocketing & waistband lining.
- Self fabric pocket bearer to finish 3cm (1⅛") deep from the zip seam.

Loops
- Center of front double belt loop level with the front of the pocket.

It is important to make sure that measurements relate to each other. The trouser front has seven measurements. As an example, does the measurement of the front yoke 4.3cm at the widest point and 1.5cm at the narrowest point look in proportion? Does the 5cm depth of belt loops look proportionately larger than the widest part of the yoke and is the pocket at 10cm approx. twice the size of the belt loop? The measurements don't have to be exactly correct, but they do need to look proportionately smaller or larger. If the measurements don't correspond in this way, your drawing is certain to look wrong and this is a good way to check the accuracy of your work.

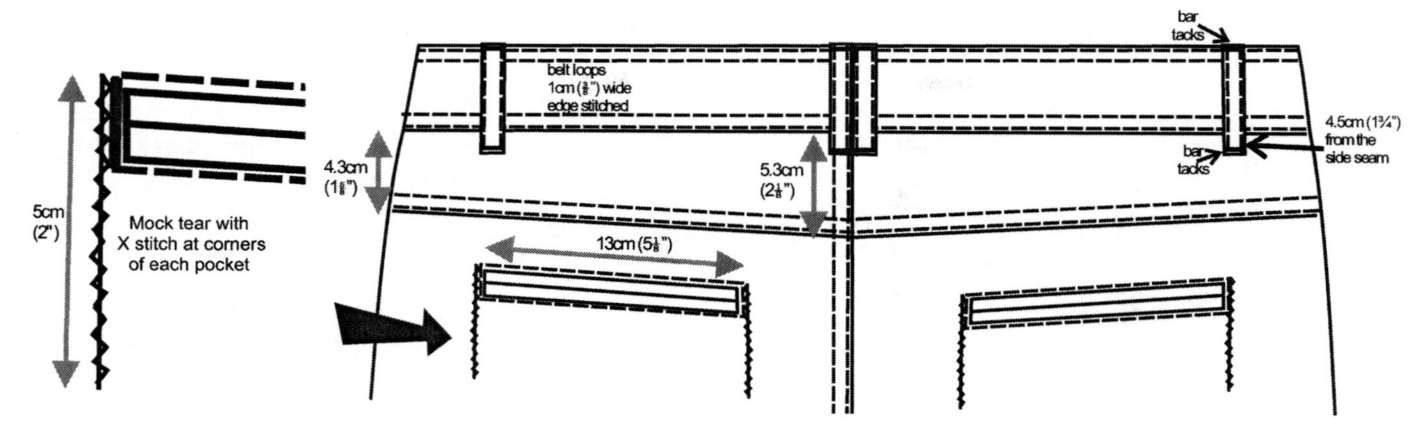

Back

- Seams 5–thread over–locked

Jetted pocket

- Effective pocket depth 12cm deep.
- Poly/cotton floral print pocketing & waistband lining.
- Self fabric pocket bearer to finish 3cm deep from the jet seam.

THE INSIDE

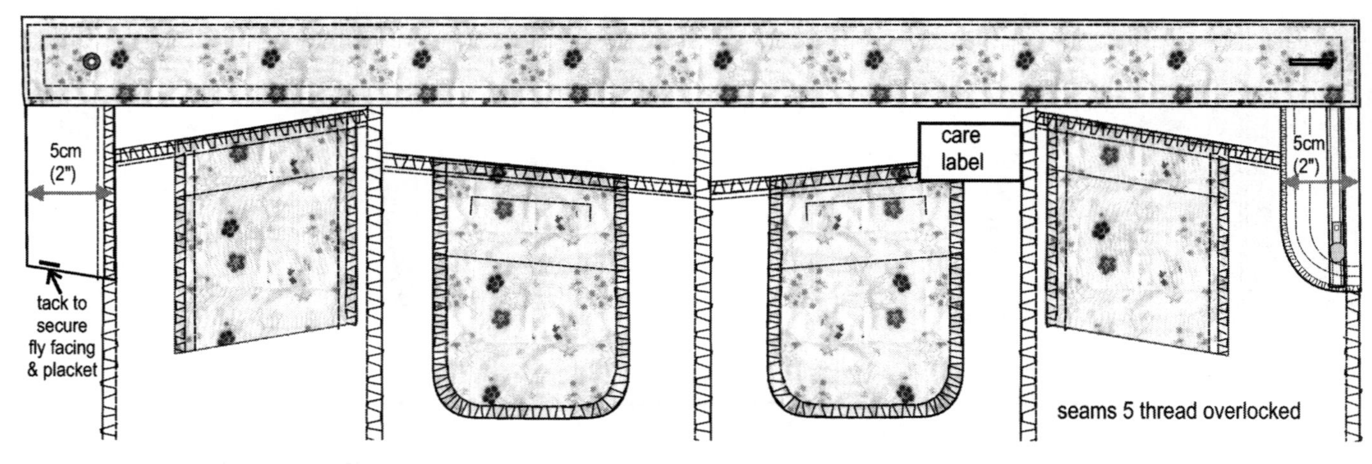

To make the trouser look different and more original it is decided to use cotton floral lining for the waistband lining & pockets. Having found a suitable design, scan the fabric and use it in the drawing to show the factory the effect you are looking for. Pockets and waistband are drawn as closed objects and the design transferred to them by the power clip application.

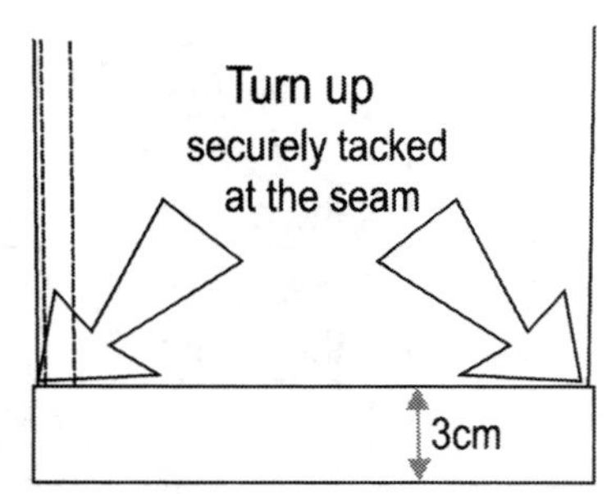

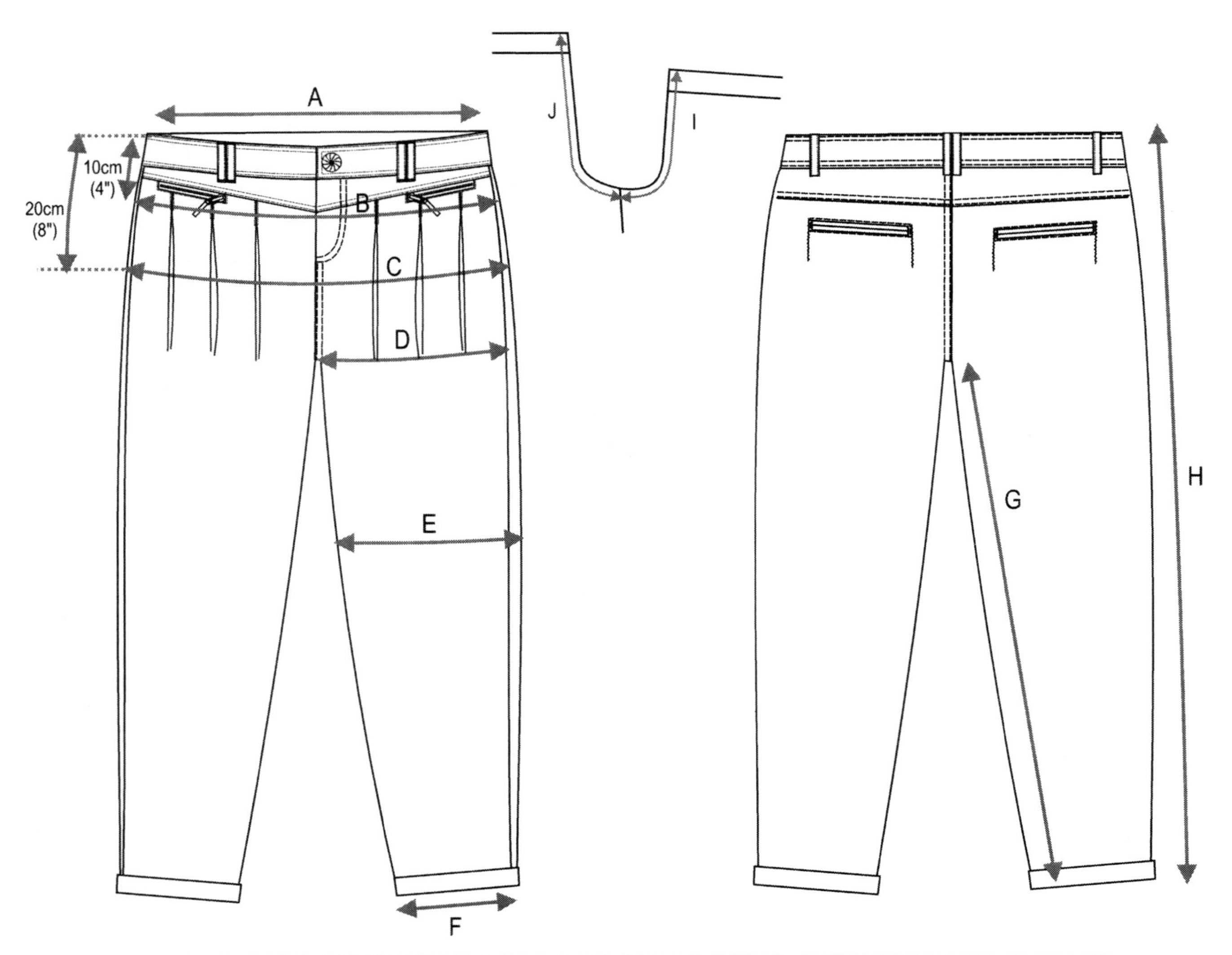

Size	UK 12	
	cms	Inches
A. Waist opening.	86	33⅞"
B. Hip 10cm below top of the waistband measured over the fullness of the pleats.	97	38¼"
C. Hip 20cm below top of the waistband measured over the fullness of the pleats.	110	43¼"
D. Thigh at crotch with pleat fullness pulled out.	70	27½"
E. Knee mid point between hem & fork.	70	27½"
F. Hem.	31	12¼"
G. Inside leg.	73.5	29"
H. Outside leg including band.	94.5	37¼"
I. Front rise including waistband.	25	9¾"
J. Back rise including waistband.	33	13"
Zip finished opening.	8	3⅛"

Packaging is sometimes overlooked. Factories you have worked with on a regular basis will get to know your packaging requirements, but more often today companies try new factories. It can be quite surprising the different ways factories have of folding a pair of trousers and placing them in a bag and packing them in a carton. Even if you are working with a familiar factory nothing should be left to chance. It is always possible that the person looking after your account is away and someone else takes over who might be used to operating differently. You must educate your suppliers to always follow your quality standards and values as this is an important factor in helping the volume of business grow between your two companies. Factories are aware of financial penalties or claims against them if a delivery is faulty. If a claim is made they instantly look for the get out clause "it wasn't specified" or "the specification wasn't clear". Factories of course want to avoid mistakes happening and prefer to work with companies who clearly specify what they want rather than having to guess. I remember working with factory managers who did not understand what was wanted, but said they did to save face.

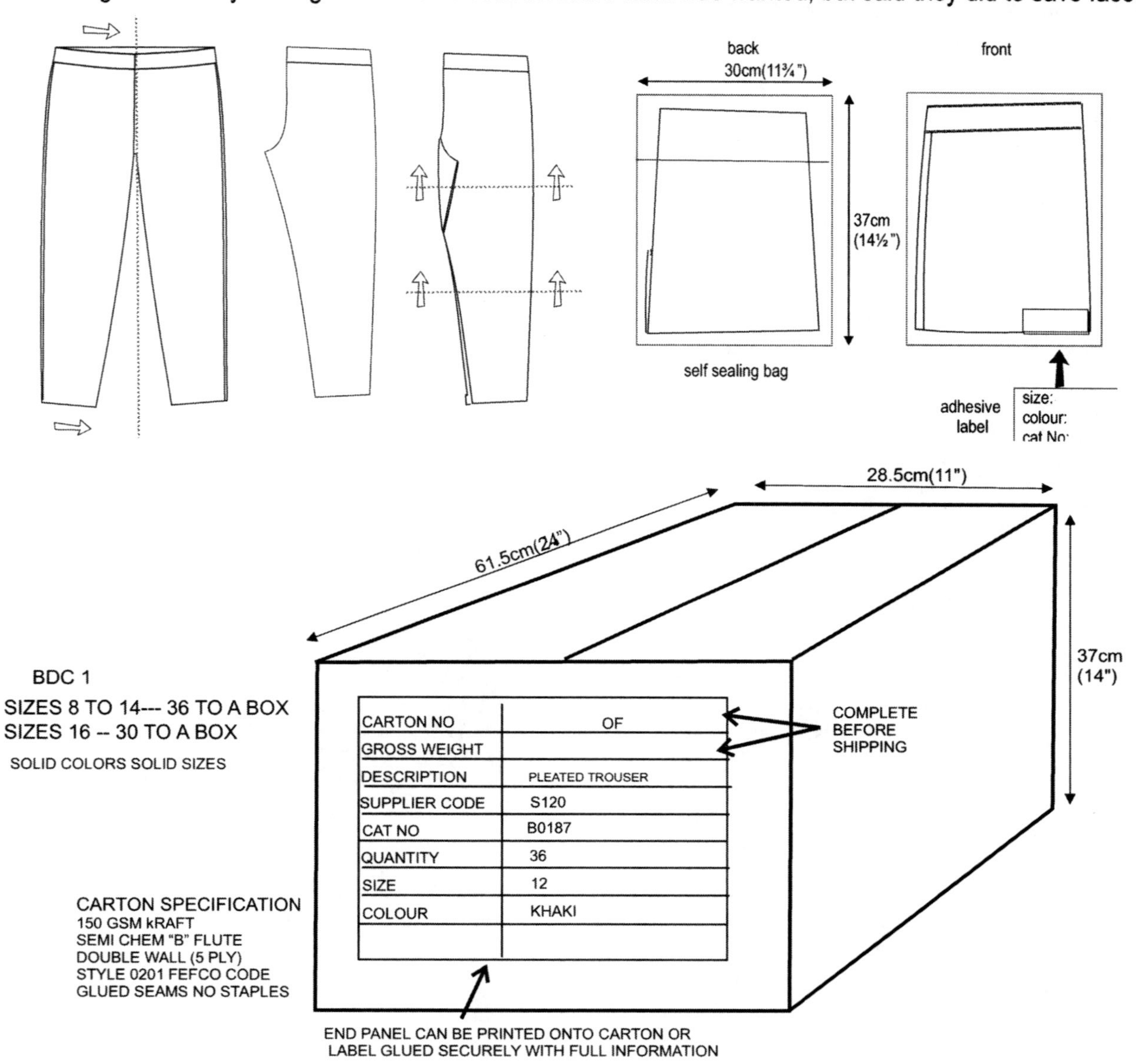

- KEEP QUANTITY PER BDC CONSTANT FOR EACH OPTION
- MAXIMUM BDC WEIGHT MUST NEVER EXCEED 12.7KG
- NEVER OVER PACK A BDC EVEN IF WEIGHT MAXIMUM ALLOWS
- ONLY ONE CATALOGUE NUMBER AND ONE OPTION MAY BE PACKED IN EACH BDC--- NEVER MIX OPTIONS
- NEVER USE STAPLES TO CLOSE BDC's TAPE MUST BE USED ON THE TOP & BOTTOM OF BDC
- PLACE A SHEET OF PAPER ON THE TOP LAYER INTERNALLY IN THE BDC TO PREVENT TAPE TOUCHING WHEN SEALING
- NEVER LOOSE FILL TO TAKE UP ROOM INSIDE BDC

CHAPTER 10

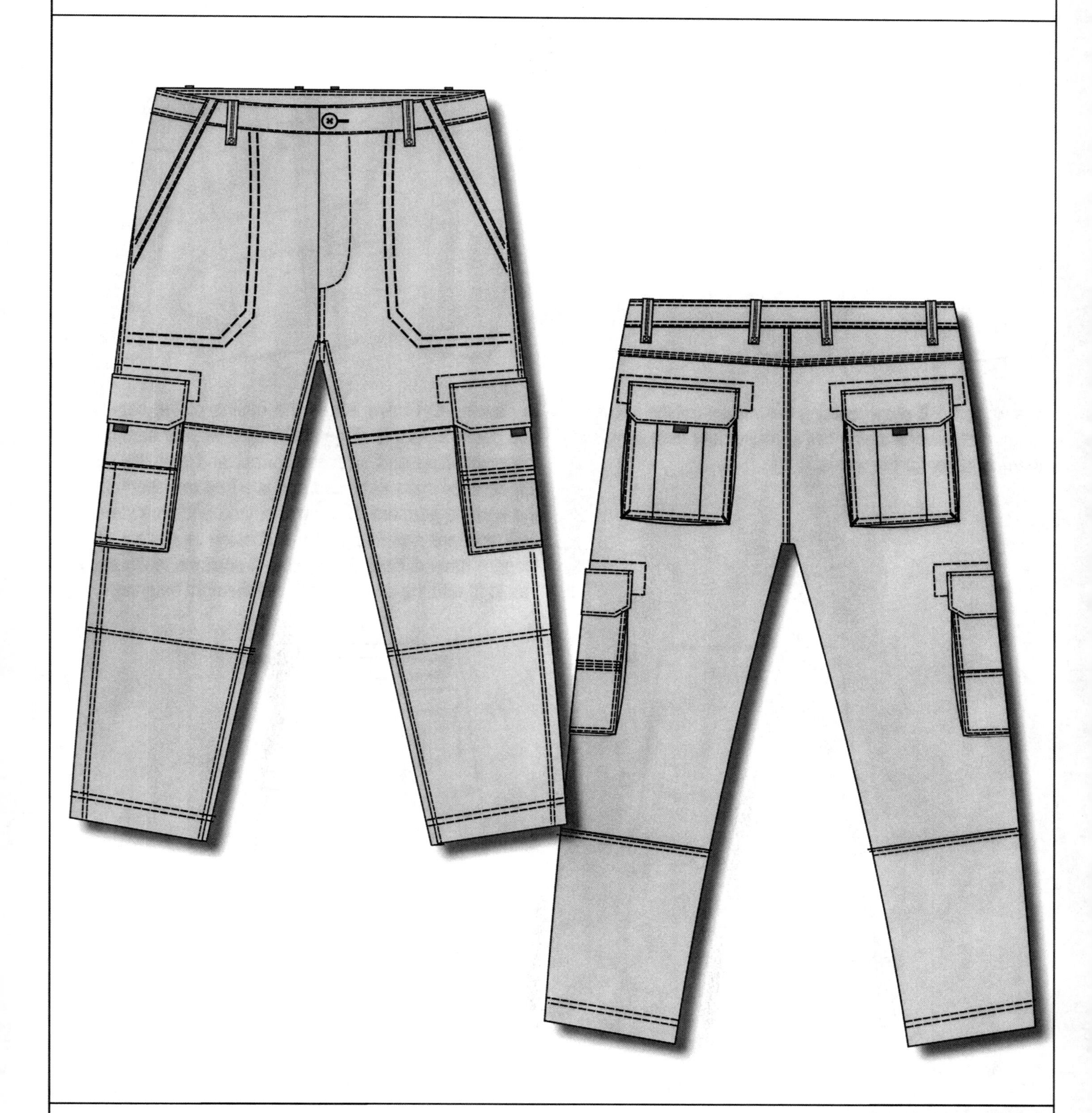

CARGO PANTS

A very popular style of pants for both men and women. Large roomy pockets with secure fastenings, plenty of seams and panels with top stitching. Fabric washed and faded giving a rugged appearance.

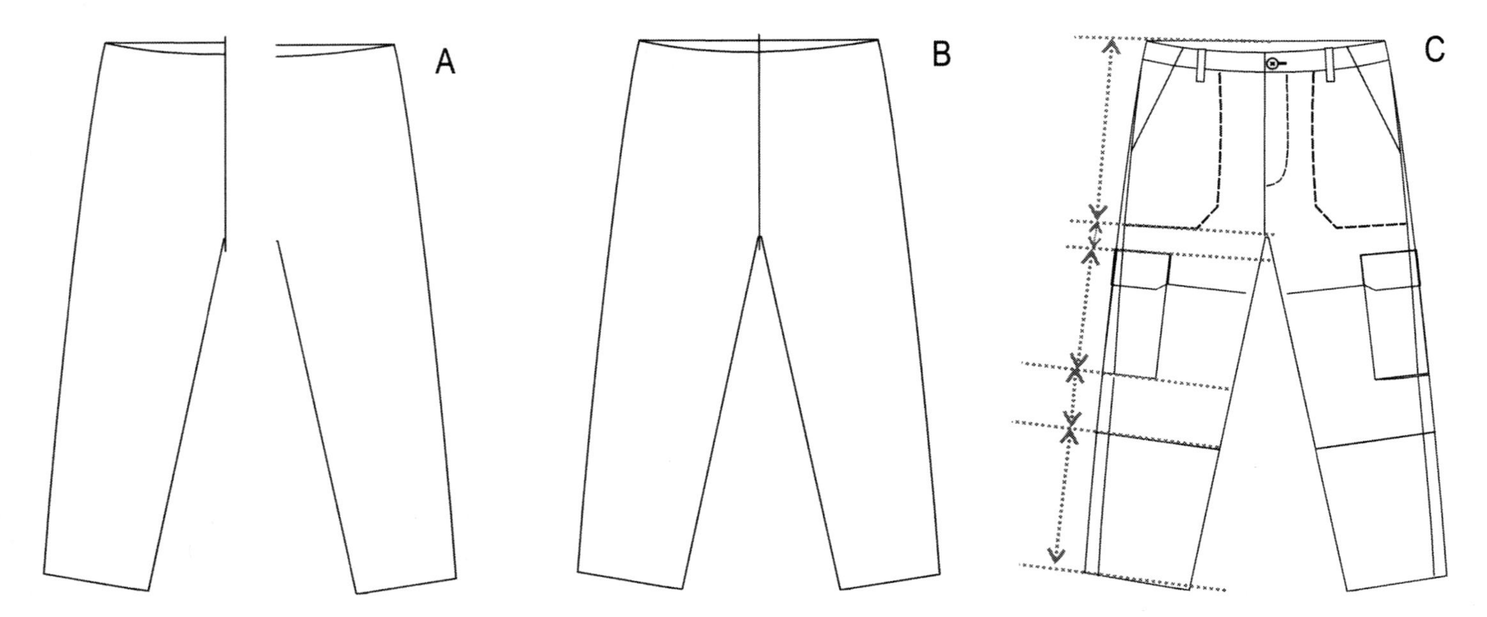

Drawings A & B show creating the trouser outline using the method of mirror imaging half a trouser and then combining them together for the whole.

In drawing C I have added the outline of the seams, fly and pockets. At this stage check against your sample that the positioning and size are correct and that the overall appearance looks balanced and is a true representation of the sample garment. Don't waste time adding style detail until you are satisfied that the drawing is correct at this stage. I have divided the leg into 5 sections, each section has to fit with the others to achieve the right balance.

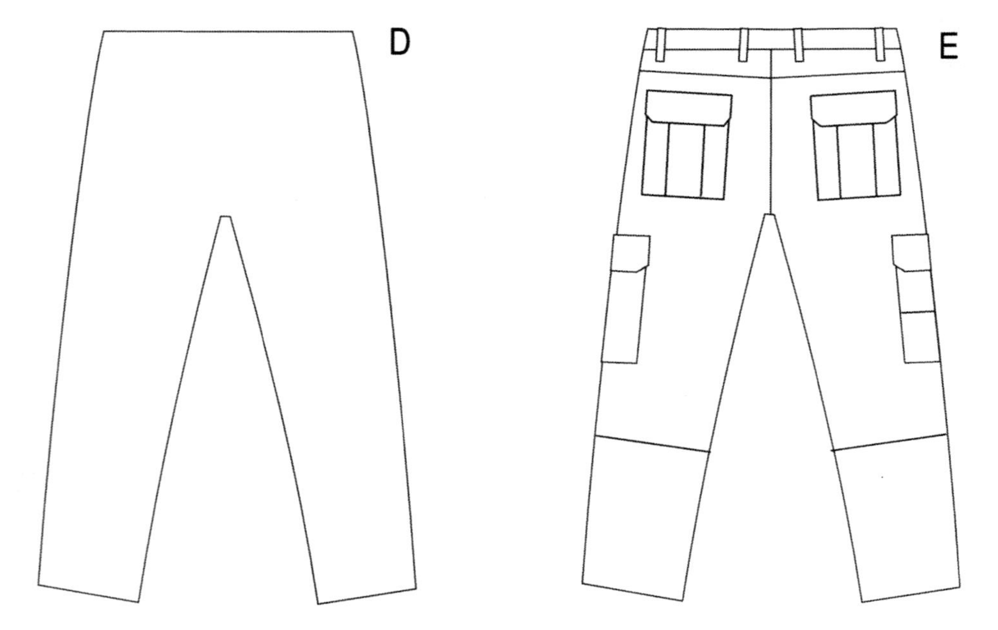

Copy the front outline D to create the back and add detail. Drawing E now completes the back and front. Do a final check and then add the details.

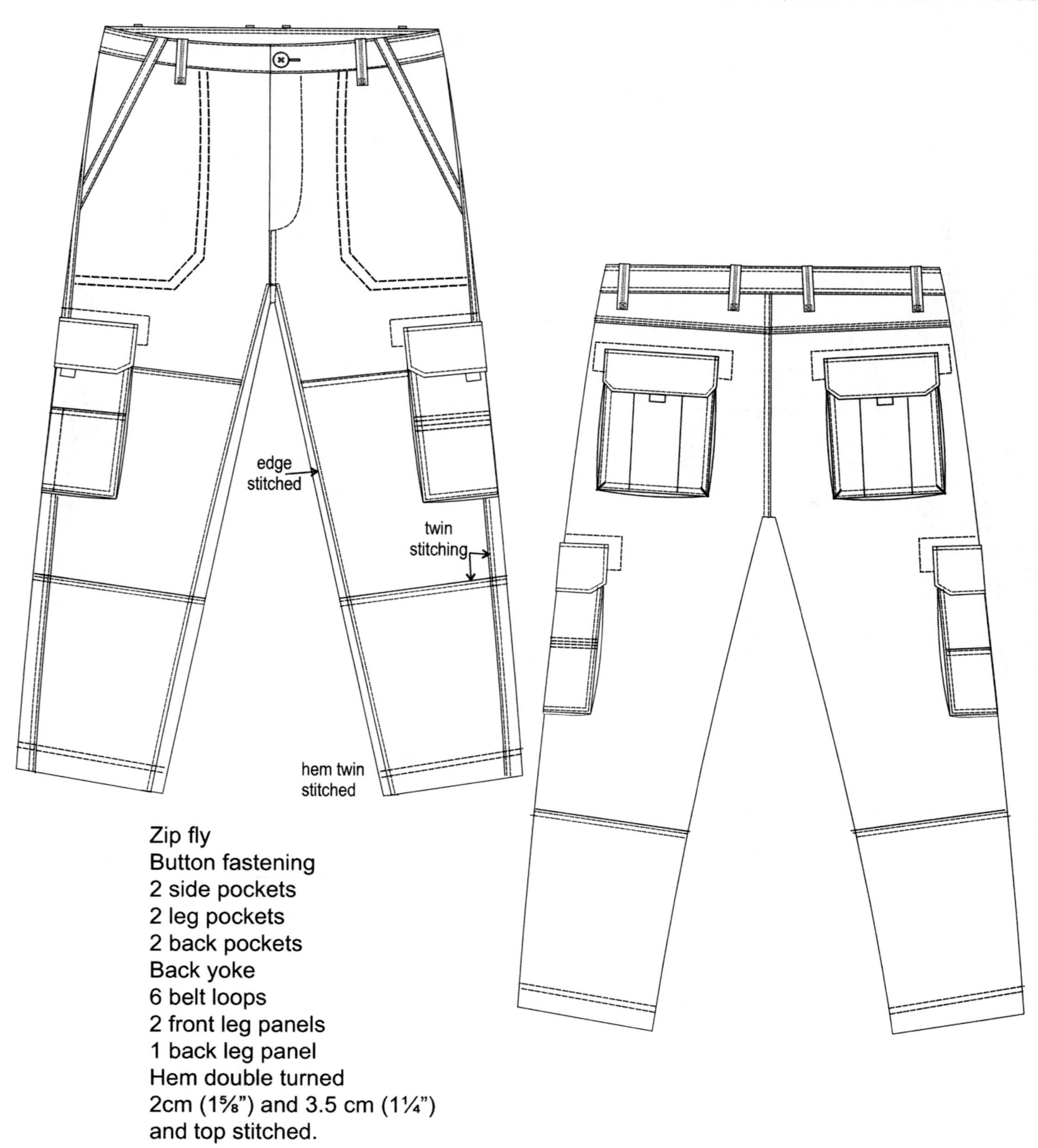

Zip fly
Button fastening
2 side pockets
2 leg pockets
2 back pockets
Back yoke
6 belt loops
2 front leg panels
1 back leg panel
Hem double turned
2cm (1⅝") and 3.5 cm (1¼")
and top stitched.

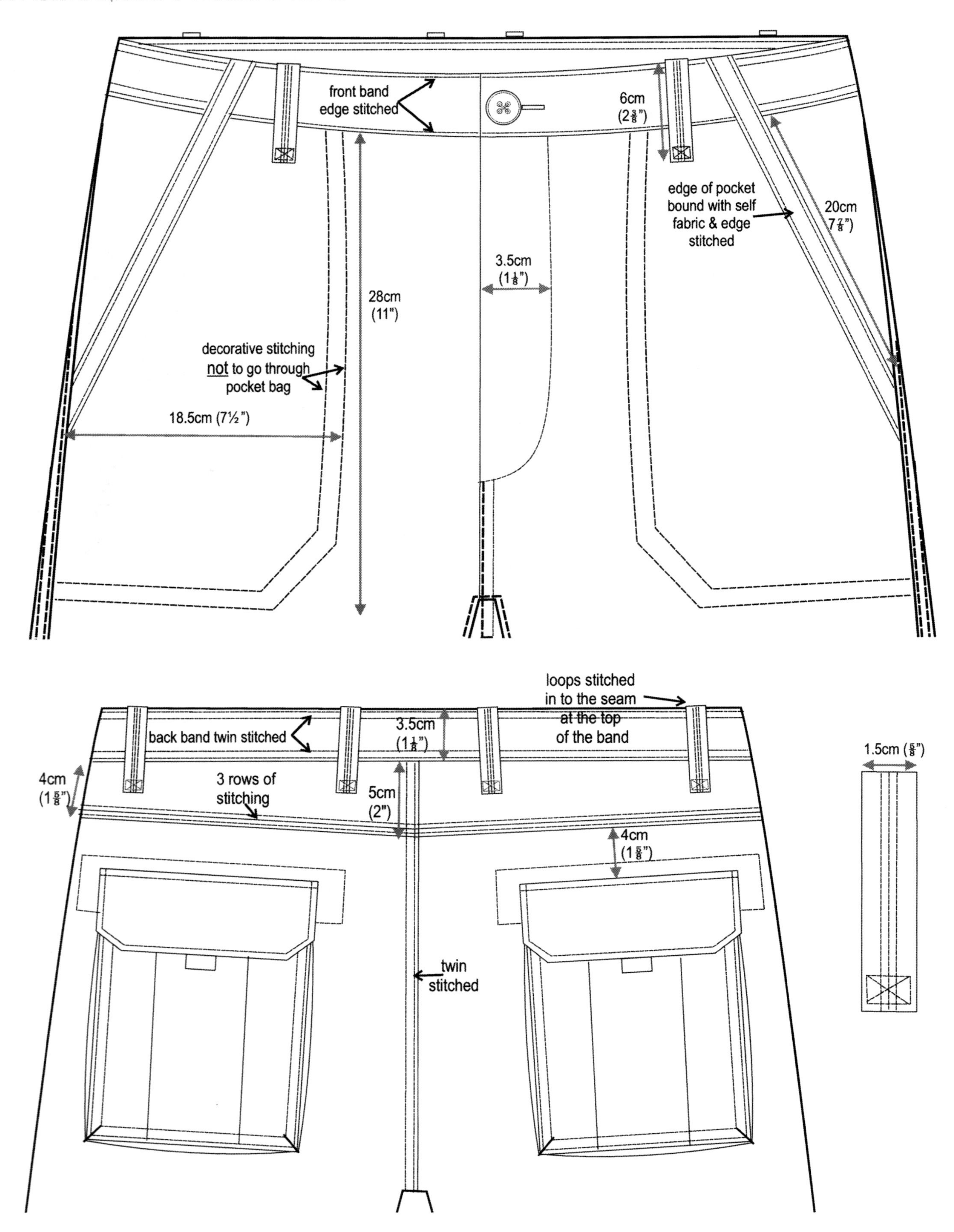

front band
edge stitched
6cm
(2⅜")
edge of pocket
bound with self
fabric & edge
stitched
20cm
7⅞")
3.5cm
(1⅛")
28cm
(11")
decorative stitching
not to go through
pocket bag
18.5cm (7½")
loops stitched
in to the seam
at the top
of the band
back band twin stitched
3.5cm
(1⅛")
1.5cm (⅝")
4cm
(1⅝")
3 rows of
stitching
5cm
(2")
4cm
(1⅝")
twin
stitched

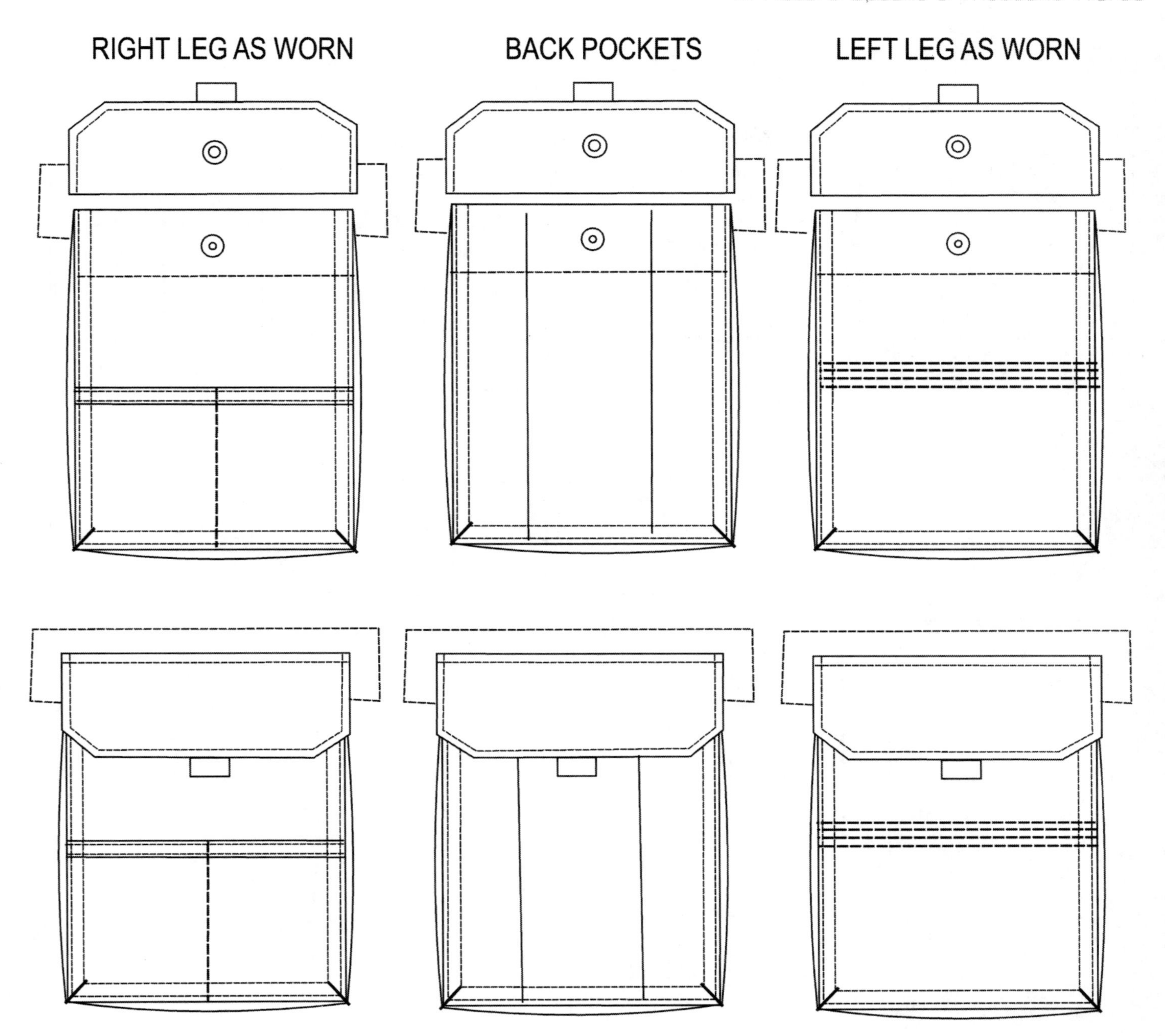

Pockets are the main feature of Cargo trousers and this style has 6 in total including the side pockets.

There are 3 styles of patch pockets but basically the construction, size and fastening are the same except for style detail on the front of the pocket.

When you have illustrated one pocket it is very easy to adapt it for the other styles and the following pages show each pocket in detail, but most details are copied and pasted from the first pocket.

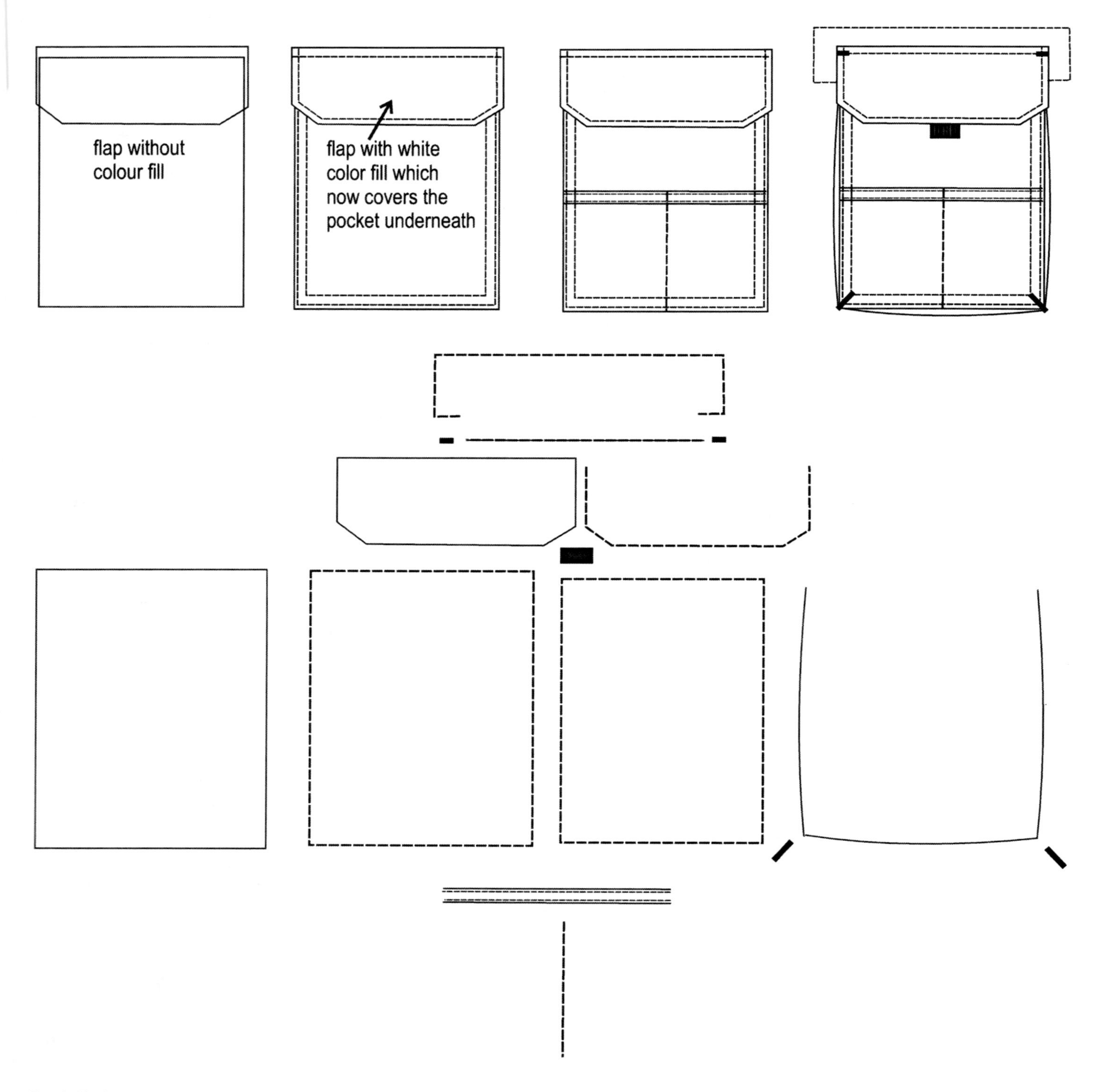

Exploded pocket to show individual drawn sections that went to make up the pocket.

The following pocket sketches will become part of your library, and because they are drawn in this detail they can easily be adapted to other styles.

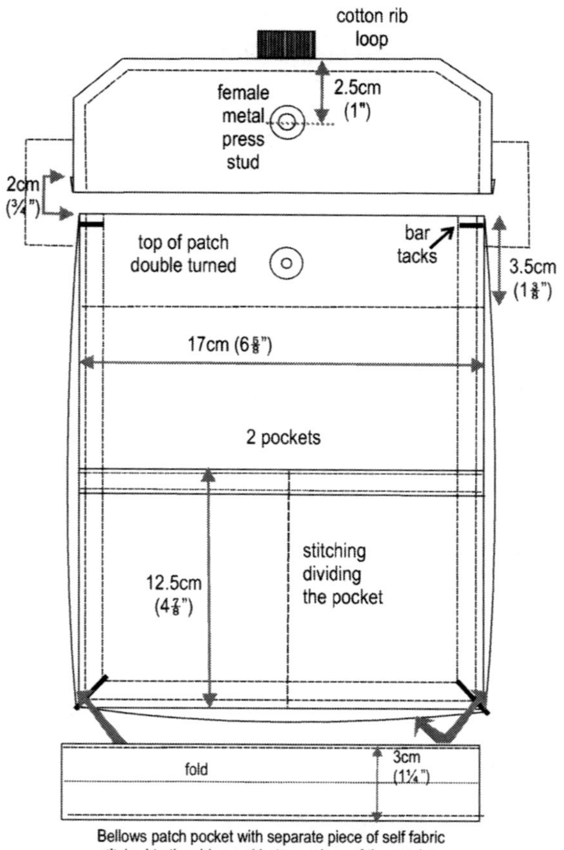

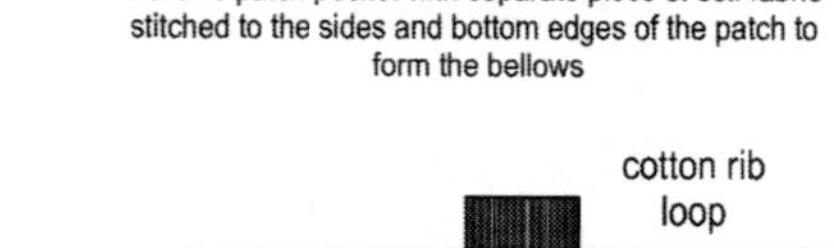

Bellows patch pocket with separate piece of self fabric stitched to the sides and bottom edges of the patch to form the bellows

leg pocket right side as worn

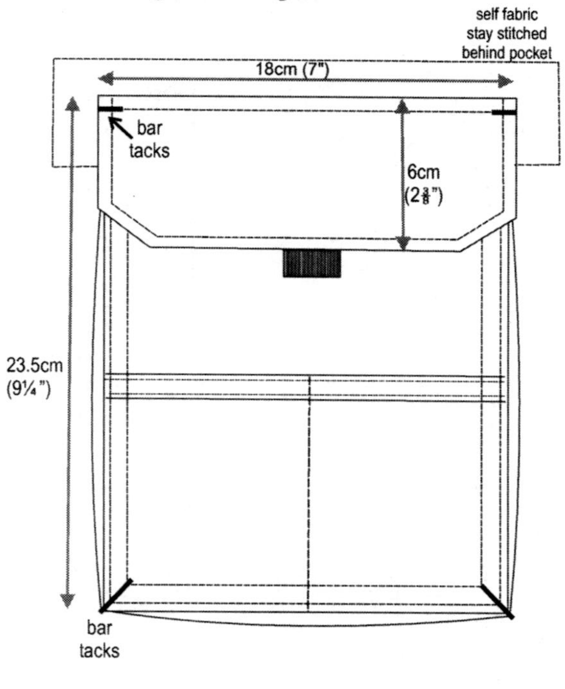

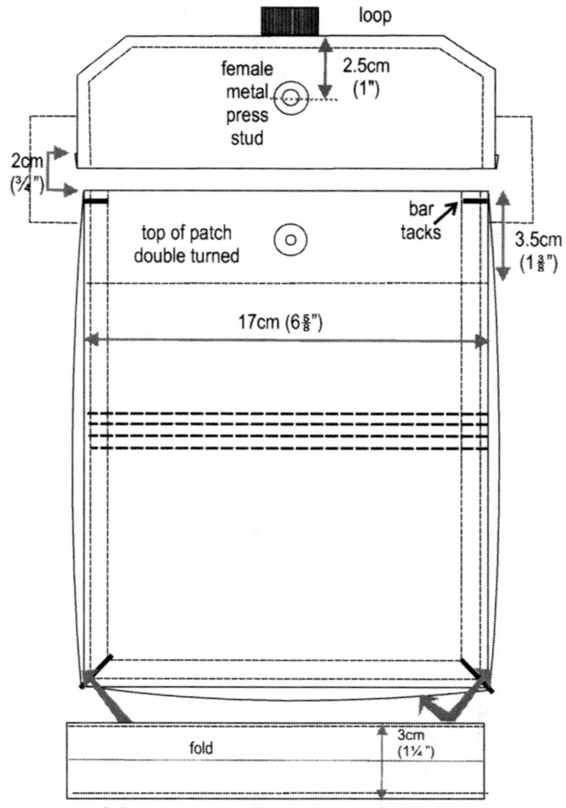

Bellows patch pocket with separate piece of self fabric stitched to the sides and bottom edges of the patch to form the bellows

leg pocket left side as worn

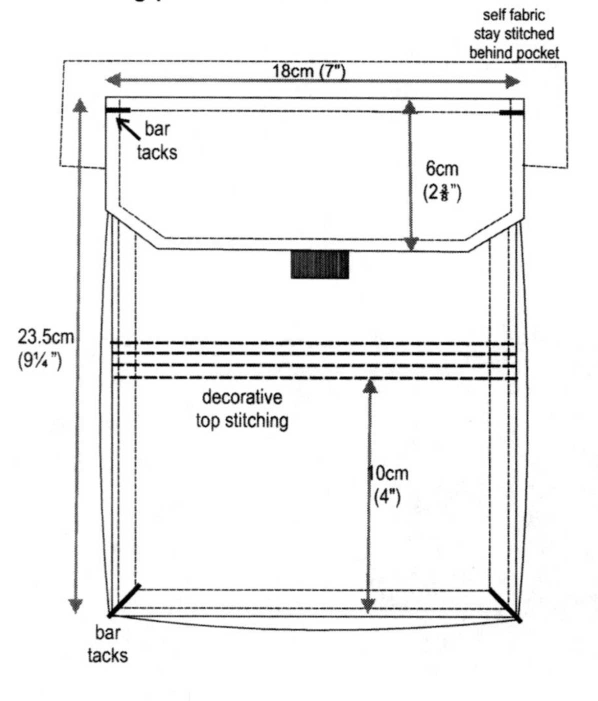

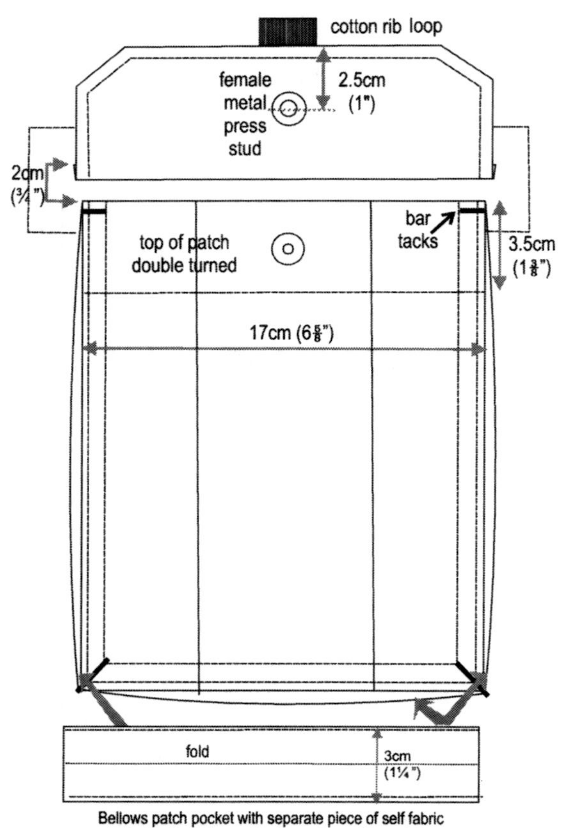

Bellows patch pocket with separate piece of self fabric stitched to the sides and bottom edges of the patch to form the bellows

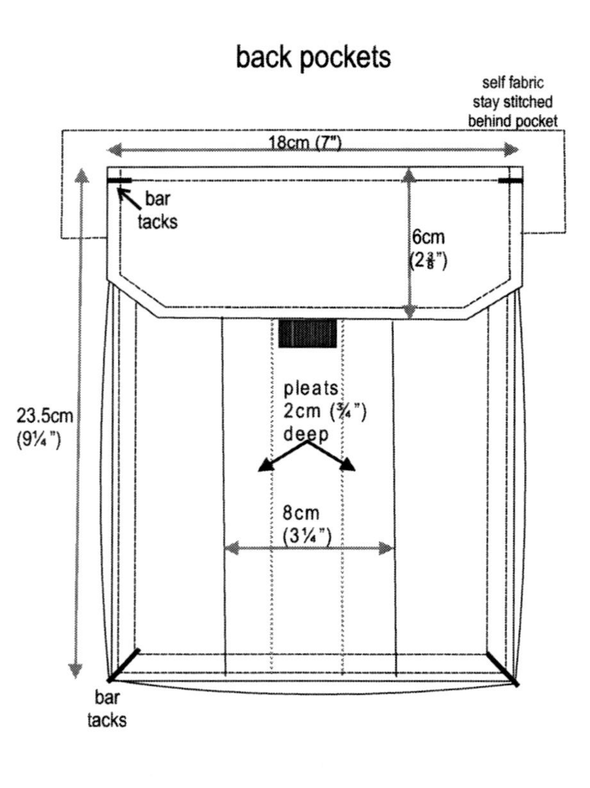

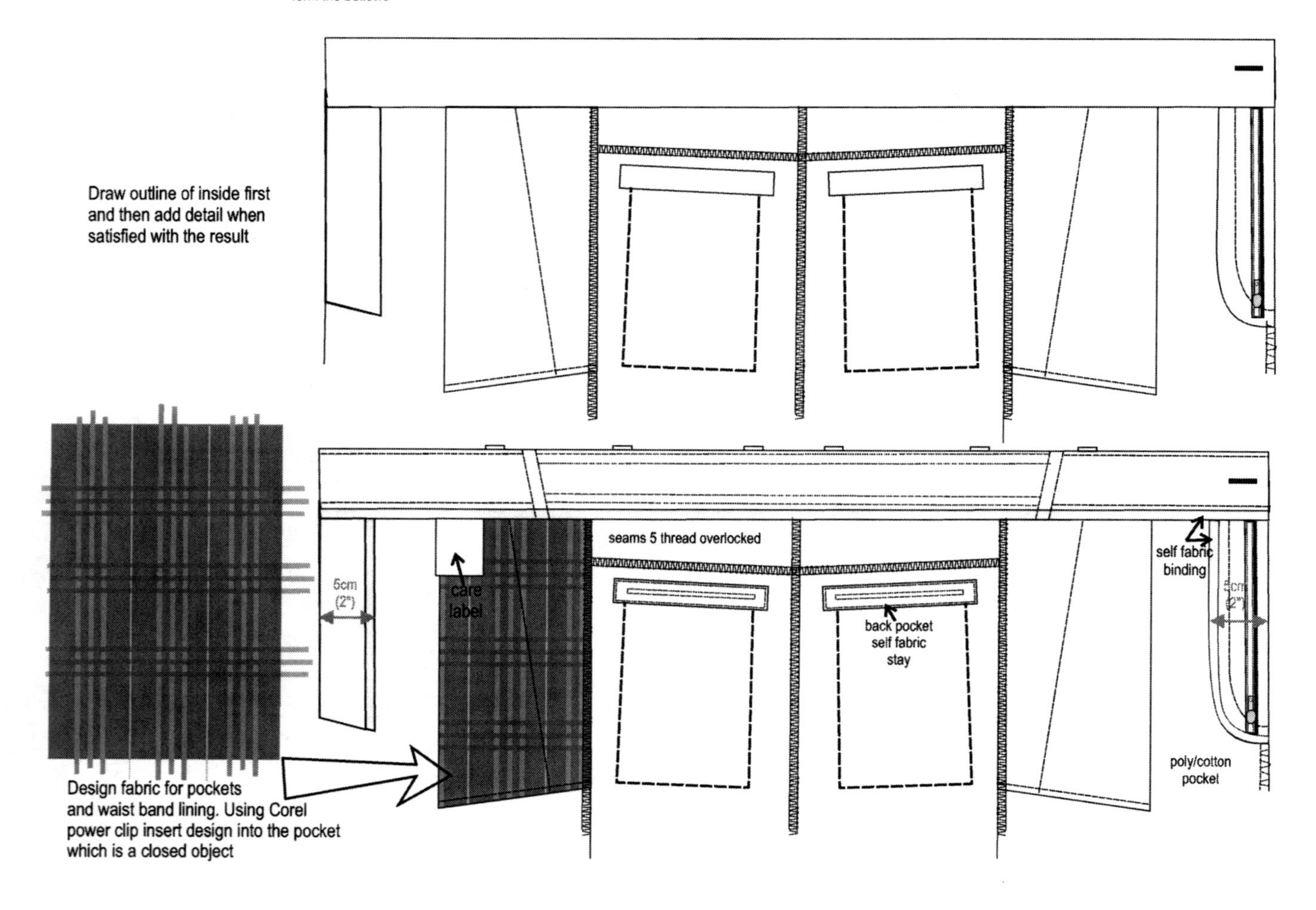

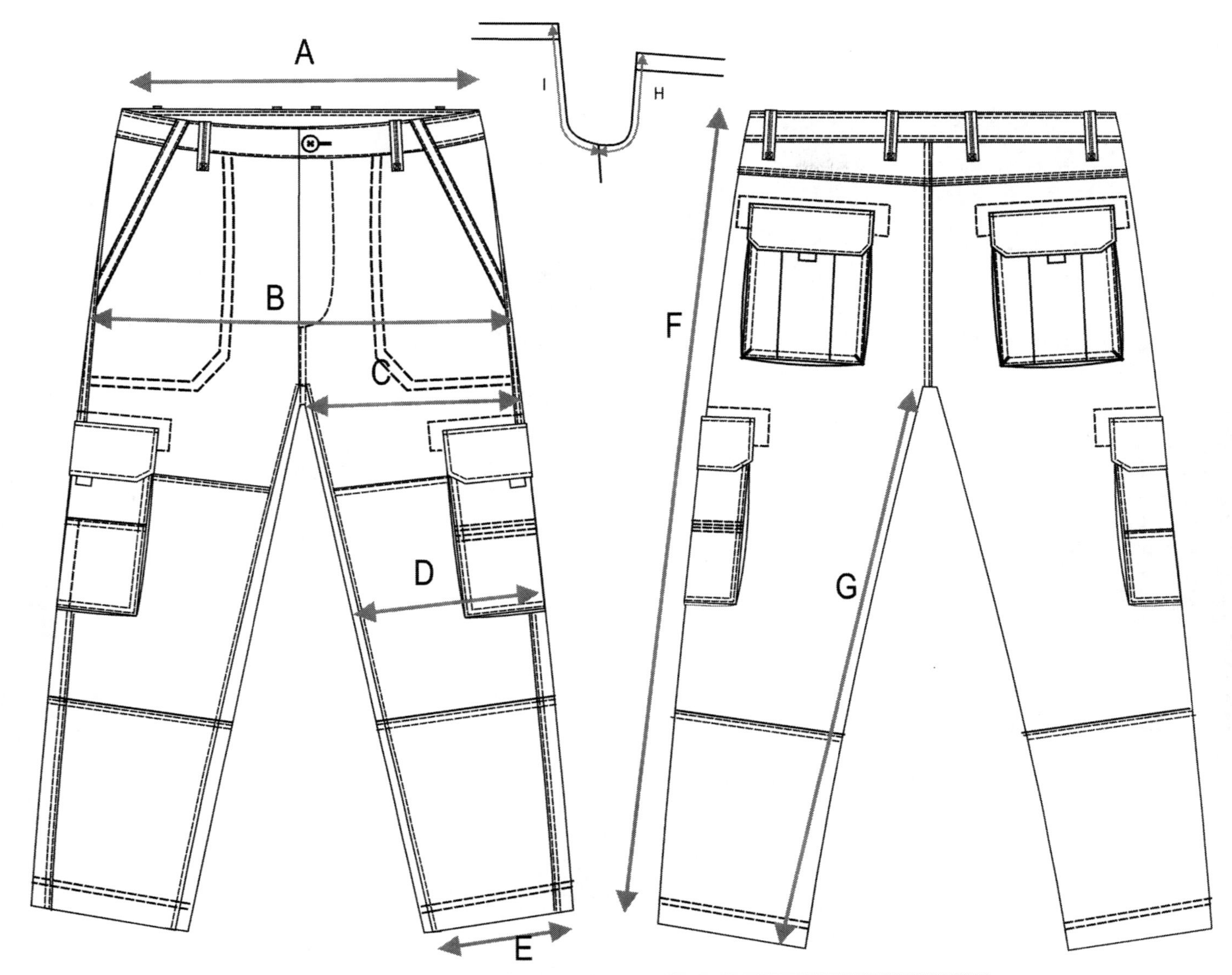

SIZE	34" WAIST	
	cms	Inches
A. WAIST OPENING	89	35"
B. HIP MEASURED AT THE BASE OF THE FLY	115	45¼"
C. THIGH AT CRUTCH	73	28¾"
D. KNEE MID POINT BETWEEN HEM & FORK	56	22"
E. HEM	48	19"
F. OUTSIDE LEG	106	41¾"
G. INSIDE LEG	81	32"
H. FRONT RISE INCLUDING WAISTBAND	28	11"
I. BACK RISE INCLUDING WAISTBAND	45	17¾"

CHAPTER 11

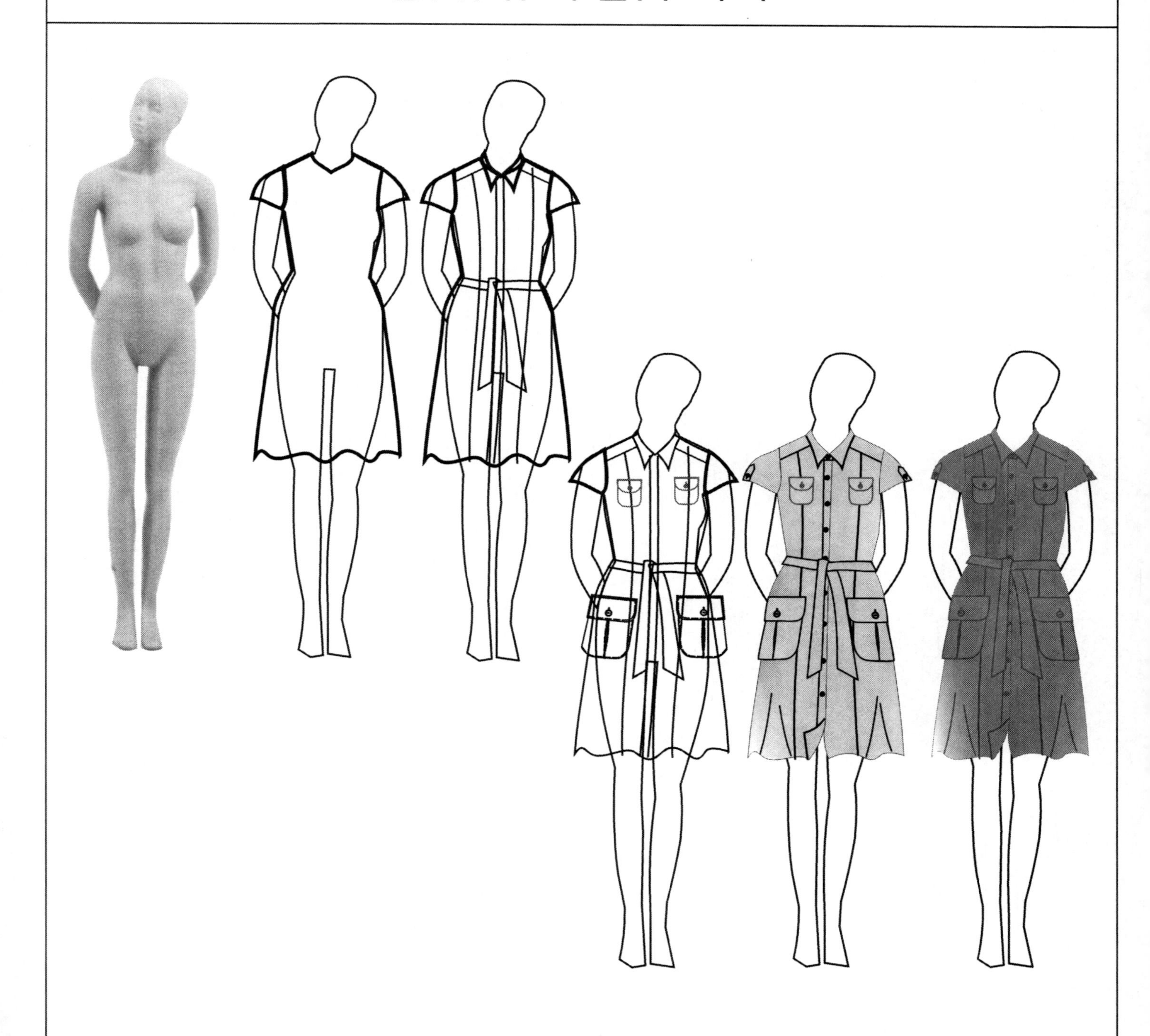

SHIRTDRESS

This dress is a blend of cotton and linen from a well-known supermarket range of clothing, and this classic shirt dress style is often found in many women's wardrobes. The dress comes in many variations and designers are always trying to re-vamp or re-invent the style. This particular dress has much detail. Most importantly the detail works, because there is a balance between all the individual parts. This results in the total design looking attractive and eye catching. The dress could have either been bought or made in your sample room; the specification is prepared to send to the factories for a price and for them to make a first sample.

Drawings 1 to 9 show the creation of the outline and details added. Drawing 1 is a rough outline of half the dress and 2 is the outline more developed. In drawing 3 the half dress is copied, pasted, mirror imaged and the two halves joined together. When starting to add style detail on the outline, I realized that the neck and bust area were too big. This placed the pockets and front panel seams in the wrong position and the dress was out of proportion. The inner line shows the corrected outline. Knowing that the silhouette is now correct, I can confidently add the remaining detail on the front and the back. Note that I have not completed the detail on the pockets, belt or added stitch detail on the seams at this stage. This is the time to double check that you are satisfied with the results so far. It is much easier to make amendments now rather than later.

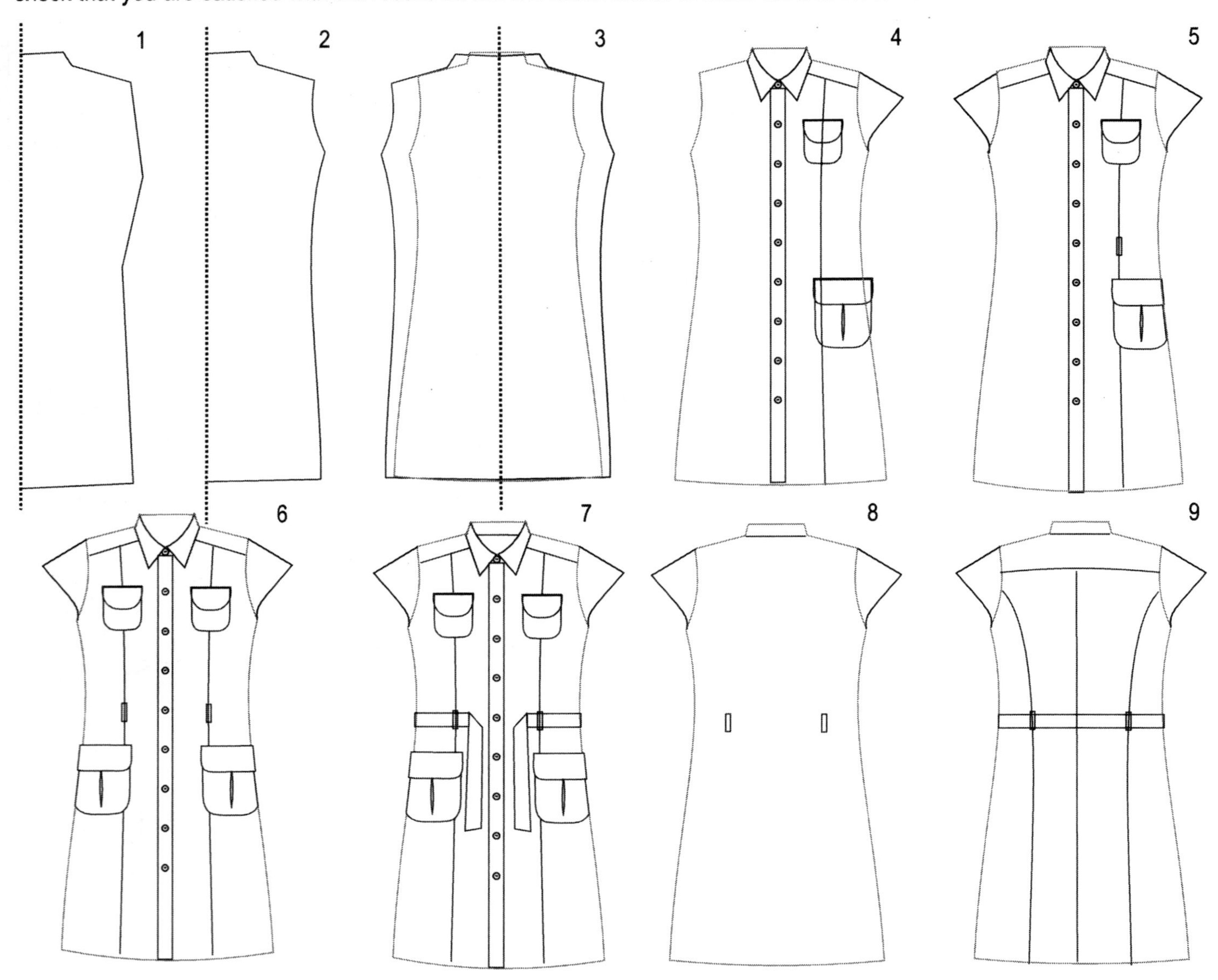

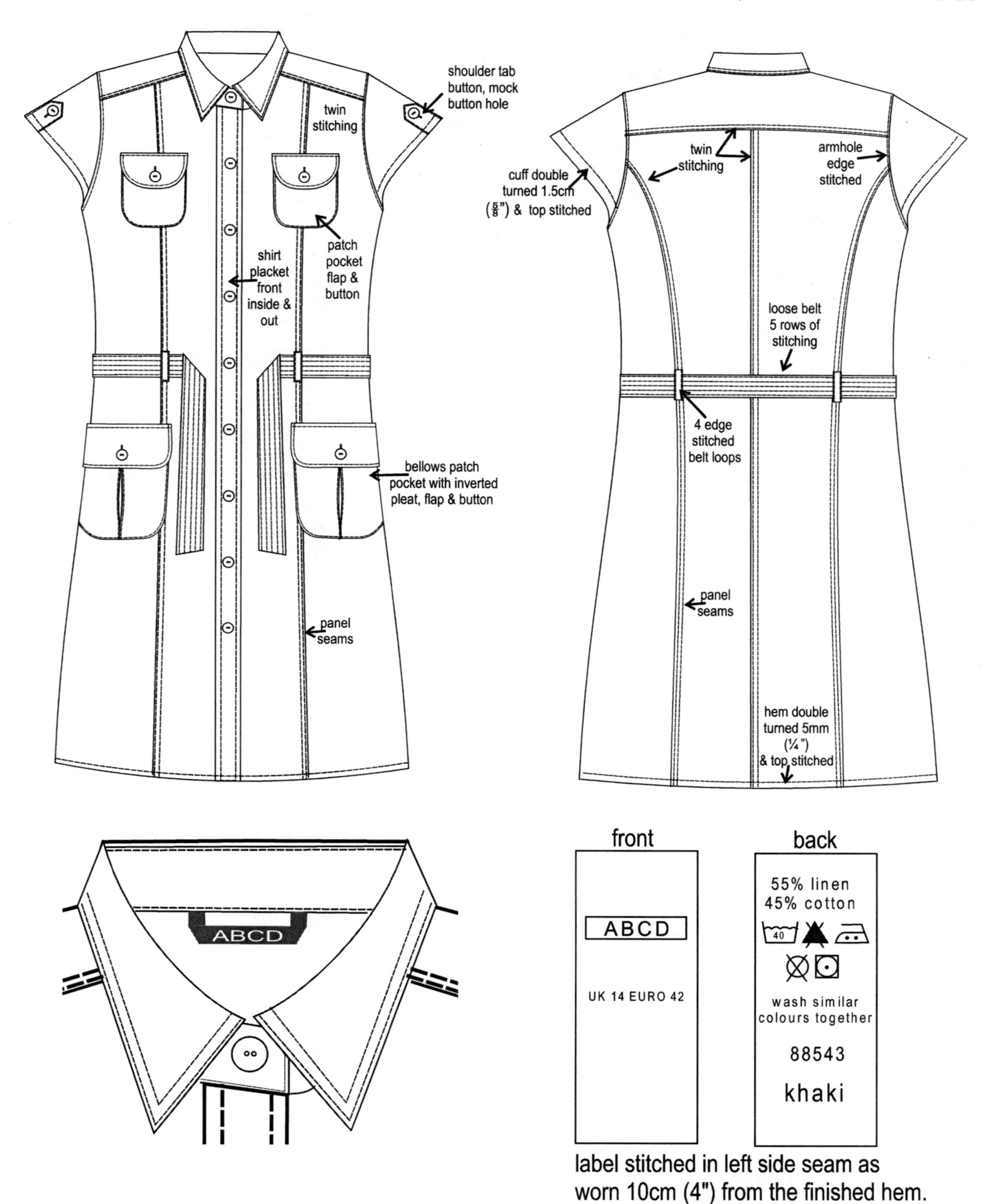

label stitched in left side seam as worn 10cm (4") from the finished hem.

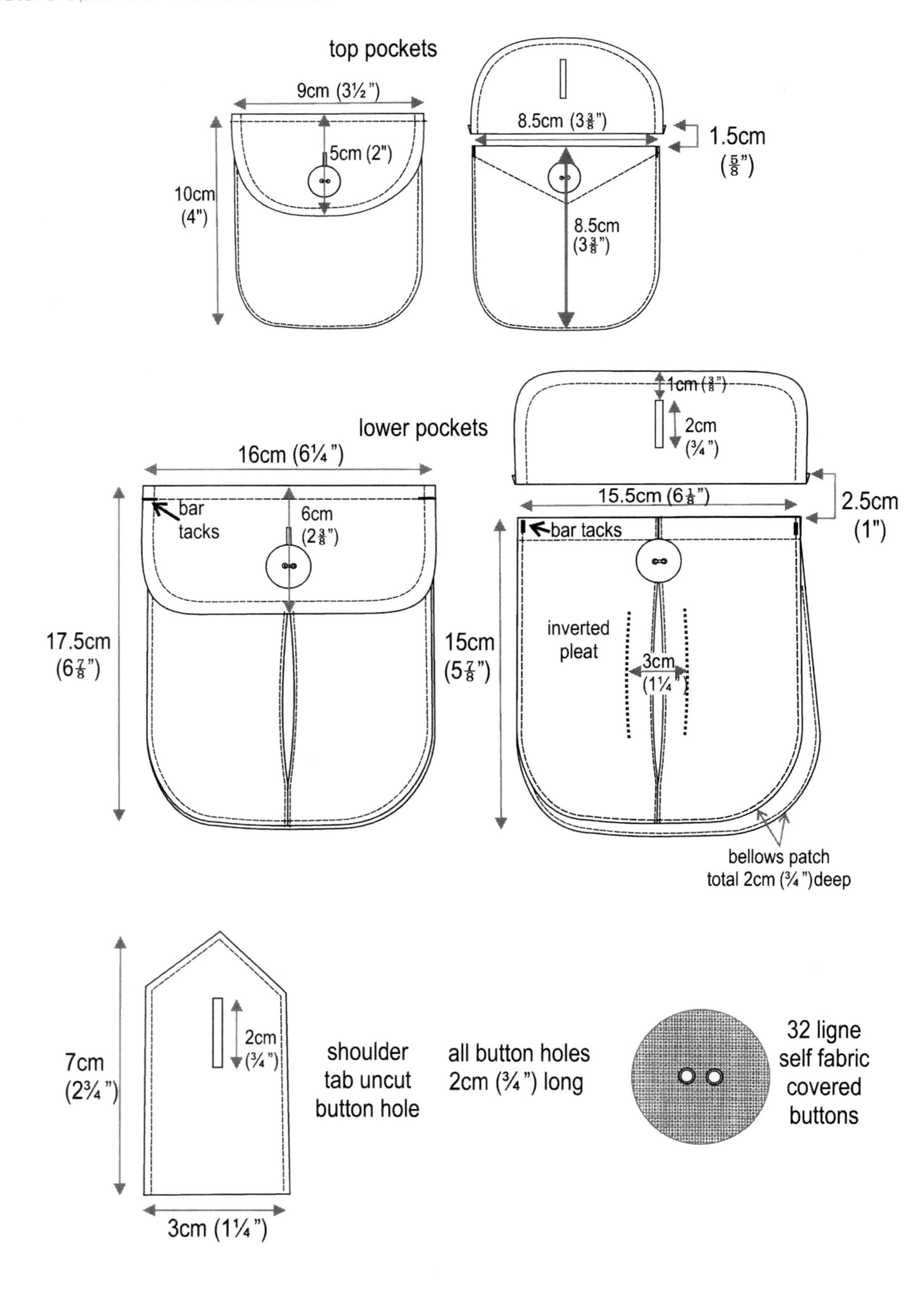

top pockets
9cm (3½")
10cm (4")
5cm (2")
8.5cm (3⅜")
1.5cm (⅝")
8.5cm (3⅜")
lower pockets
1cm (⅜")
2cm (¾")
16cm (6¼")
15.5cm (6⅛")
2.5cm (1")
bar tacks
6cm (2⅜")
17.5cm (6⅞")
15cm (5⅞")
bar tacks
inverted pleat
3cm (1¼")
bellows patch total 2cm (¾")deep
7cm (2¾")
2cm (¾")
3cm (1¼")
shoulder tab uncut button hole
all button holes 2cm (¾") long
32 ligne self fabric covered buttons

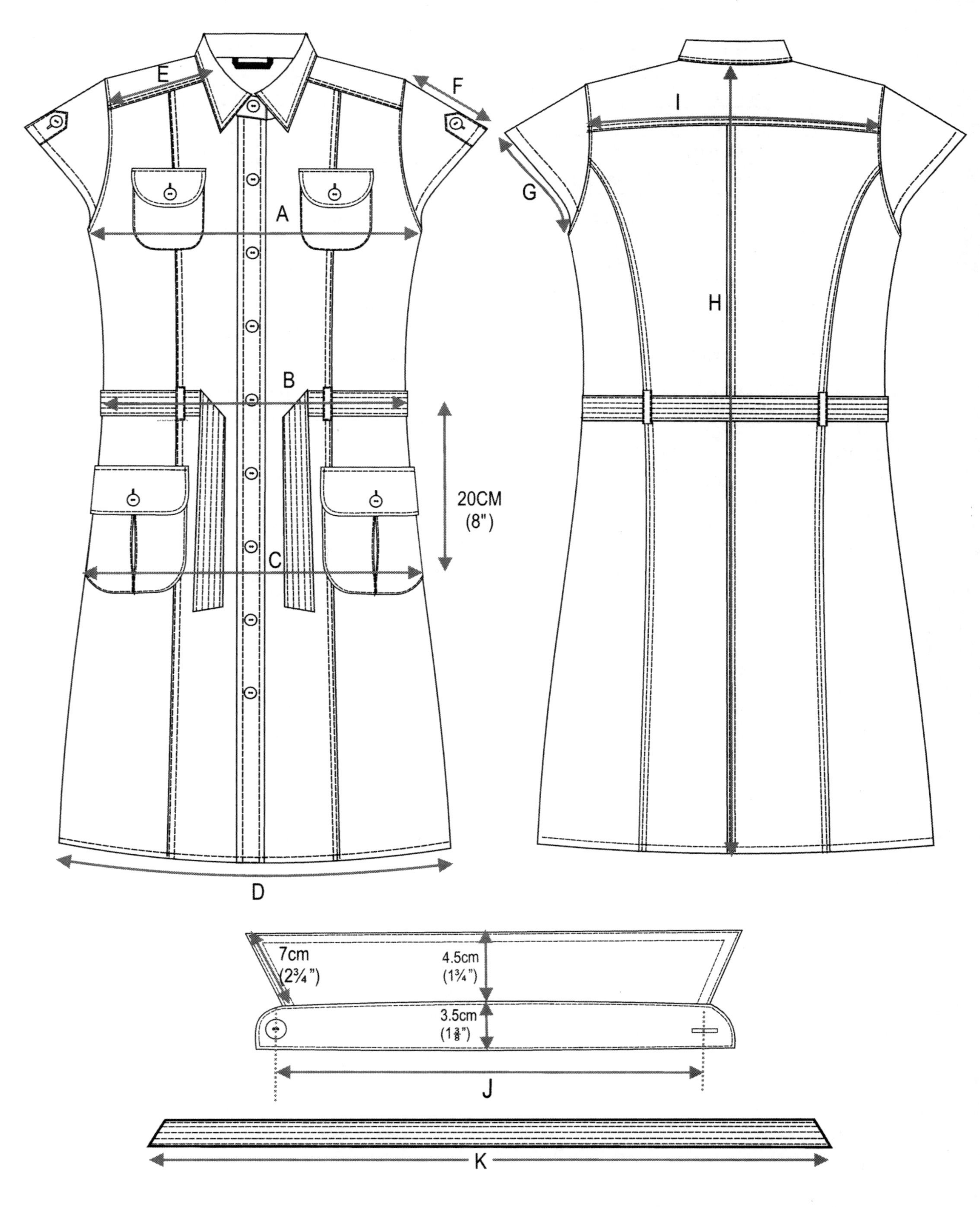
E
F
A
I
G
H
B
20CM
(8")
C
D
7cm
(2¾")
4.5cm
(1¾")
3.5cm
(1⅜")
J
K

SIZE	UK 12	
	CMS	INCHES
A. Bust at armhole - half measurement	50	19¾"
B. Waist-Half measurement	45	17¾"
C. Hip 20cm below waist - half measurement	54	21¼"
D. Hem sweep - half measurement	62.5	24⅝"
E. Shoulder yoke	11.5	4½"
F. Sleeve crown to cuff	16.5	6½"
G. Sleeve opening - half measurement	19	7½"
H. Center back length	92.5	36⅜"
I. Back yoke	38.5	15¼"
J. Collar - center of the button hole to the center of the button	42	16½"
K. Belt length	160	63"

CHAPTER 12

PARTY DRESS

These are examples of a classic style of party dresses with straps and without. Fully lined. Self fabric flower corsage at the waist. Pleating on the skirts back and front. Invisible back zip with hook and eye fastening.

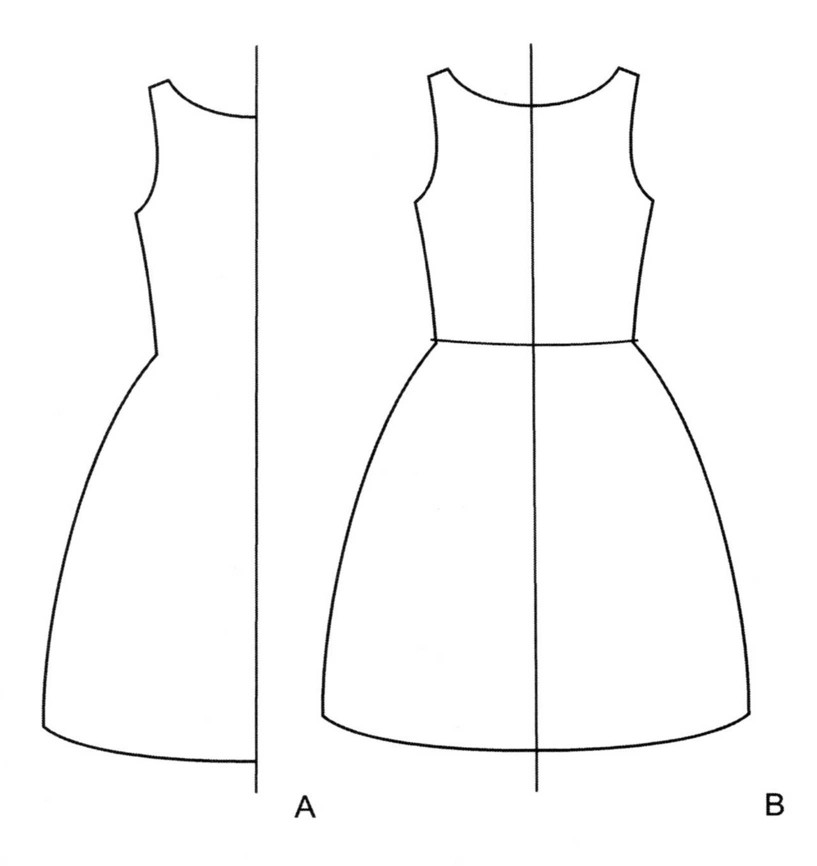

Dresses have a very distinctive outline and shape, so drawings A & B are the most critical. It is advisable to do these in 2 halves, mirror image. Put the 2 together until you get the right result, then merge the 2 halves.

Final style details are added to drawings C & D.

Using the front shape E add the back details and complete with drawings F & G.

Drawings H & I show the outlines added for strapless style. Drawing J is the method of drawing the corsage made from the dress fabric.

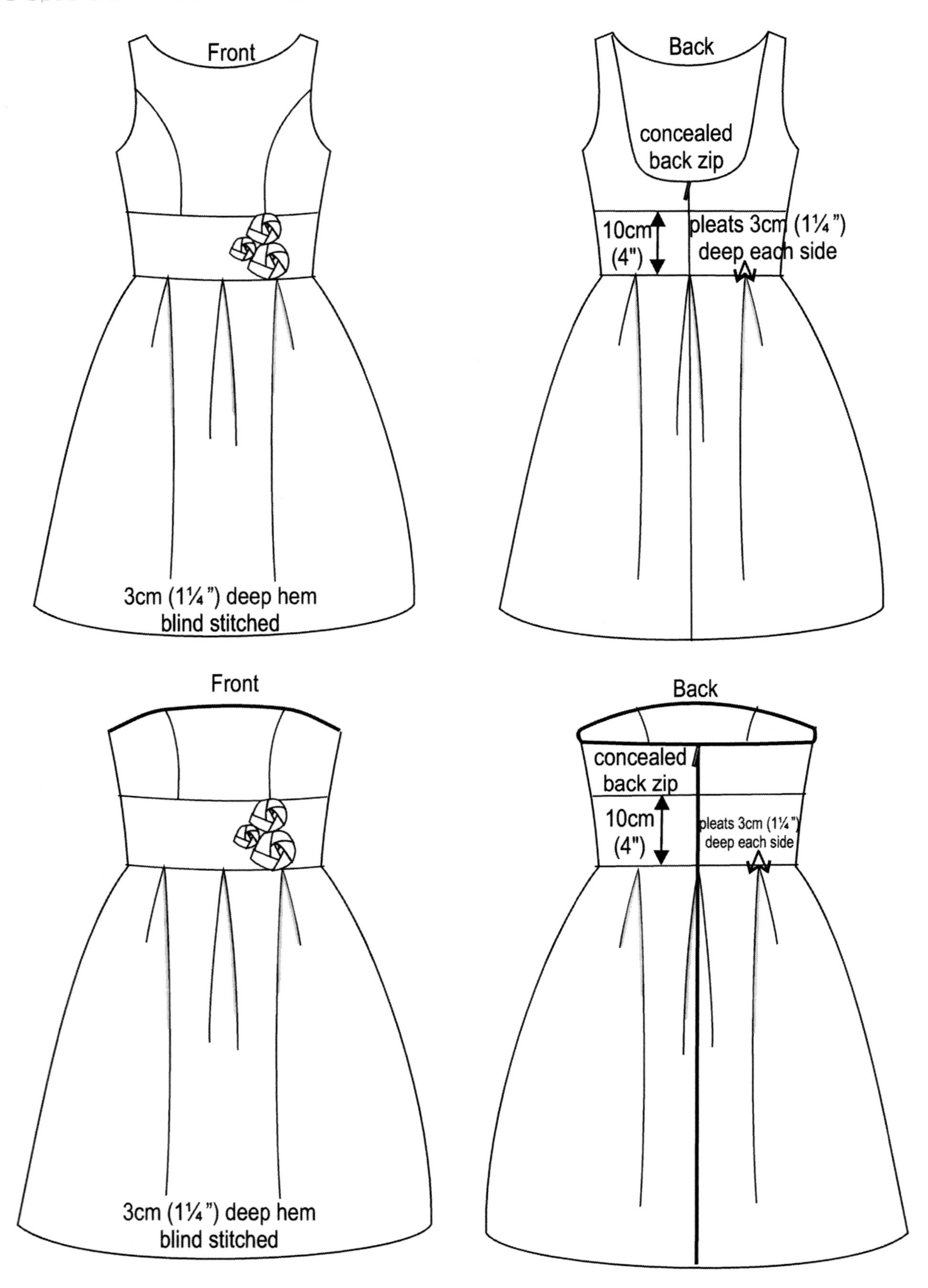
Front
3cm (1¼") deep hem
blind stitched
Back
concealed
back zip
10cm
(4")
pleats 3cm (1¼")
deep each side
Front
3cm (1¼") deep hem
blind stitched
Back
concealed
back zip
10cm
(4")
pleats 3cm (1¼")
deep each side

Knitted polyester lining secured at the top edges and the zip seam. Hem double turned 1cm (⅜") & 2.5cm (1")and top stitched.

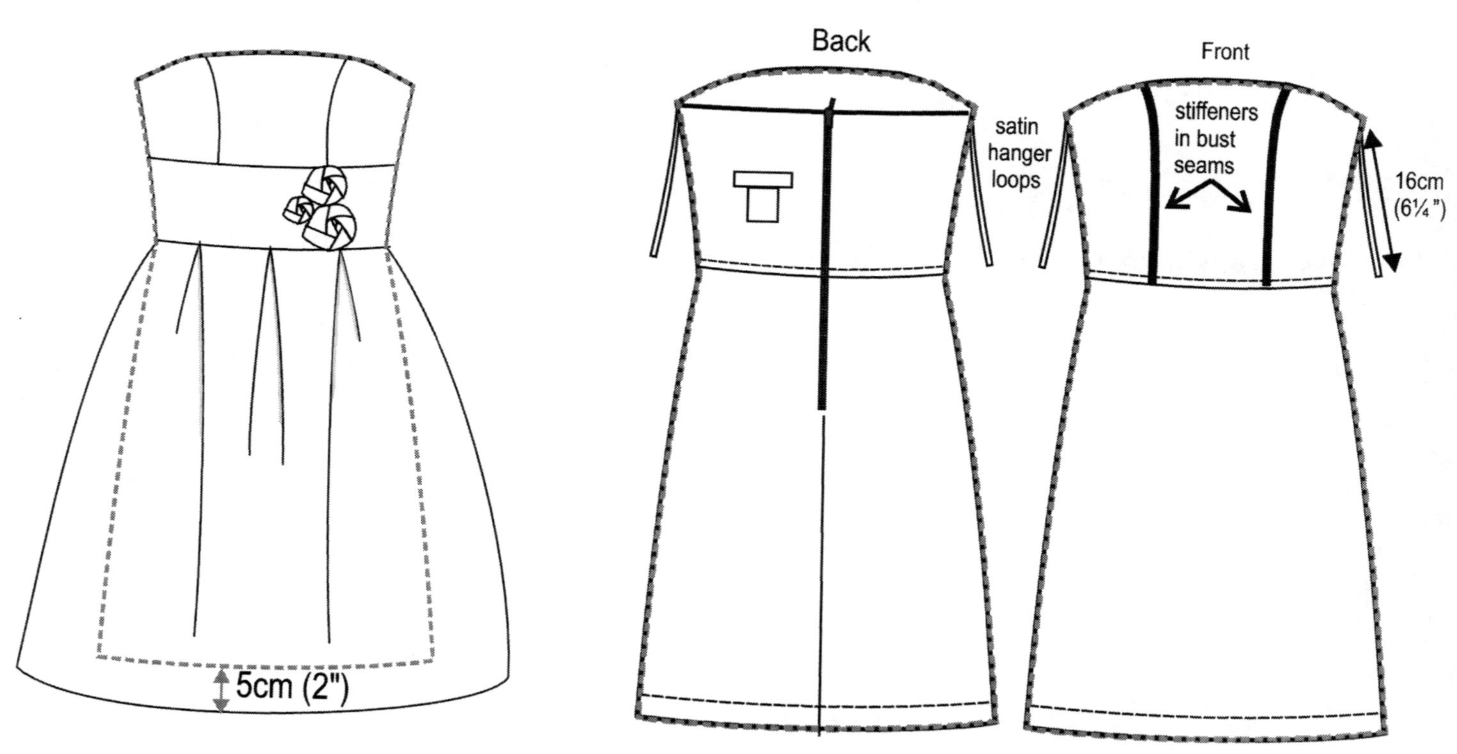

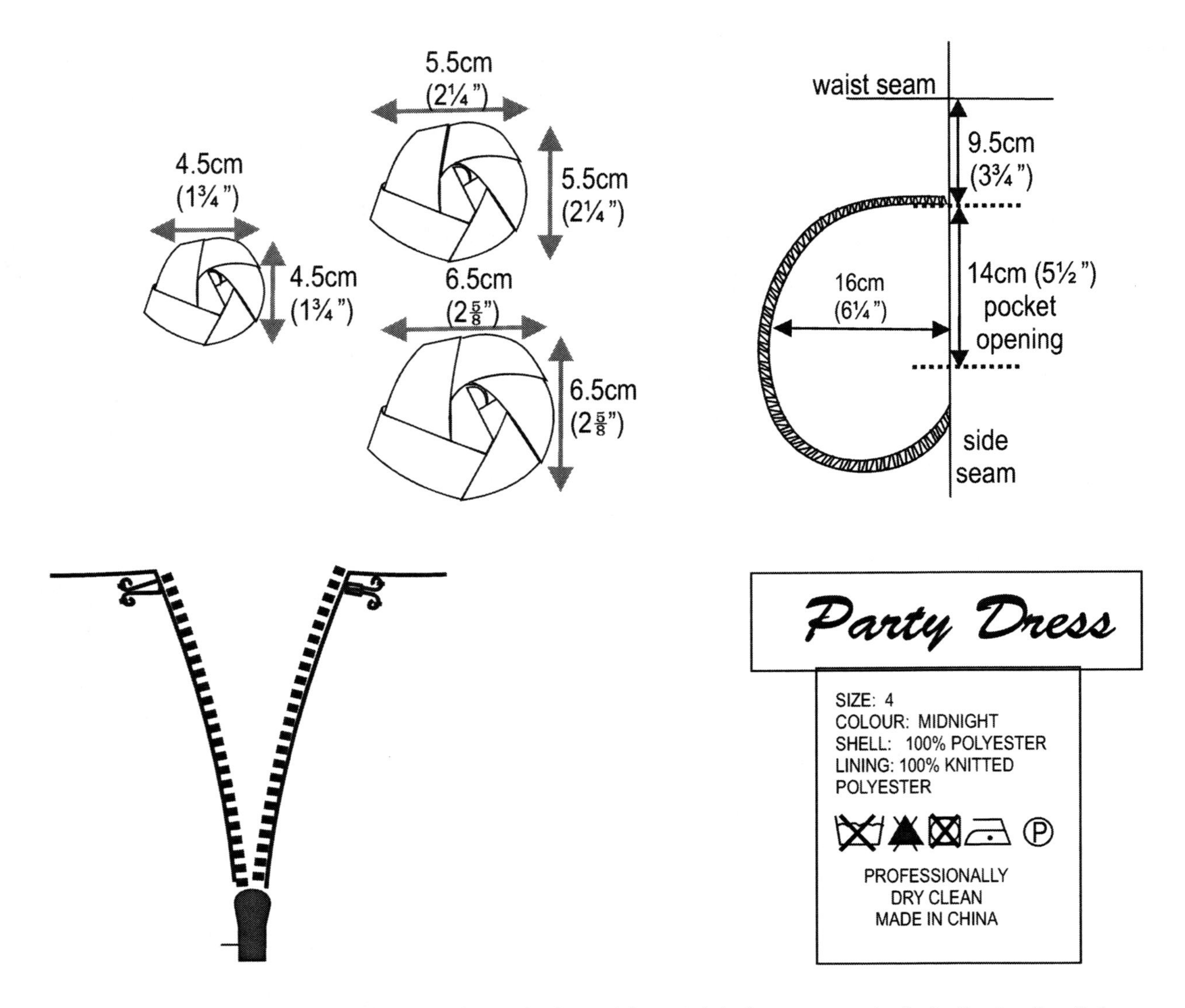

Hook & eye fastening at the top of the zip brand & care labels sewn centrally to the bodice lining panel.

Dress with shoulder straps

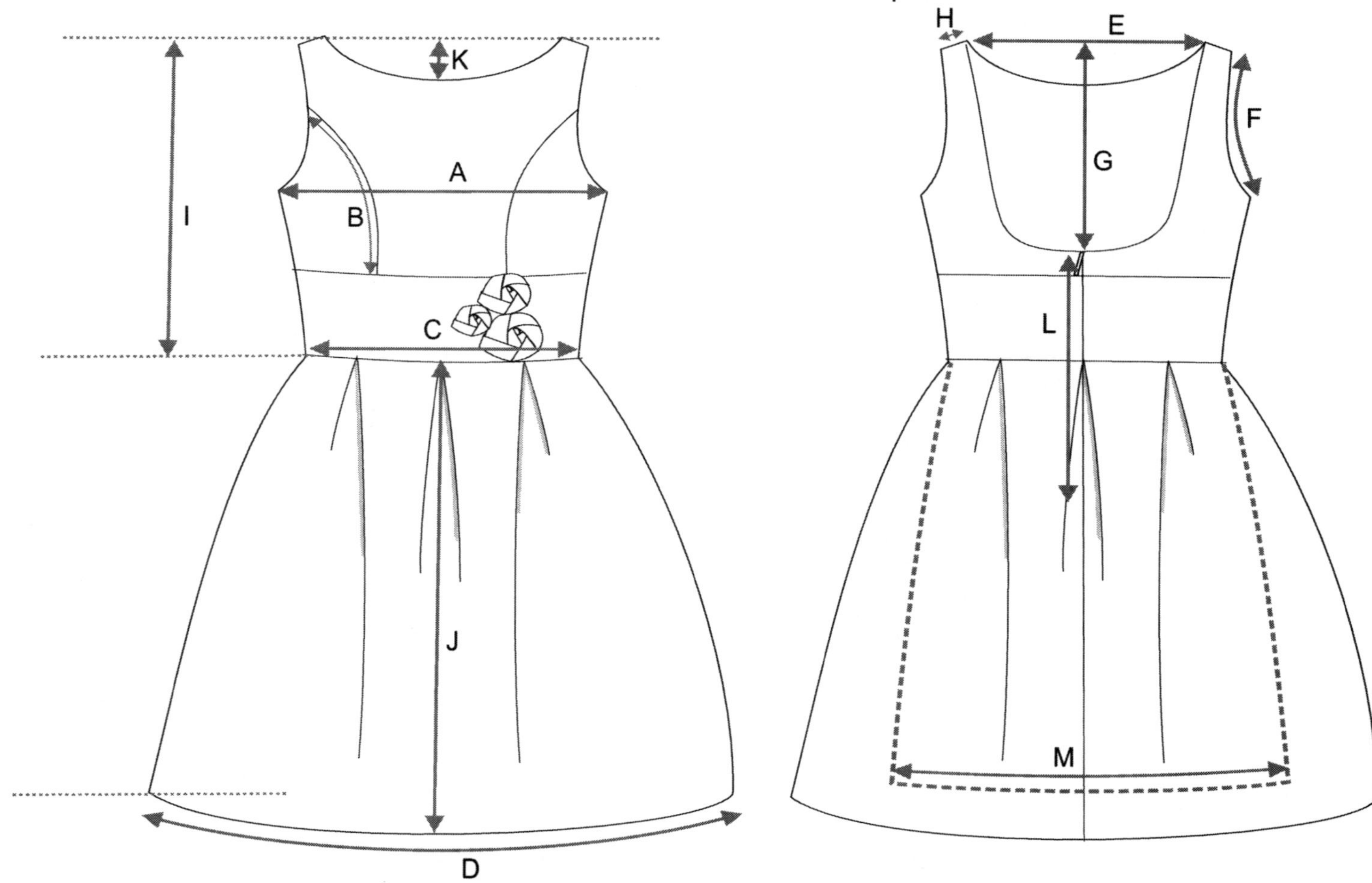

SIZE UK 14 with straps	CMS	INCHES
A. Bust at armhole with fullness smoothed out	94	37”
B. Bust seam measured on the curve	24	9½”
C. Waist-on seam	82	32¼”
D. Full hem sweep	214	84¼”
E. Neck opening	28.5	11¼”
F. Armhole measured on the curve, back & front edges together-half measurement	22.5	8⅞”
G. Back neck drop	18	7⅛”
H. Shoulder width on seam	4.5	1¾
I. Shoulder to waist seam	39.5	15½”
J. Skirt length from the waist seam	56	20½”
K. Front neck drop	7	2¾”
L. Zip length	36	14⅜”
M. Lining hem	126	49⅝”

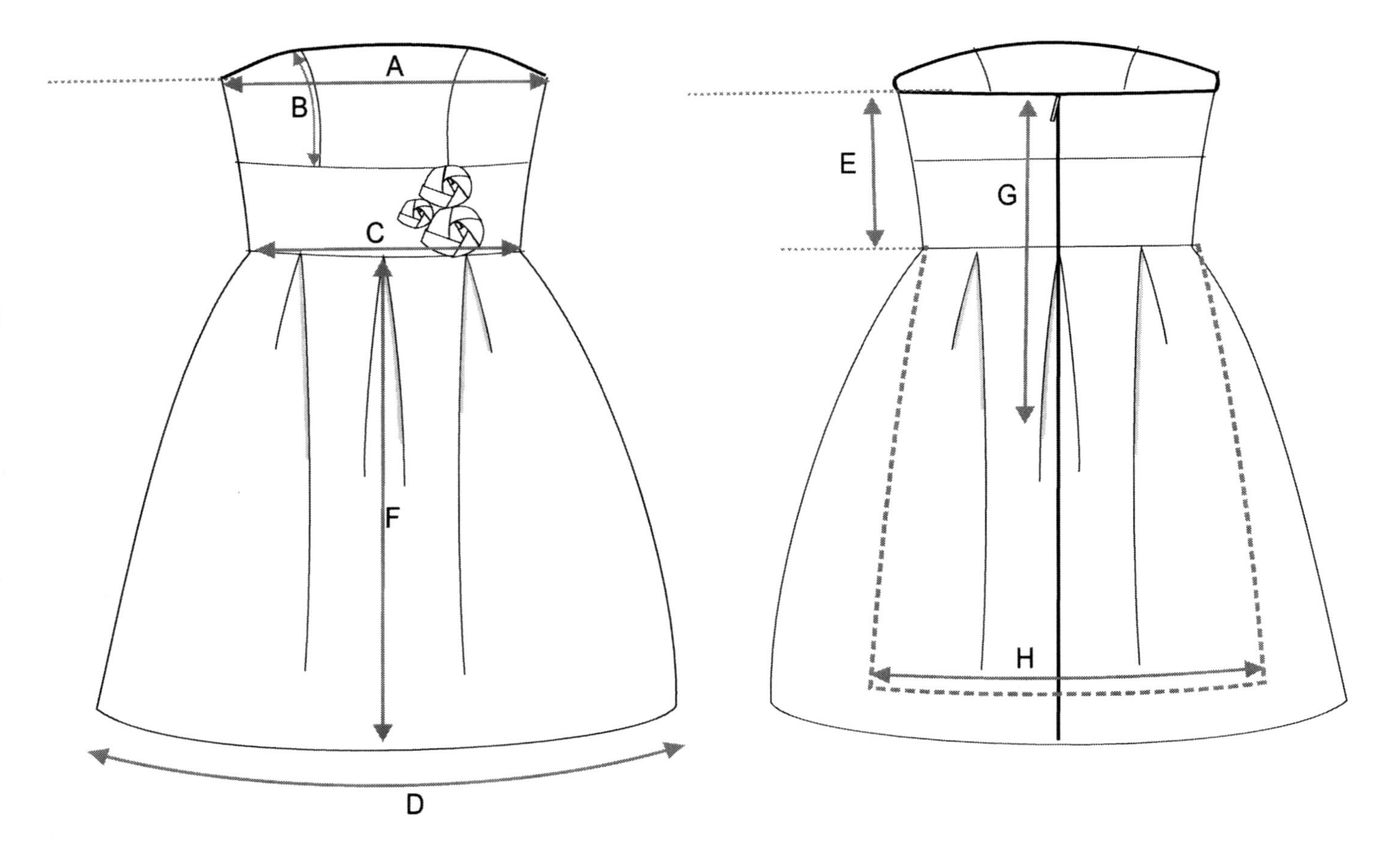

SIZE UK 14 Strapless	CMS	INCHES
A. Bust at armhole with fullness smoothed out	90	35⅜"
B. Bust seam measured on the curve	19	7½"
C. Waist-on seam	82	32¼"
D. Full hem sweep	214	84¼"
E. Top of armhole to waist seam	23	9⅛"
F. Skirt length from the waist seam	56	22"
G. Zip length	36	14⅜"
H. Lining hem	126	49⅝"

CHAPTER 13

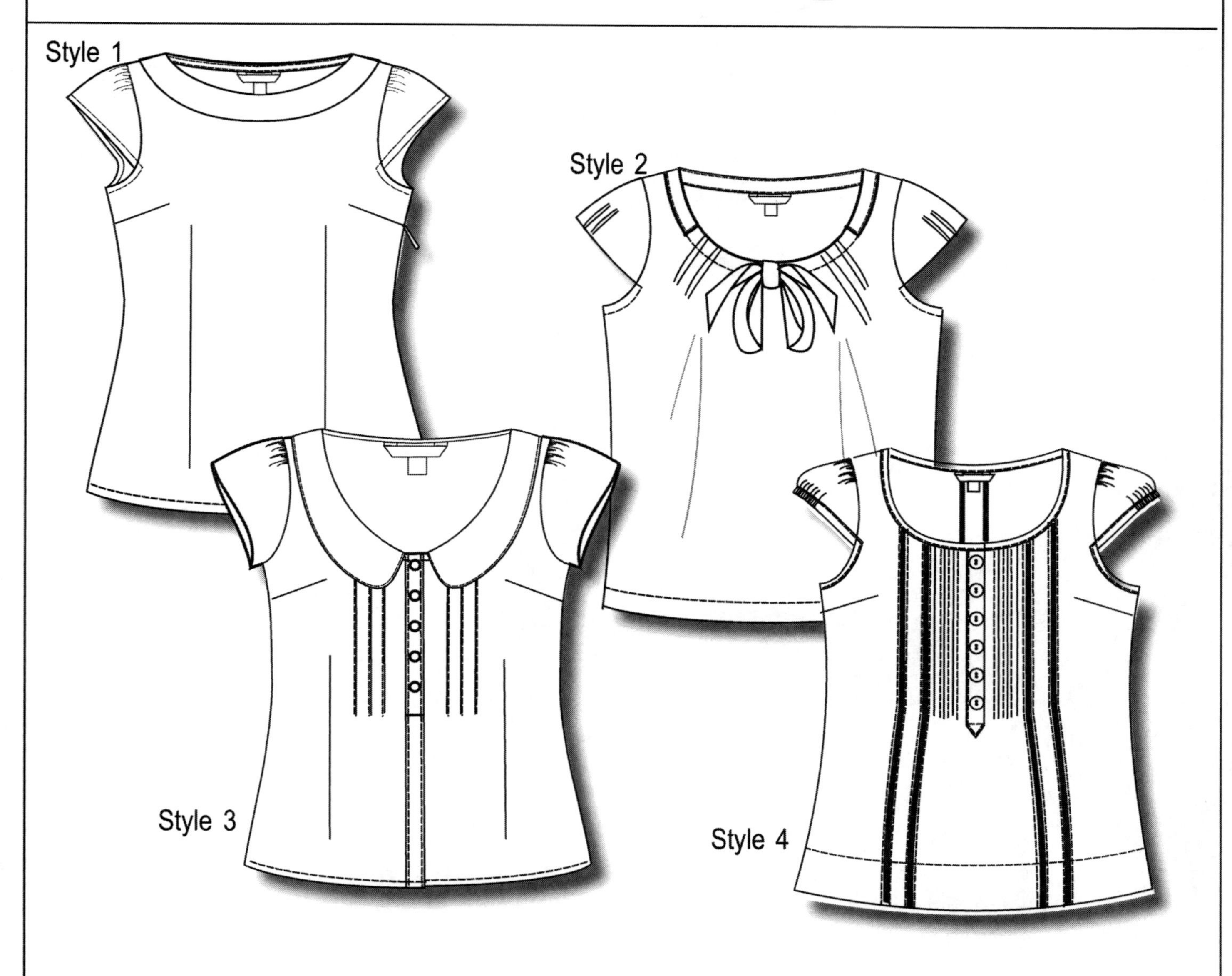

BLOUSES

Four different blouses from one High Street retailer, made in four different countries. This is a good example of a retailer sourcing globally, and probably each factory could have made any of the four styles. This type of retailer will have its own design department that will be constantly working on new styles, but before orders can be placed prices must be agreed upon and first samples approved. Specifications can be e-mailed quickly to any number of factories. I have created specifications for the four styles to provide sufficient information for the factory to produce costing and then approval samples. I have concentrated on style details and key manufacturing points–other details can be added or changed later when the first samples are received. Part of the retailers own brand, packaging and labeling details could be in a separate manual. I have presented the sample measurements in a different way by adding them to the drawings that show the measuring points. The shapes of the blouses are similar, but there are differences. After creating the outline for style 1, it was used as the template for the other 3 styles. On the page with the measurements I have shown the variation of each style from style 1.

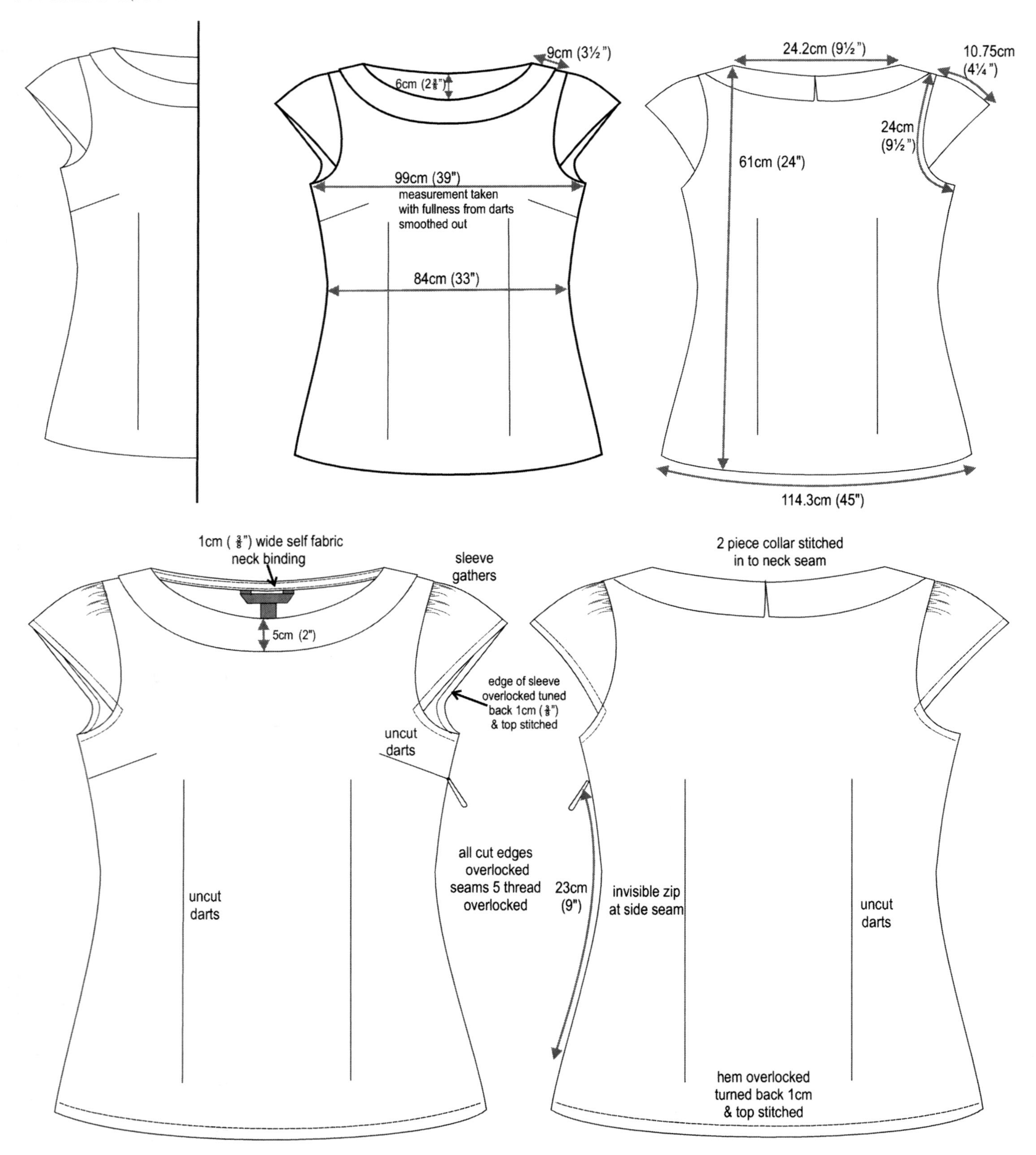

Style 1 Size USA 12 Euro 42

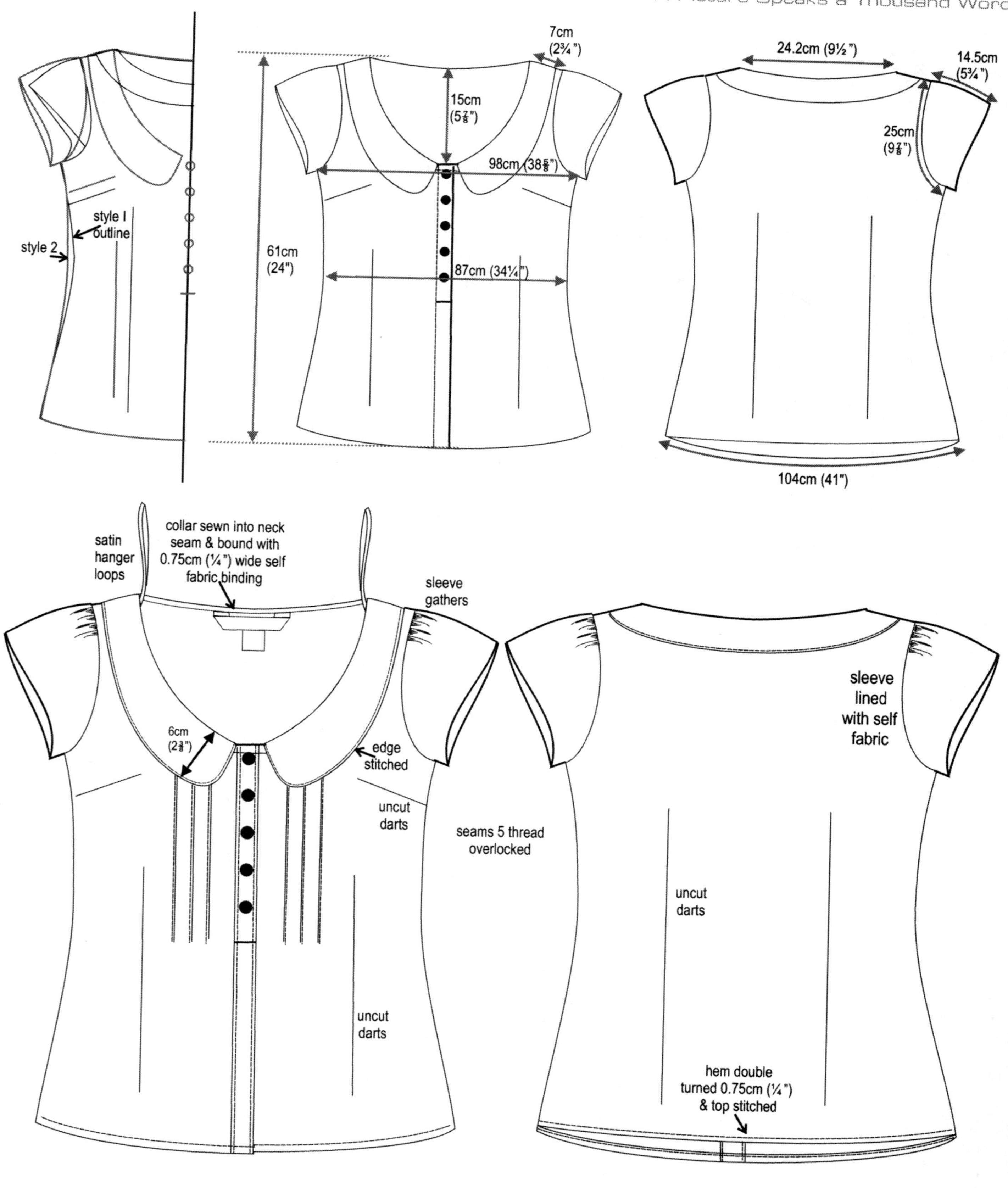
style I outline
style 2
7cm (2¾")
15cm (5⅞")
98cm (38⅝")
61cm (24")
87cm (34¼")
24.2cm (9½")
14.5cm (5¾")
25cm (9⅞")
104cm (41")
satin hanger loops
collar sewn into neck seam & bound with 0.75cm (¼") wide self fabric binding
sleeve gathers
6cm (2⅜")
edge stitched
uncut darts
seams 5 thread overlocked
uncut darts
sleeve lined with self fabric
uncut darts
hem double turned 0.75cm (¼") & top stitched

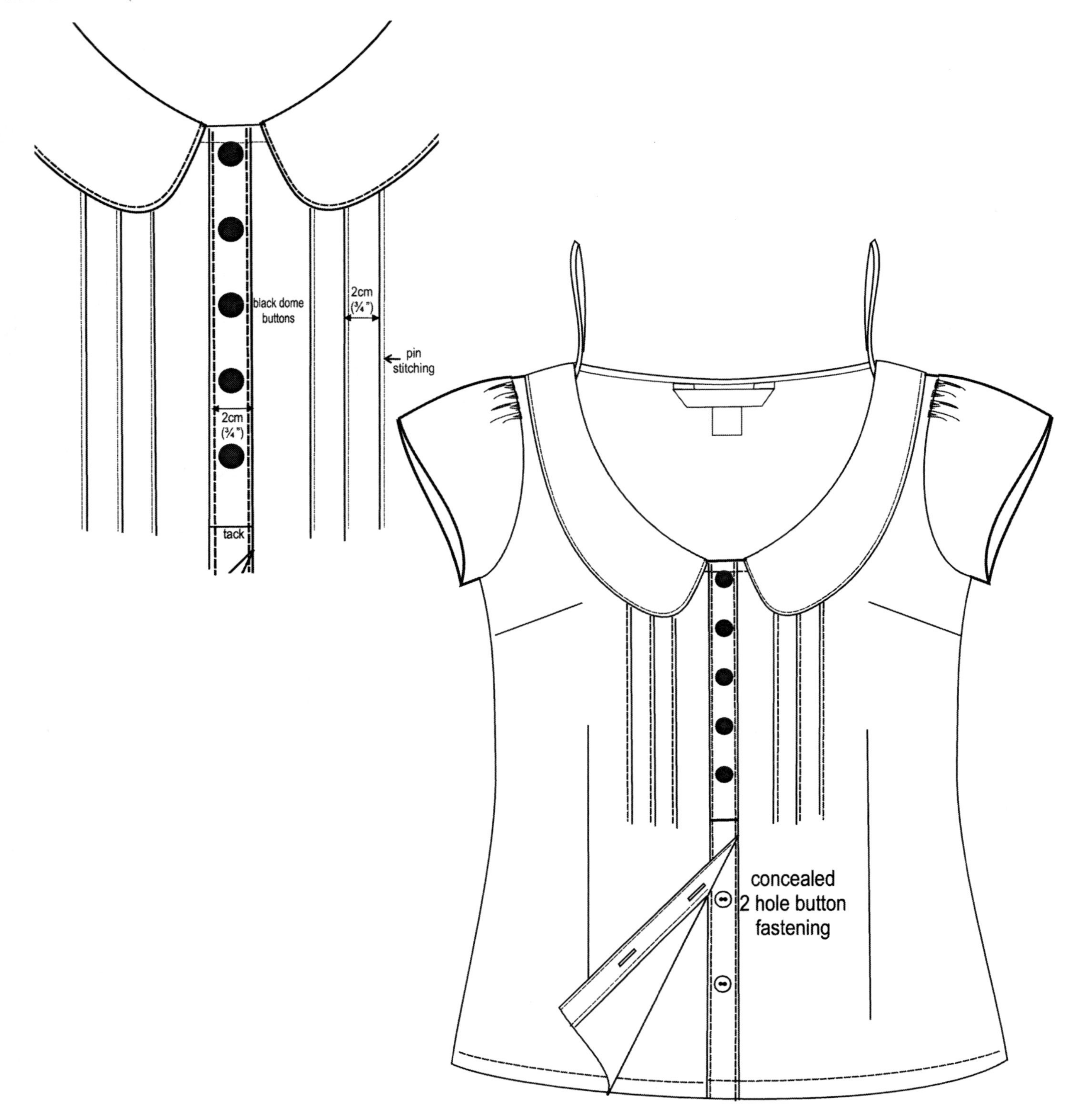

Style 2 Size USA 10 Euro 40

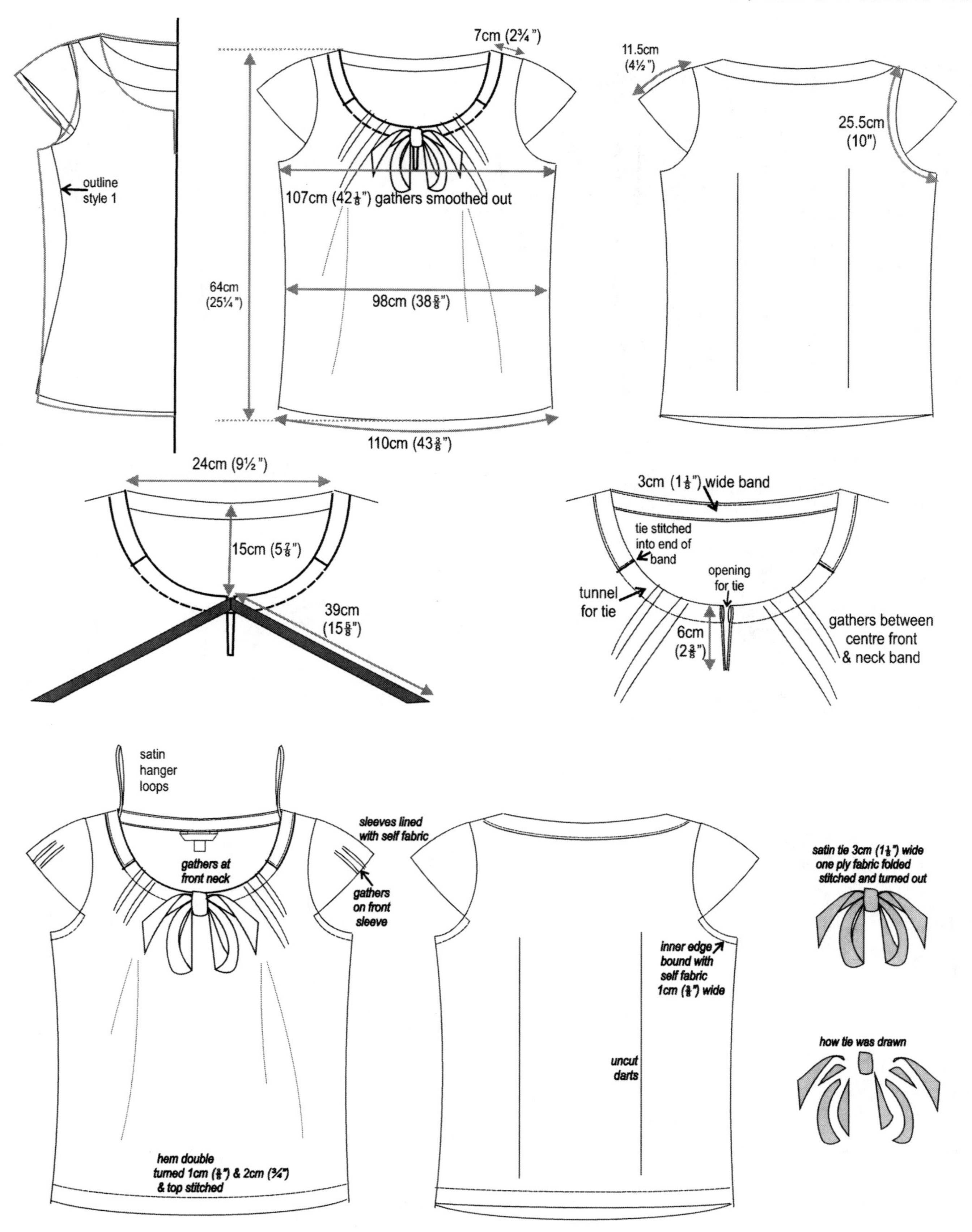

Style 3 Size USA 10 Euro 40

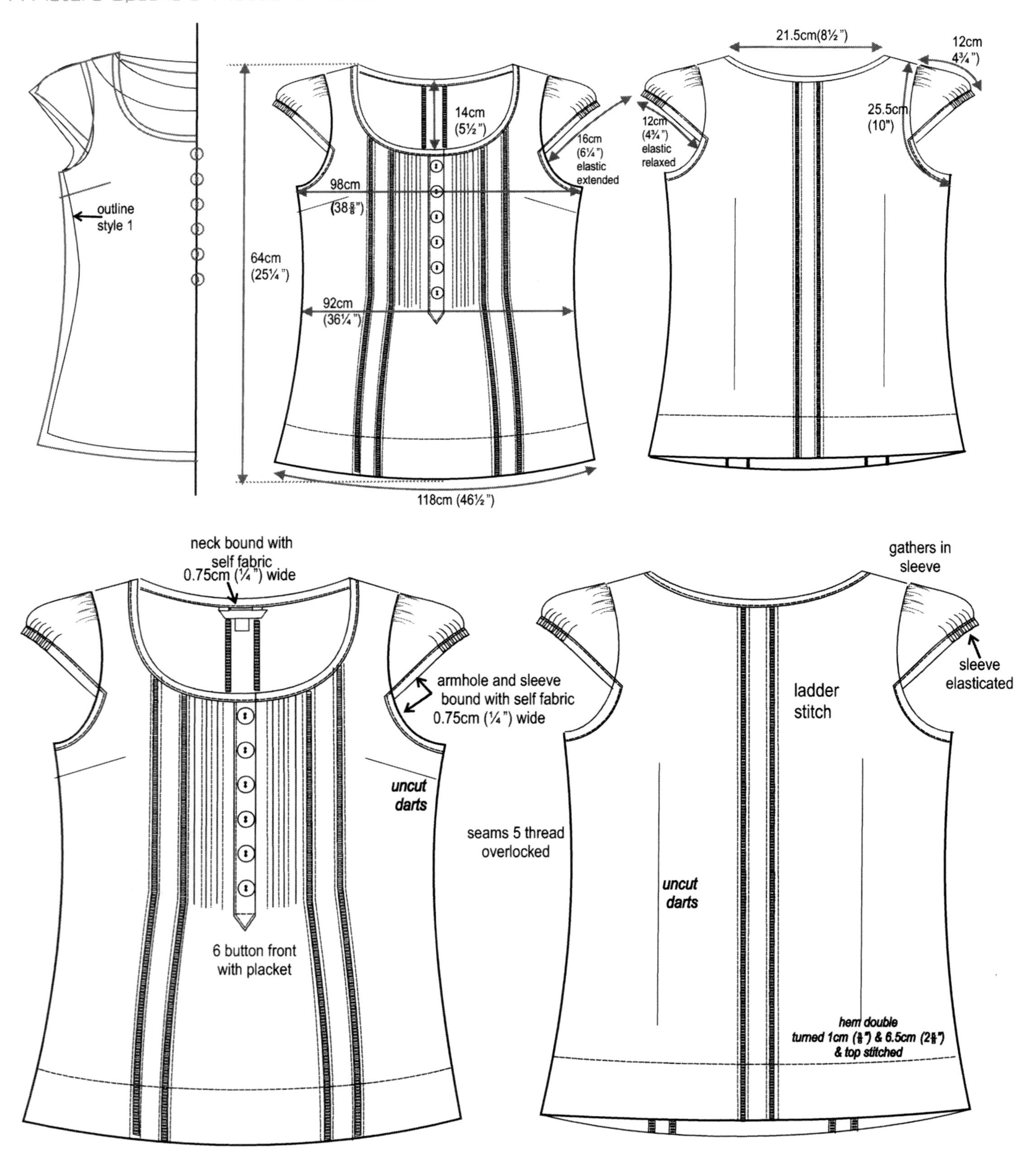

Style 4 Size USA 8 Euro 38

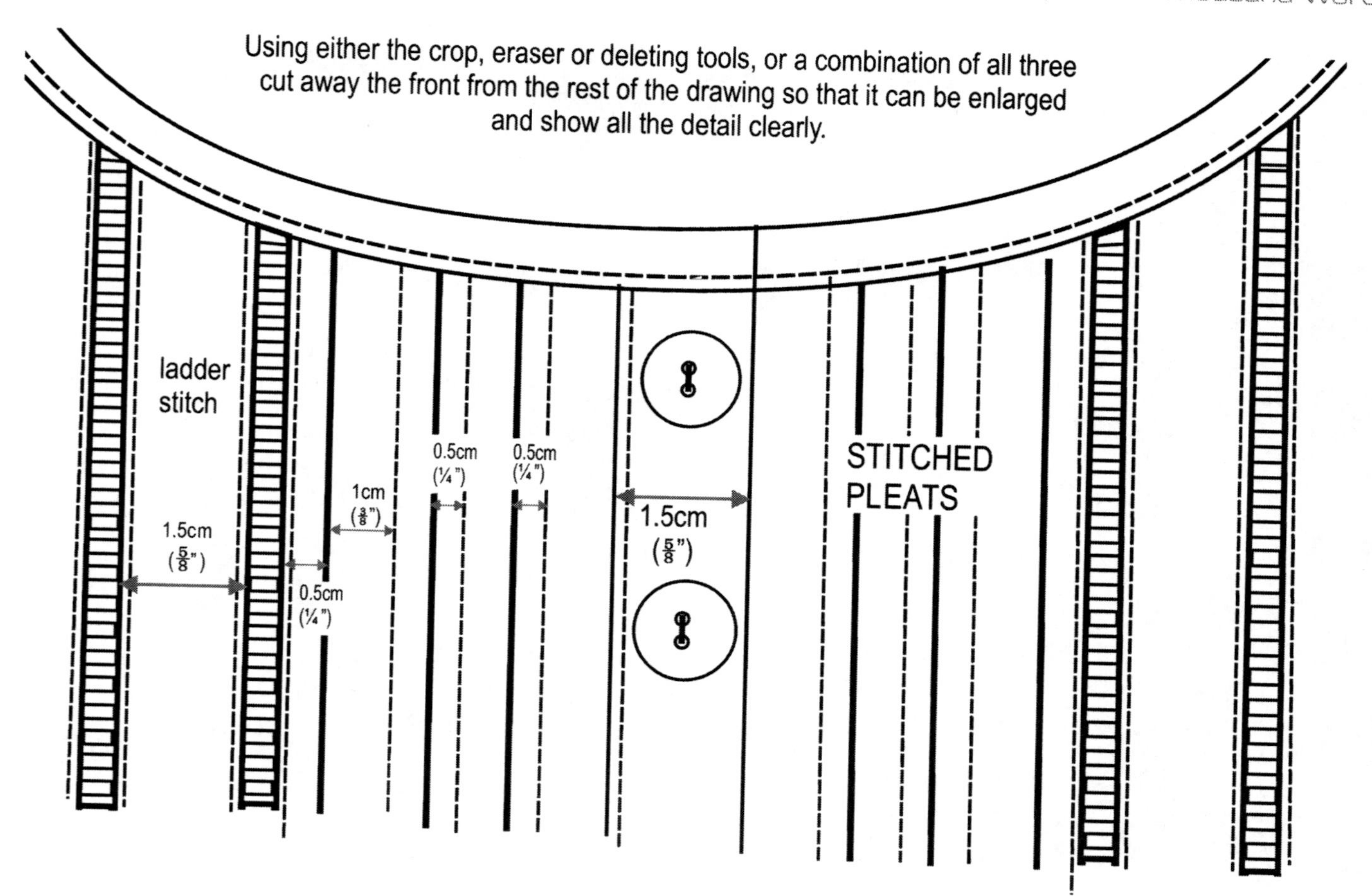
Using either the crop, eraser or deleting tools, or a combination of all three cut away the front from the rest of the drawing so that it can be enlarged and show all the detail clearly.
ladder stitch
1.5cm (⅝")
0.5cm (¼")
1cm (⅜")
0.5cm (¼")
0.5cm (¼")
1.5cm (⅝")
STITCHED PLEATS

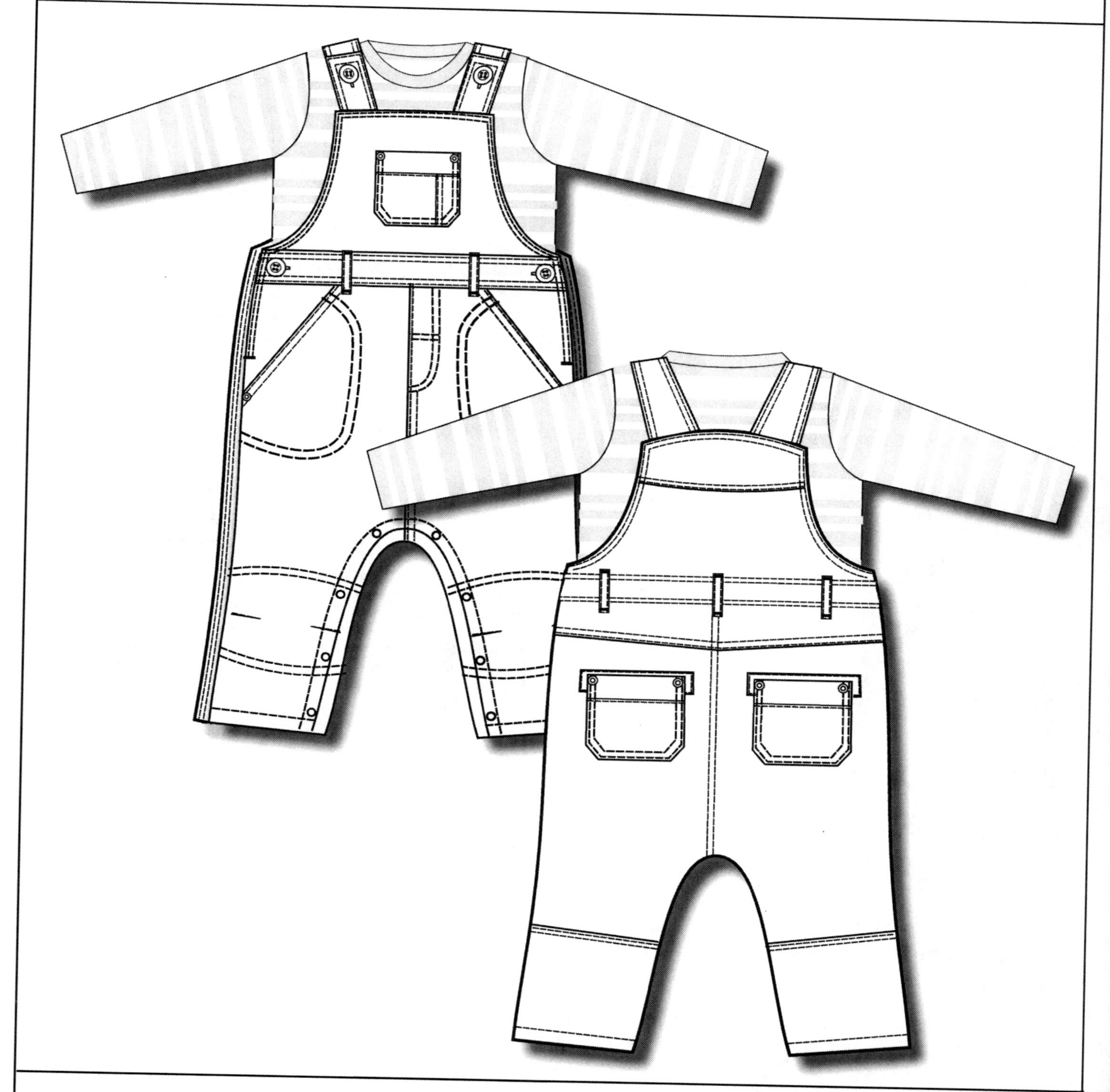

CHAPTER 14

DENIM OVERALLS

Baby and children's wear is a growing market. Parents will sometimes go without buying themselves new clothes so as to make sure their kids are always dressed in the latest fashions. Denim overalls are usually from denim and like their parents' jeans have lots of pockets and stitch detail. They are often sold with a matching top. It should not be overlooked that babies and children's garments must be practical. Chlidren's clothes should be cut with plenty of room, should not be restrictive and must be easy to get on and off.

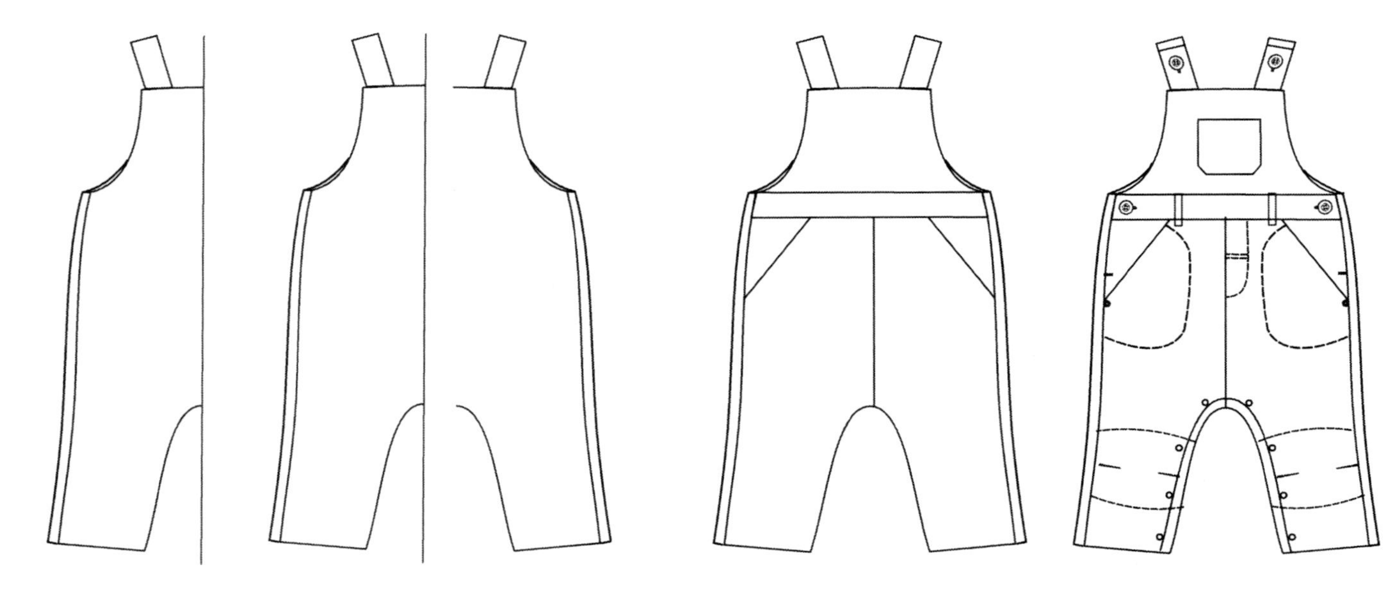

Draw half outline, mirror image and combine 2 halves together when satisfied with the result.

Add band, side pockets and center frontline, check against sample and add outline of other detail.

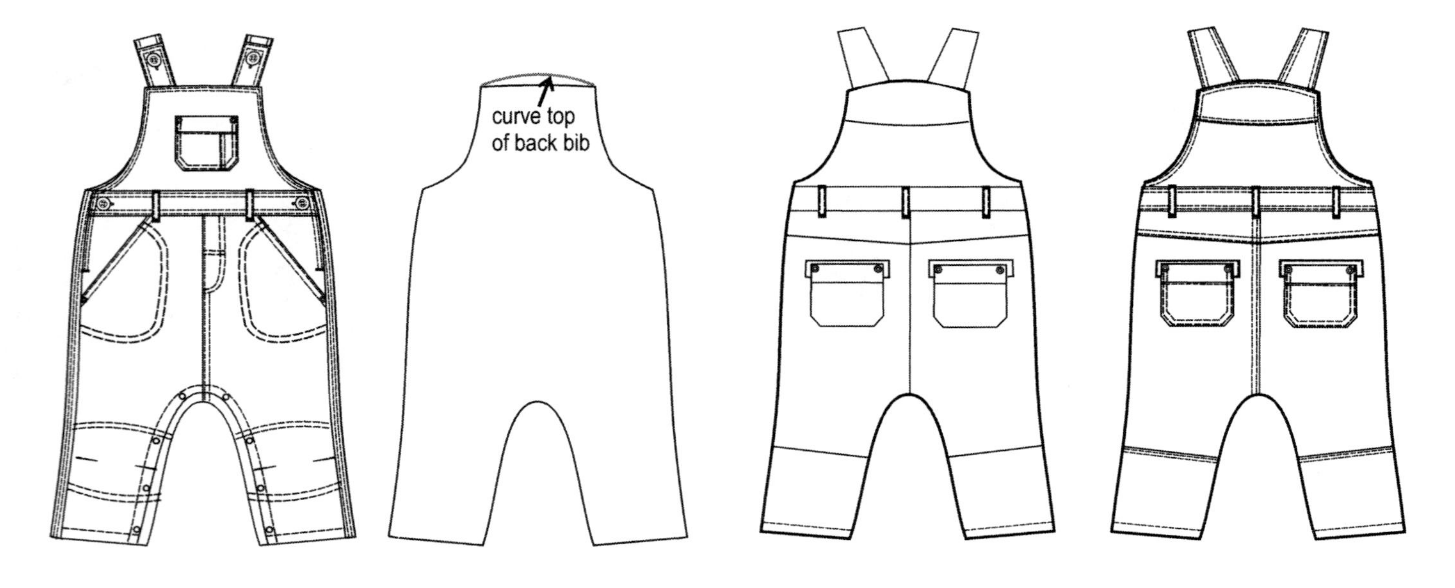

Front completed.

Take outline of the front and sketch outline of the back details.

Back completed.

Add band, side pockets and center frontline, check against sample and add outline of other detail.

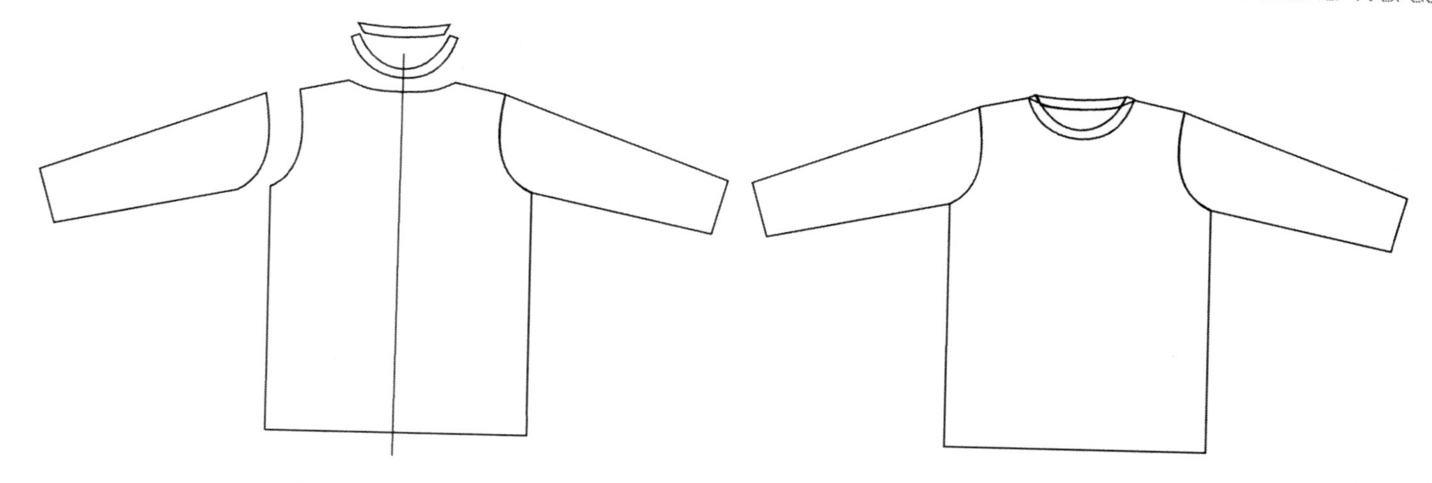

Draw front, back, sleeves and neck bands as solid objects.

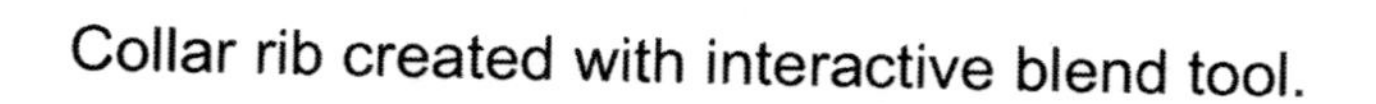

Collar rib created with interactive blend tool.

Create stripes, select and place in body and sleeves with the power clip tool

Stripes added to the body and sleeves.

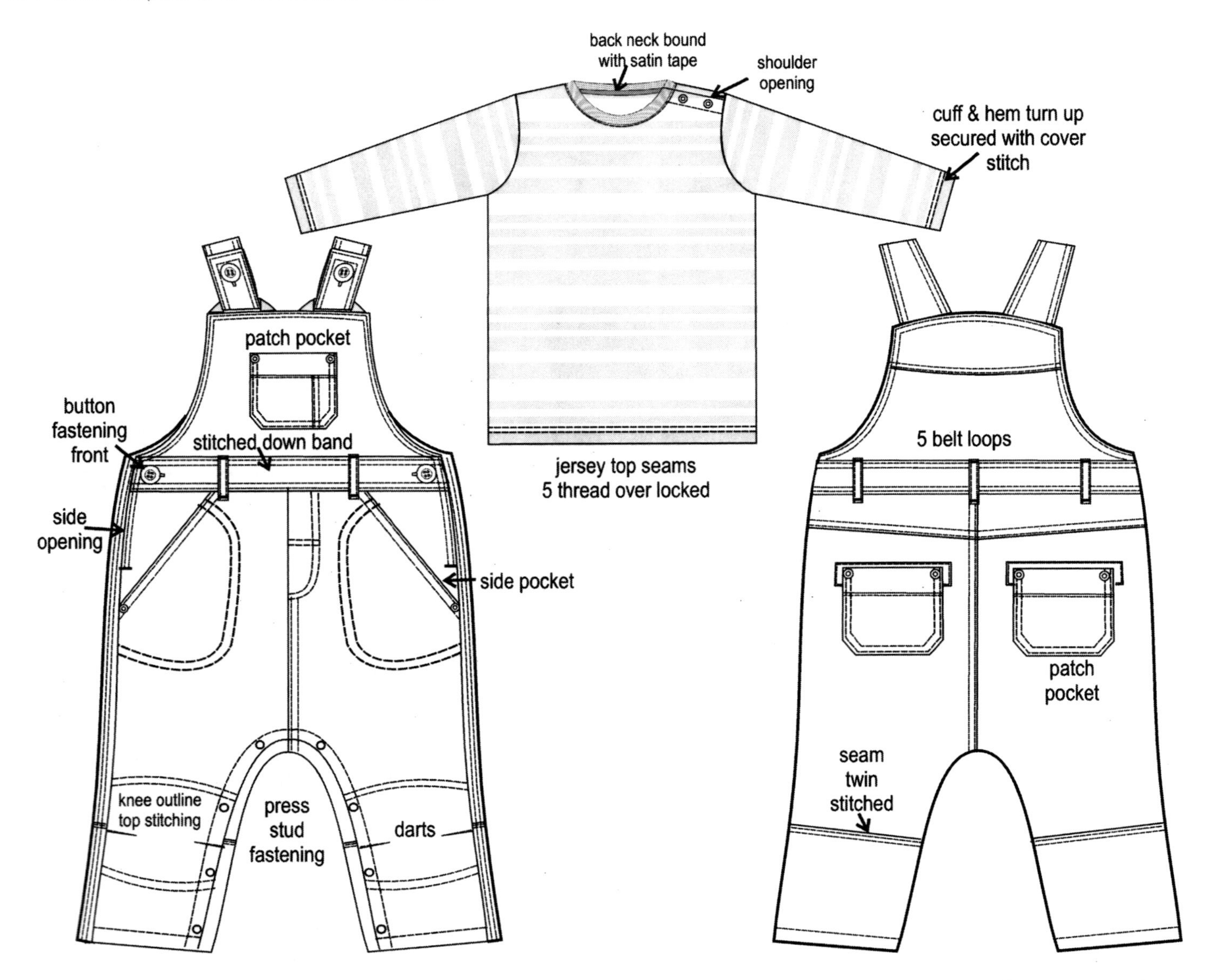

The following pages show sections of the denim overalls in more detail. Having already drawn the pockets, copy and paste to enlarge them. Detail can now be more clearly shown with descriptive text added. I have broken the lines of the front to separate the upper section from the legs to show a larger image with added text. The same is done with the straps to show the size of the straps and the positioning of the buttons. I have added an extra drawing for the leg openings, showing the number of studs and their positions. Using the existing drawing of the front I added a drawing of the bib when unfastened to show more of the inner details. Factories always appreciate as much information as possible helping them to make the sample quickly with fewer mistakes.

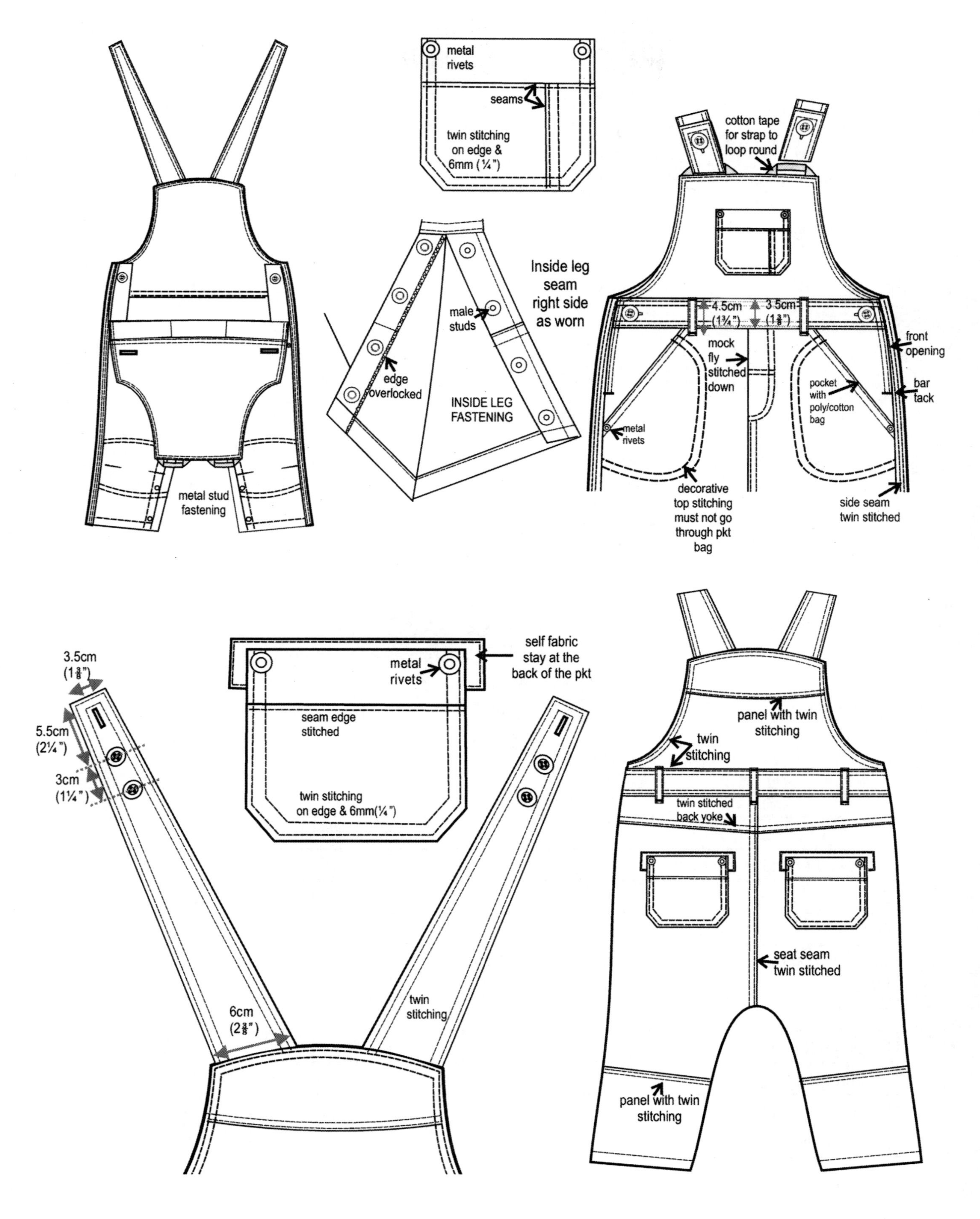
metal rivets
seams
twin stitching on edge & 6mm (¼")
cotton tape for strap to loop round
Inside leg seam right side as worn
male studs
edge overlocked
INSIDE LEG FASTENING
4.5cm (1¾")
3.5cm (1⅜")
mock fly stitched down
front opening
bar tack
pocket with poly/cotton bag
metal rivets
decorative top stitching must not go through pkt bag
side seam twin stitched
metal stud fastening
3.5cm (1⅜")
5.5cm (2¼")
3cm (1¼")
metal rivets
self fabric stay at the back of the pkt
seam edge stitched
twin stitching on edge & 6mm(¼")
6cm (2⅜")
twin stitching
panel with twin stitching
twin stitching
twin stitched back yoke
seat seam twin stitched
panel with twin stitching

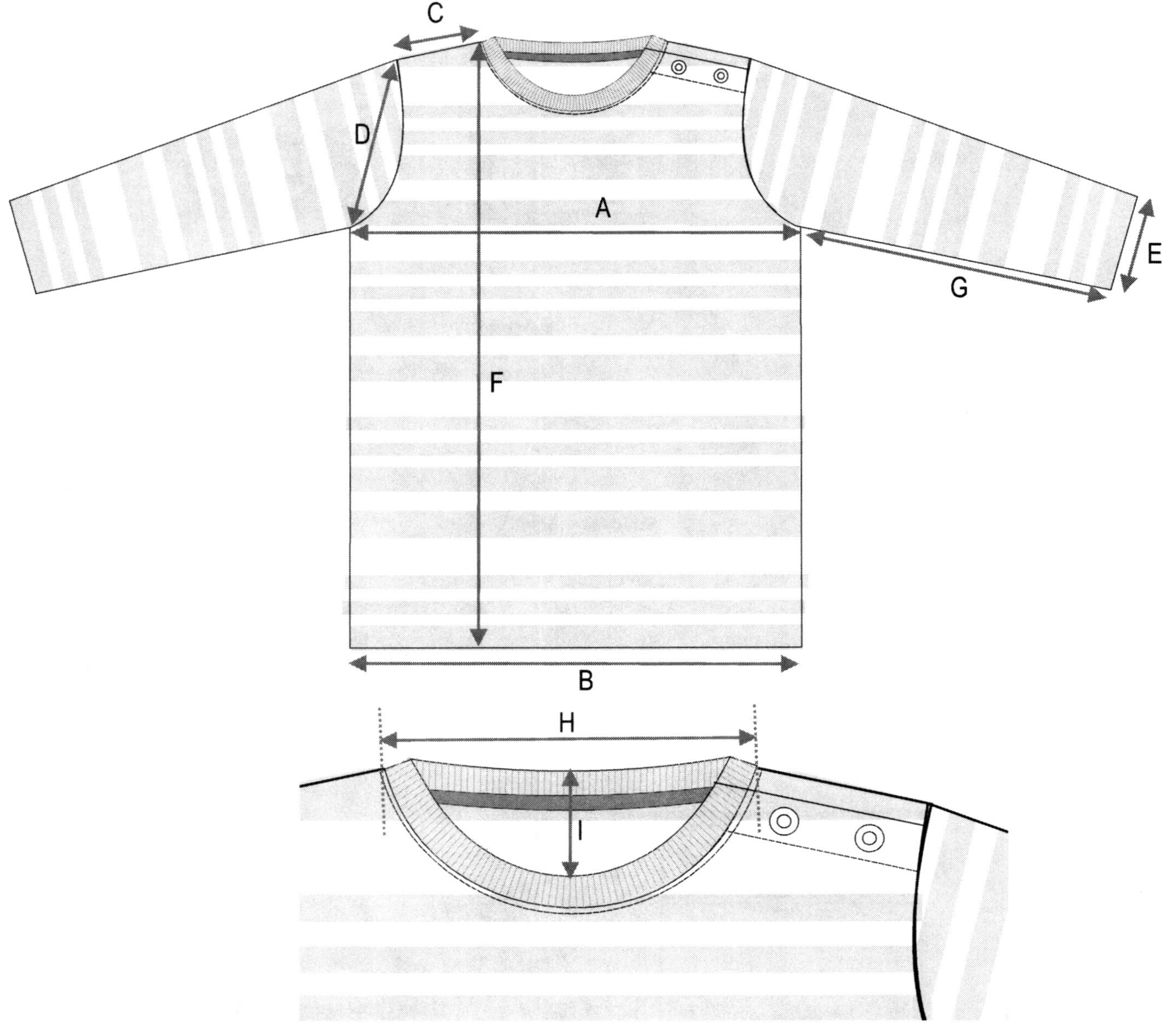

SIZE 3-6 Months	CMS	INCHES
A. Width at the under arm	54	21¼"
B. Hem	54	21¼"
C. Shoulder not including rib	5	2"
D. Armhole measured in a straight line from the shoulder to the top of the side seam	12	4¾"
E. Cuff opening	14	5½"
F. Length from the neck point	31	12¼"
G. Under arm	18.5	7¼"
H. Distance from the neck points	12	4¾"
I. Front neck drop.	3	1⅛"

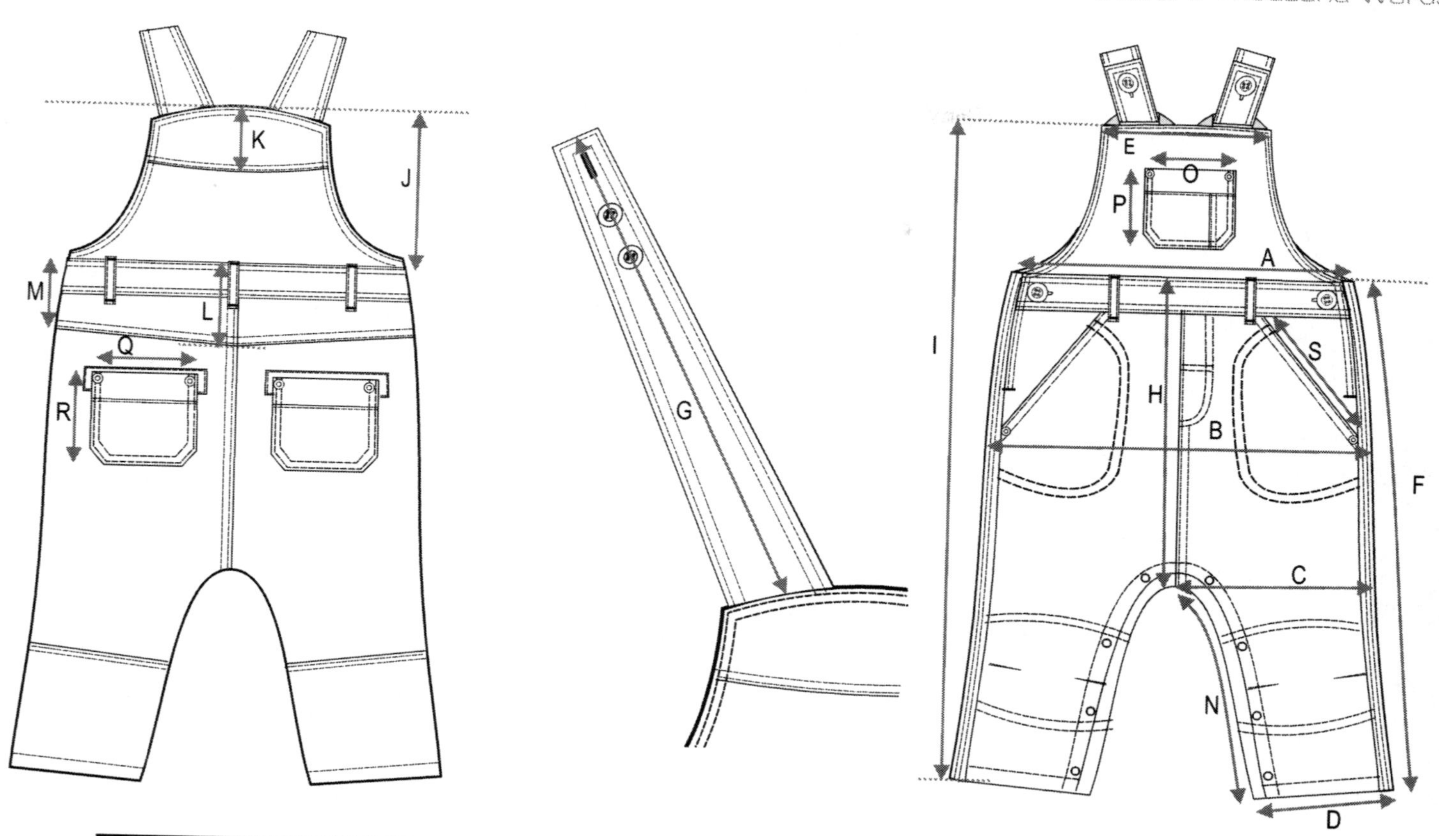

SIZE 3-6 MONTHS	CMS	INCHES
A. Width across waist band	48	18⅞"
B. Width at the bottom edge of the side pocket	52	20½"
C. Width of thigh at the bottom of the crutch seam	35	13¾"
D. Leg opening	23	9"
E. Top edge of the bib.	14	5½"
F. Out side leg from top of the waist band	37	14⅝"
G. Strap length	20	7⅞"
H. Front and back rise from the top of the waist band	19	7½"
I. Length from the top of the bib to the bottom of the leg.	47.5	18¾"
J. Top of the bib to the top edge of the waist band.	10	4"
K. Depth of the back bib panel.	4	1⅝"
L. Yoke depth from the top of the waist band at the center back.	6.5	2⅝"
M. Back yoke at the side seam from the top of the waist band.	4	1⅝"
N. Inside leg.	18	7⅛"
O. Width of the front patch pocket	7.5	3"
P. Depth of the front patch pocket	7.5	3"
Q. Width of the back patch pocket	9	3⅝"
R. Depth of the back patch pocket	9	3⅝"
S. Side pocket opening	9	3⅝"
There may be more measurements in this size chart than normal. This is because as we grade up to larger sizes the child will grow noticeably in height and all parts of the garment will increase in proportion.		

DENIM OVERALLS

CHAPTER 15

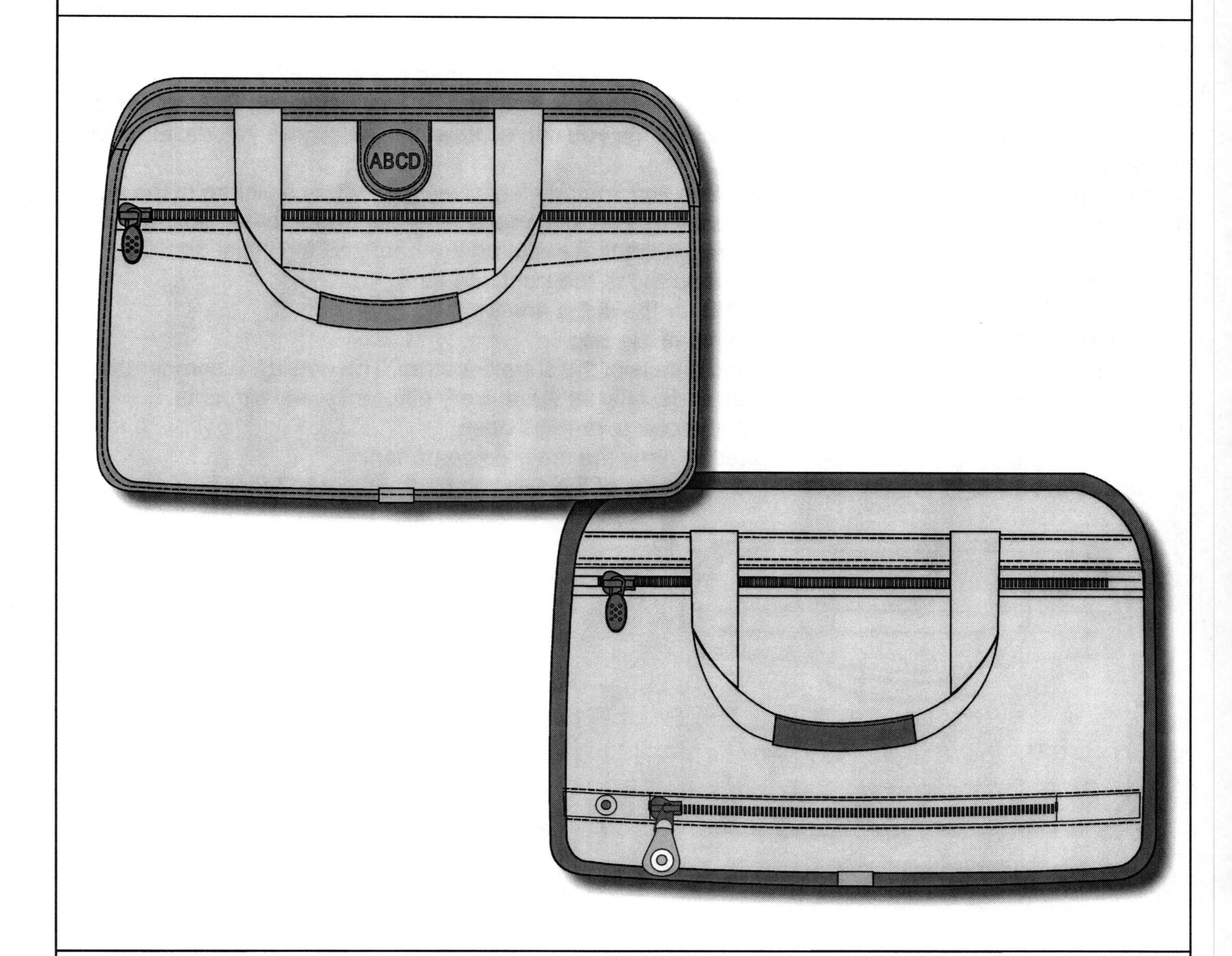

TRAVEL BAG

Companies keen for new business sometimes get inquiries for products they don't normally supply. Sometimes an ambitious salesperson will say if we could source a good travel bag from China we could sell them by the container load. They know the perfect bag to add to the company's range of products, but it belongs to the Managing Director and no way would he allow it to be sent to China for a factory to copy. The Technologist is now faced with a challenge—to create a specification to send to China of a product with which they are not technically proficient, and of which they have no sample to send. The company will therefore attempt to send as much information as possible for the factory to produce a reasonable first sample and costing. Photos could help, but the bag is black and details would not show up very well. The bag I have illustrated is my own, which I have used for many years for work and traveling overseas and doubt that I could now find one similar. The bag has many useful features; these include 3 inner compartments with numerous pockets, 2 outer zip pockets and a zipped section that extends the size of the bag. There are similar bags on the market, but if we want to reproduce all the features of this particular bag, we need to specify as much detail as possible.

A question I often ask myself is how much information do I send? The answer is always the same, as much as possible if it will help the factory. This specification is split in two, the outer and the inner. You could send the outer sketches with style details, fabric description and measurements and leave the factory to design the inner pockets, but the inner detail of this bag is so very well designed and was probably the factor that made me decide to buy it, so you can't afford not to specify the inside. Draw the outline templates for both as shown with illustrations 1, 2 and 8. The remaining illustrations are taken from the originals with detail added. With time you can achieve this quickly as you develop your drawing skills.

Illustration 1 & 2 is a snapshot of the outer bag and immediately gives the factory a picture of the style. These initial drawings are important to finalize as they become a template for the other illustrations.

- Illustration 3 shows the individual drawn pieces that make up the front and top initial drawing.
- Illustration 4 shows the remaining detail added to the front and back.
- Illustration 5 shows the detail completed for the sides and top.
- Illustration 6 are the outer measurements of the bag.
- Illustration 7 are the measurements and details of the shoulder strap. The outside is comparatively easy; the inside is more of a challenge especially as there are 3 different compartments.
- Illustration 8 shows the side view with the compartments open.
- Illustration 9 shows the stages required to draw the inner compartments.
- Illustration 10 & 11 are the completed drawings of the two compartments with inner pockets.

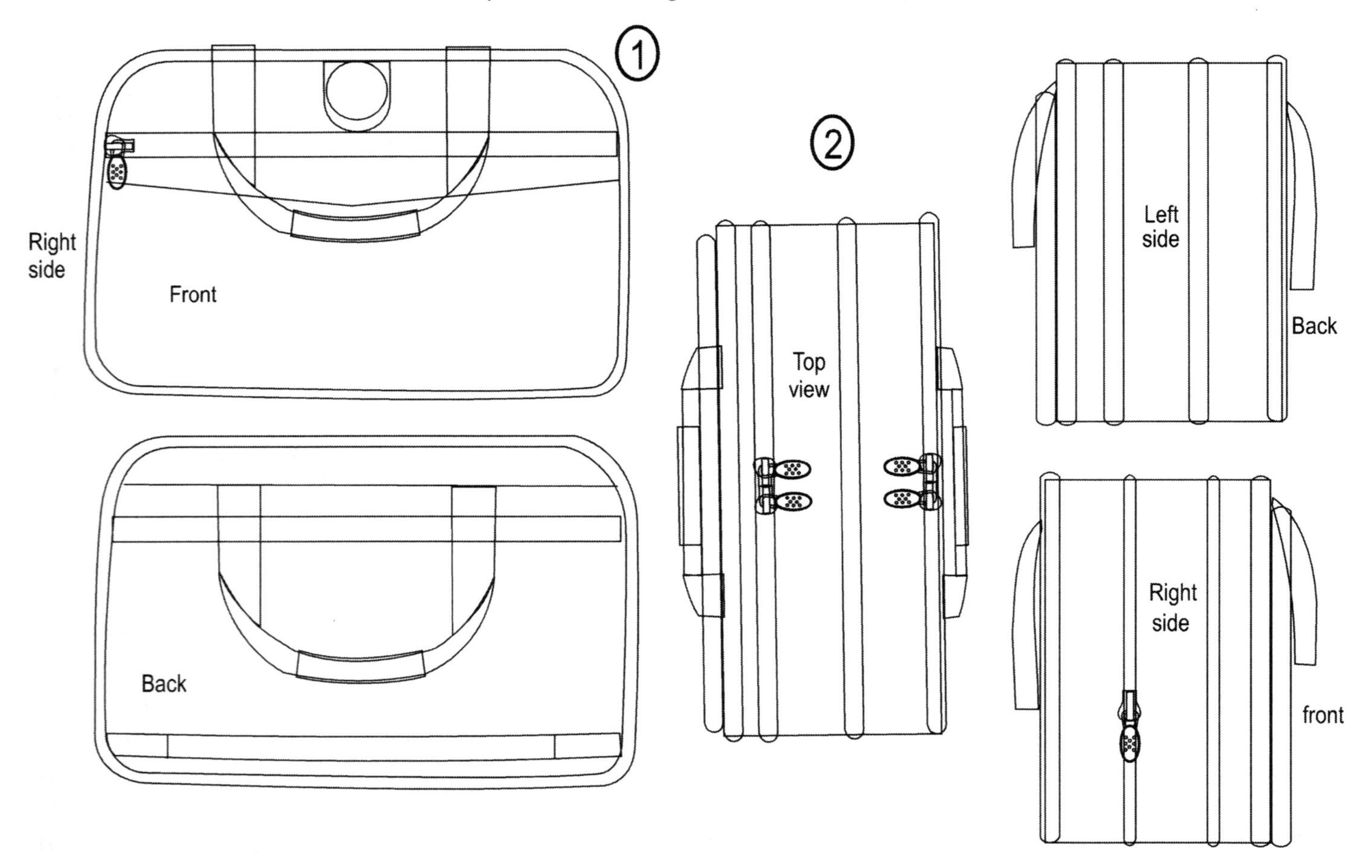

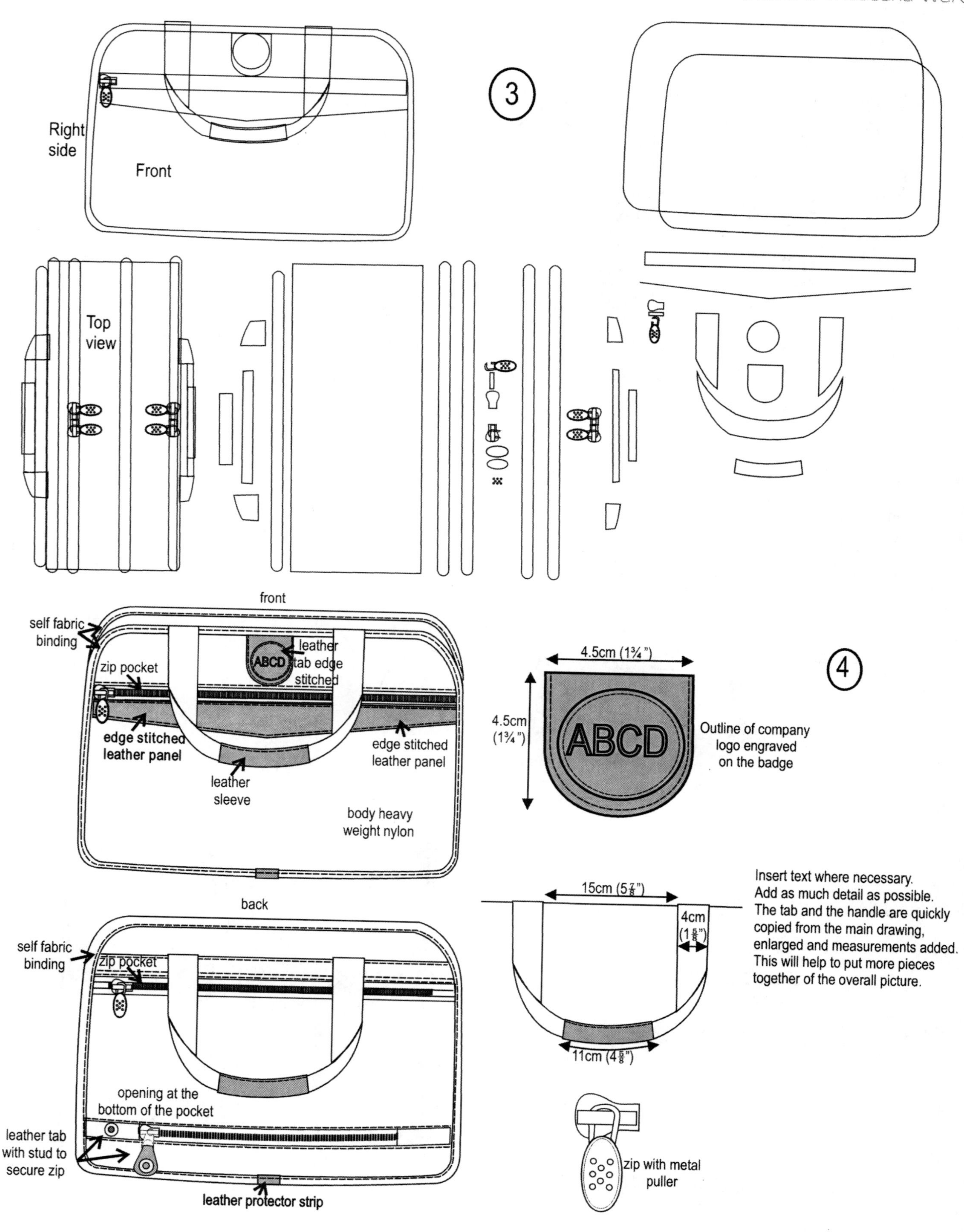

Insert text where necessary. Add as much detail as possible. The tab and the handle are quickly copied from the main drawing, enlarged and measurements added. This will help to put more pieces together of the overall picture.

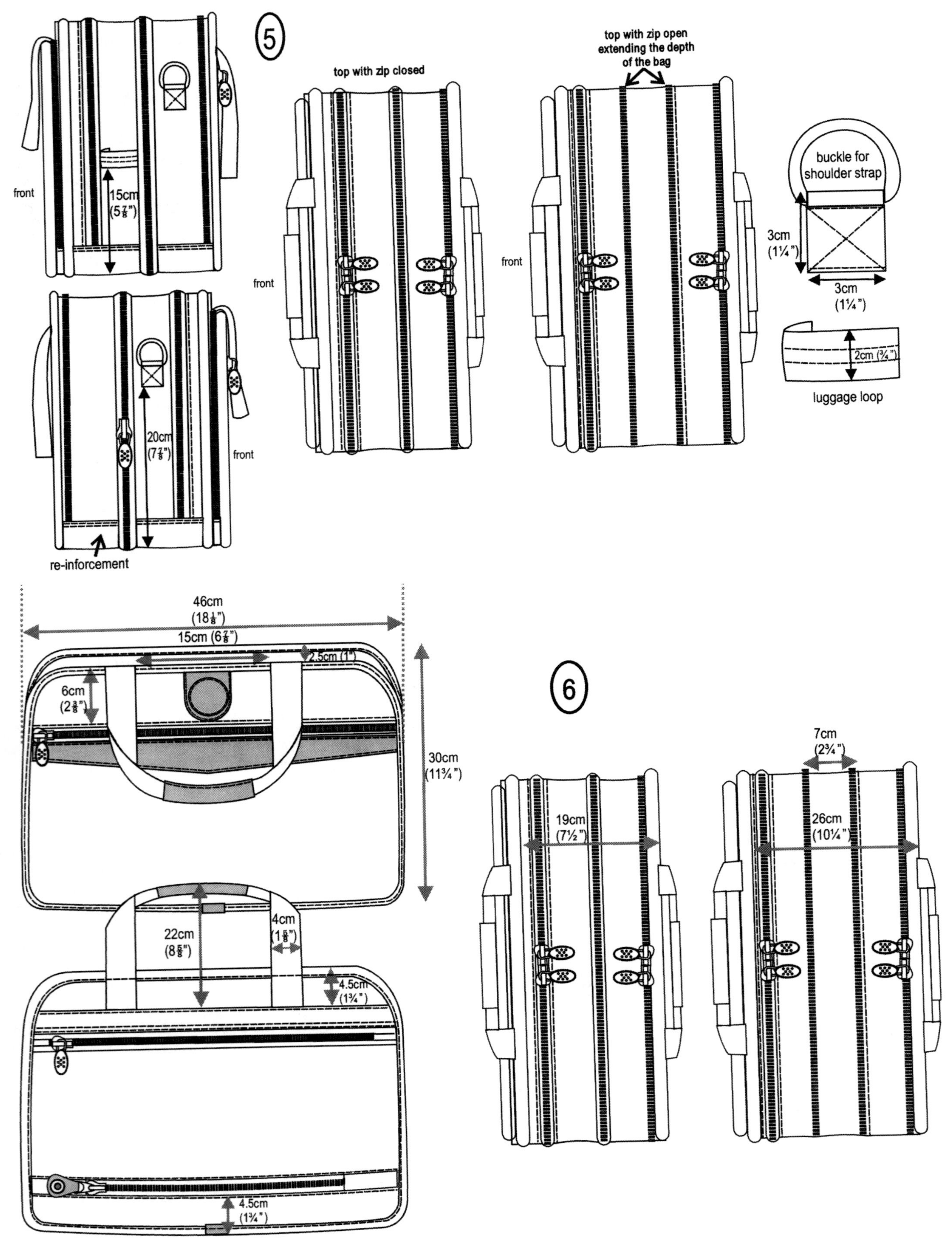
5
front
15cm
(5⅞")
20cm
(7⅞")
front
re-inforcement
top with zip closed
front
top with zip open
extending the depth
of the bag
front
buckle for
shoulder strap
3cm
(1¼")
3cm
(1¼")
2cm (¾")
luggage loop
46cm
(18⅛")
15cm (6⅞")
2.5cm (1")
6cm
(2⅜")
30cm
(11¾")
22cm
(8⅝")
4cm
(1⅝")
4.5cm
(1¾")
4.5cm
(1¾")
6
7cm
(2¾")
19cm
(7½")
26cm
(10¼")

The specification would not be complete if I did not show the side view with the compartments open drawings. See illustration 10 & 11.

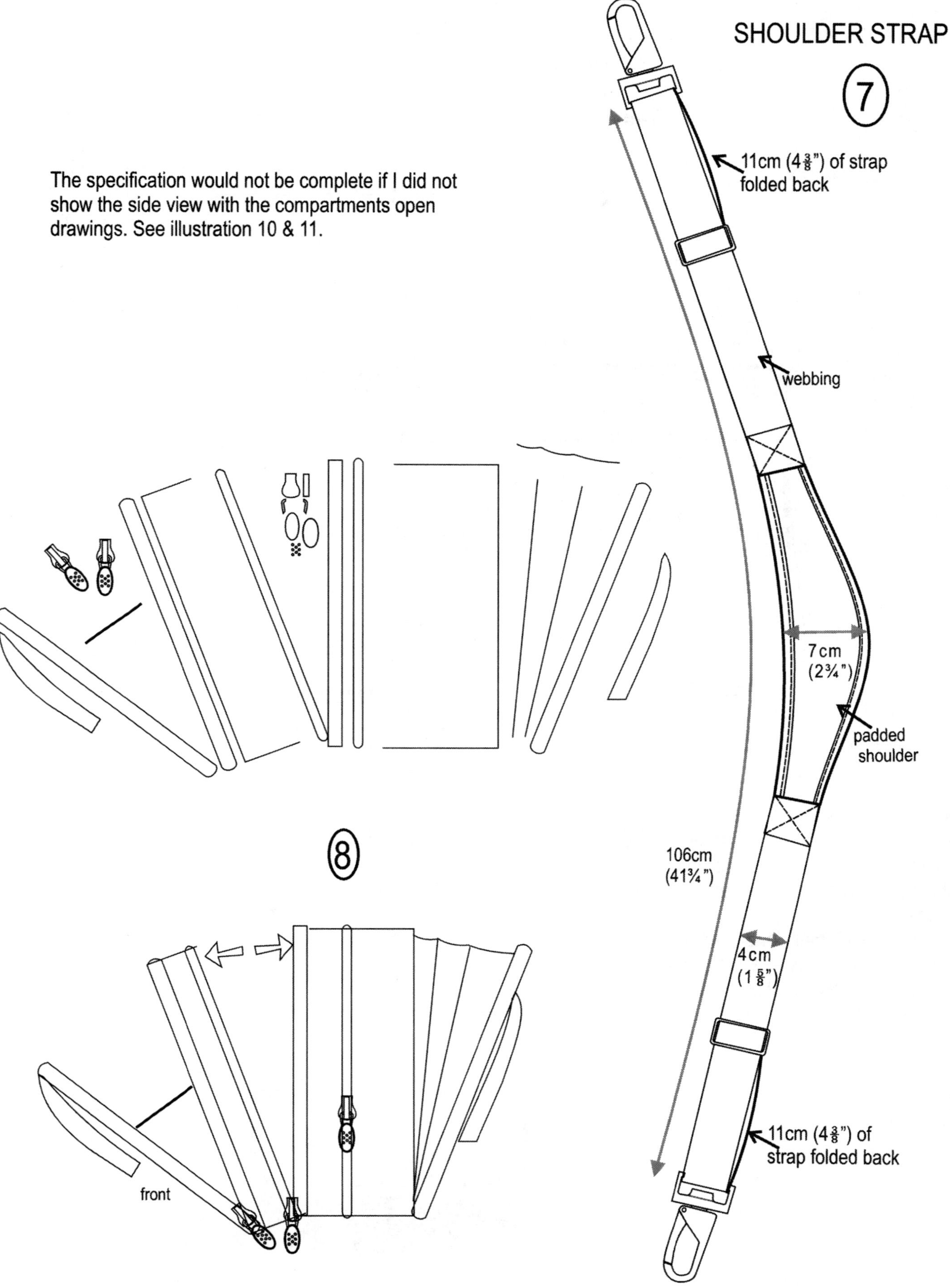

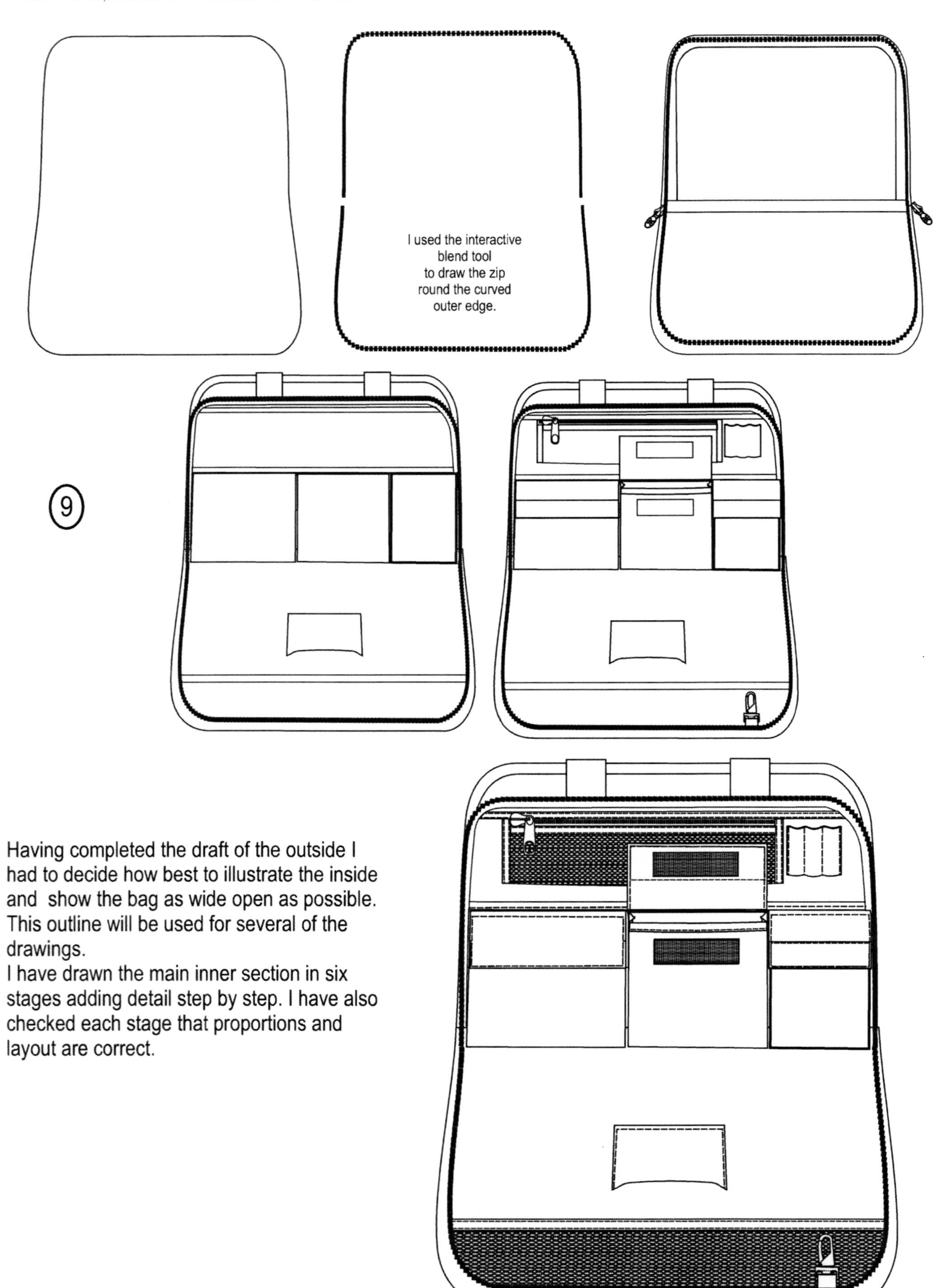

Having completed the draft of the outside I had to decide how best to illustrate the inside and show the bag as wide open as possible. This outline will be used for several of the drawings.
I have drawn the main inner section in six stages adding detail step by step. I have also checked each stage that proportions and layout are correct.

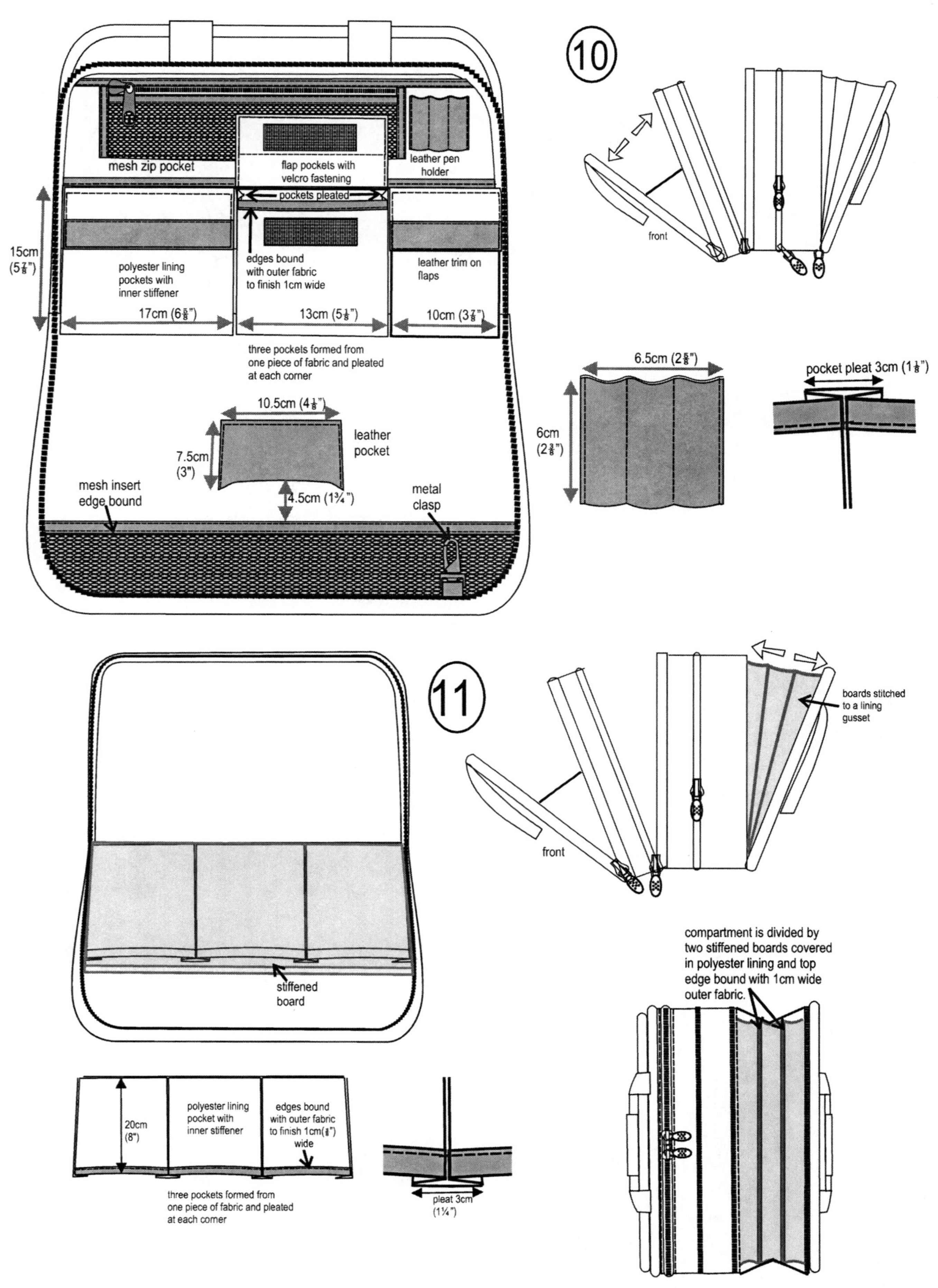
10
mesh zip pocket
flap pockets with
velcro fastening
leather pen
holder
pockets pleated
15cm
(5⅞")
edges bound
with outer fabric
to finish 1cm wide
polyester lining
pockets with
inner stiffener
leather trim on
flaps
17cm (6⅝")
13cm (5⅛")
10cm (3⅞")
three pockets formed from
one piece of fabric and pleated
at each corner
10.5cm (4⅛")
leather
pocket
7.5cm
(3")
mesh insert
edge bound
4.5cm (1¾")
metal
clasp
front
6.5cm (2⅝")
6cm
(2⅜")
pocket pleat 3cm (1⅛")
11
boards stitched
to a lining
gusset
front
stiffened
board
20cm
(8")
polyester lining
pocket with
inner stiffener
edges bound
with outer fabric
to finish 1cm(⅜")
wide
three pockets formed from
one piece of fabric and pleated
at each corner
pleat 3cm
(1¼")
compartment is divided by
two stiffened boards covered
in polyester lining and top
edge bound with 1cm wide
outer fabric.

SUMMARY

This book has been somewhat of a personal journey for me reflecting on the industry I have been involved with all my working life and some of the remarkable changes I have seen over that time.
When I first started work in clothing manufacturing in Leeds West Yorkshire there were literally hundreds of manufacturers within a short radius of the city center. Gradually over the years production began to move to other countries and today there are very few manufacturers left.

One of the defining moments in the UK textile industry was in the 1970's when High Street tailoring companies with their own factories in the UK realized they could buy men's suits from Eastern Europe much cheaper than from their own factories. At first the Eastern European suppliers dictated what fabrics and styles they were making, and retailers were only too happy to go along with this, benefitting from the higher profits margins.

Today trading is a global business and the supply chain can extend from London to New York to Shaghai, or to any Far Eastern country. The operation of subcontracting work either to cheaper factories in your home country or offshore through importing agents or even setting up overseas offices to control production brings its own problems. The specification becomes an integral part of the process.

The specification has to operate at various levels and satisfy different criteria. For example:

- Act as a reference point for technical and non technical management.
- Be a document that your customers can relate to.
- Serve as a reference and instruction to pattern cutters.
- A document that machinists and factory operatives can follow.
- Be usable as part of the quality assurance procedure.
- Be a template to be used for future specifications.

I have seen many examples of badly written specifications, often from companies that put out tenders for clothing or equipment they want. They can comprise pages of neatly written text describing the product. I am sure they fully understand every word and exactly how the finished product should look, so they assume all their suppliers will also be able to follow what they have written. On the front page there might be a photo of the item (which is usually of very little help).

Unfortunately, even the product developers whose mother tongue the specification is written in spend hours trying to figure out what is required. It reminds me of a popular game show that ran for many years on television called the Krypton Factor which tested mental agility by presenting the contestants with random shapes and pieces of information that they had to fit together to make a whole object.

It was once said to me that the instructions in a specification should be "simple enough for monkeys to follow". Please do not take this the wrong way, it is not meant to disrespect monkeys or factory personnel. We have all been in this position ourselves. Don't we appreciate instructions to assemble flat packed furniture, use a new camera or washing machine where it is clearly spelled out and easy to follow? Don't we get frustrated when these instructions are difficult to understand? As the end users, we look for easy to follow graphics to identify the parts and clarify the instructions we are trying to understand.

As a team member in any business we have our own part to play in the supply chain, and this means communicating clearly and efficiently what we want to the next person down the line.

I hope the book will help you see that technical design is equally as important as fashion design, as they both work together to give a complete picture of the product.

Wishing you all success in an always interesting and fascinating industry.

Stanley Brahams

Q

R

S

T

V

W

Z